Ocaña

Ocaña

Carlos Arribas

Ocaña

English edition first published in 2014
by:

Mousehold Press
Victoria Cottage
6, Constitution Opening
Norwich, NR3 4BD
www.mousehold-press.co.uk

Originally published in Spain in 2013 by Cultura Ciclista

Translated by Antonio Cuadrado-Fernández & Adrian Bell

Cover photograph: Presse Sports

ISBN 978-1-874739-72-2

Printed by Page Bros (Norwich)

Contents

A Word to the Reader

It is customary in works of fiction to warn readers that any resemblance to reality that they might encounter in the lines they are about to read is pure coincidence. I would like to warn my readers that in this particular book any resemblance to reality is not coincidental. It is just that – reality. This warning is necessary because instead of the academic biography one might have expected of a book about Ocaña, what I finally produced is a book that resembles more a fictionalised life, or a biographical novel, whichever you prefer to call it. It is a book in which the facts of the cyclist's life, those things that really did occur and are duly corroborated form what one might call a solid skeleton, to which, with a good deal of licence and a certain exercise of imagination, I have added 'muscle', 'flesh and blood'. I have done this in order to arrive at a portrait of a person with whom I barely had a relationship.

Most of the situations narrated and described in the book, as well as the dialogues guiding such narrations (except the most strictly sport-related) are like scenes from a film. They represent the emotional recreation of the memories of the people who lived with him, the people who loved him, and those who coped with him. This does not mean these events could not have happened exactly as they are narrated; they are not in any way implausible.

If there is an excuse for this methodology which might clash with some people's ideas of a biography, it is the passion with which I am forced to take on certain undertakings, such as that of writing about the Tour, or about an age of cycling that I want to relive, or the telling of the life of someone whose misfortunes marked me as a child and whose mystery I have not managed to unravel. Or, to put it simply, to describe something that I feel attracted to; or to write about someone who made the expression 'solitary escape into a headwind' an icon of absolute freedom and enviable liberation. For this reason, I hope that none of the people who are still alive and who have helped me fill the life of the cyclist with their memories, and whose names figure in the book, will be upset by their appearance in certain scenes. Some might say, 'this is not the Luis I knew', or 'this is not Ocaña', and also 'that is not me'. To all of those I apologise in advance.

Whenever an unexplained death puts an end to an inexplicable life, a family ends up broken. This not mere rhetoric in the case of Ocaña, the cyclist from Priego (Cuenca), who committed suicide on the 19th of May, 1994, on a Thursday, just a few days before turning 49 years of age. This is why some people may take offence at some of the things I write in the book; I hope that is not the case. After talking to some of the people who were closest to Ocaña, his widow, his sister, his son, and his friends, I believe that, almost 20 years on from his death, most of them have come to terms with the tragedy and assessed their share of influence in the destiny of a cyclist like no other. And of a man whose life and death embraced all the elements that made most of the twentieth century in Spain so miserable.

Apart from talking to all the people still alive who have a voice in the book, and apart from cannibalising some of the paragraphs from the chapter dedicated to Ocaña and Fuente in my part of the book *Locos por el Tour* [Mad About the Tour], I have immersed myself in as many books related to Ocaña as I have been able to find; most of them were published in French and mostly devoted to his years of success up to 1974, except Jean-Paul Ollivier's book. They are old books, written by French journalists (some of them now dead) like Roger Bastide and François Terbeen, as well as Bertrand Lucq and the great Jean Cormier. Also crucial have been the chronicles in *L'Équipe* by Antoine Blondin, Pierre Chany and Jacques Goddet, Raphaël Géminiani's authobiography and that of Raymond Poulidor, *Viva la Vuelta!* by Lucy Fallon and Adrian Bell, and Paul Fournel's book about Jacques Anquetil, Philippe Kohly's *Merckx/Ocaña* documentary, produced in 2004 by Art channel within the series 'The Great Duels of Sport', and the archives of *Pueblo* and *El Mundo Deportivo* as well as the website www.memoire-du-cyclisme.eu.

Carlos Arribas
Madrid,
4 November 2013

Part One

1

Matías Soria, nicknamed 'Short-arse' had to tiptoe in order to place the water jar on the donkey in perfect and silent equilibrium. He was blinded by the smoke from the poorly rolled cigarette, held in his fleshy lips. He turned his face just enough to avoid it, and also to stop himself from dropping his beret. He also did it to avoid losing his balance and to prevent the water jars from clashing together. He wanted to avoid the noise caused by an accidental fall which might wake up the cock and the dog, the poor hens in the henhouse, and finally his mother, who had managed to fall asleep in the grey, mist of dawn that were only waiting to be burnt off by the sun's scorching rays.

Once again, Matías had achieved his daily, wary objective and straddled nimbly and triumphantly on to the animal. He then whispered a 'giddy up' in the donkey's big ears and set off just next to the ditch which extended from the Borbotón to the vegetable garden. The air was still odourless when he crossed the Escabas to take the rocky way to Cañamares, which, after passing two young vines and a gorgeous patch of ancient olive trees, climbed a hill covered with box and pine trees. As he entered a small clearing in a hollow, the sun suddenly hit the back of his neck.

'Stop right there, my friend,' shouted a voice hidden in the shadows, behind tall shrubs. He followed the voice, which took the shape of two men with a máuser, both with sunken eyes and angular, weather-beaten faces. Instinctively, Matías put his hand on the satchel where he kept a piece of bread, a rasher of streaky bacon and a bit of oil.

'No, we don't want food. Have you got tobacco?' They confiscated his packet of rolling tobacco and the cigarette papers, and without taking their eyes off the load of water jars hanging from the donkey, they asked him: 'What about money?'

'No, I haven't got any money. When I sell the water jars this afternoon in the market in Cañamares, I may have a few coins.'

'You are Matías the Short-arse, aren't you? Your brother Cándido was very clever; he certainly did things right. This afternoon we'll see how well you did.'

'Yes, my brother,' replied Matías. He was a man of few words; he preferred to think of every word he used and not to waste it. He thought: 'Yes, my brother; he had balls.'

He had a successful day in the Cañamares market. He sold all his water jars. He had four pesetas in his saddlebag and he wanted to avoid the men who stole his tobacco. So he opted to take a detour along a rocky path climbing up to the north, almost reaching Alcantud, this side of the sierra of naked stone, through the mountainous passage between gorges. These were threatening mountains populated with oaks, low evergreen oak shrubs, rosemary, savin, pine trees and other shrubs. Then he went southwards to poor, dry Priego, the red sun on his right, the air pregnant with the scent of fragrant and medicinal plants.

'I bumped into some Maquis[1] on the way to Cañamares,' he told his mother that night. 'They knew Cándido.'

Matías was 12 years old the last time he saw Cándido, and he would have had to have been at least twenty, like his elder brother, to have gone with him. He was strong, tanned, robust, bony and frugal; that's what gancheros[2] were like. And that's how he remembered his brother, dancing on the trunks while going down the irregular, narrow and dangerous Escabas River, then the Guadiela and the tame Tajo River until he reached Aranjuez, guiding the pine trees with his hazelnut tree pole. He slept freely, naked and barefoot on the riverbank, with the stars above within reach of his hand and his dreams. At the beginning of spring, when they arrived in Aranjuez, they used to stay at the workers vegetable garden, watering and harvesting asparagus. Some

---

1. Maquis - guerrillas exiled after the Civil War who fought against occupying Nazi and the Vichy regime in France during World War II and continued to fight against the Franco regime until the early 1960s.
2. Gancheros - the men whose job was to float the tree trunks down river.

nights they used to go dancing *paso doble* in the camp site. But one day, well into a very hot summer, the *paso doble* became a military fanfare. It was the same *paso doble*, the same joy, but it didn't call for dancing, it called for war.

On 18 July 1936, Cándido and Pedro Pernia, a friend from his group, did not come back to Priego; they went further north, beyond the Tajo, as far as Teruel, in Aragón, where they enlisted in the Republican Army. Matías knew about this, hearing his mother cry every single night. His mother cried with every battle. If the Nationalists won she cried for Cándido, who was suffering there in Brunete, fighting against the chilblains and lice in Teruel, retreating across the Ebro time and again. If the Republicans won she then cried for another son of hers, the eldest, who had become a Carlist militia man[1], and was now a prisoner. His father silently received the monthly payment from the Republican Army sent by Cándido. Matias remembered him carefully folding the peseta notes, and keeping them in a sack that he buried and unburied among the vegetables on moonless nights. Had they won the war, they would have a treasure now. But they lost the war and only the Carlist militia man came back home – his mother saw him coming through the path next to the ditch and the Borboton brook, and from far off she confused him with Cándido. She ran like crazy to hold him, but it was the other one. And it was he, the militia man who dug up the sack of rotten paper and burned it just when other people were burning stubble, so you could not tell where the smoke was coming from.

Ten years had passed since then and Matias continued to receive news about Cándido, as if his life had become a novel in instalments. His was a moving novel of fight, battles, hope and freedom. All of it became a family legend, told on black winter nights whilst hemmed in the dark house, lit with just a black smoky oil lamp, and barely heated by a brazier of poisonous coal dust that forced them to keep a small slit open in the window.

When they lost the war, the inseparable Cándido and Pedro, and a gypsy friend of theirs, Doroteo, joined the column of exiles. They

---

1, Volunteers for the Nationalists, who were based mainly in Navarra in northern Spain.

arrived at the French frontier on foot following the coastline from Sagunto, longing for the sun of their childhood, and the dry air of the sierra that smelled like medicinal plants, which made them stronger. They survived bombings, hunger, disease and defeat like few others. However, like many others, they were received in Perpignan, further north from the misery that was the camp at Colliure, by the barbed wire of a concentration camp established, with Marshal Pétain's permission, by the Nazi occupying army. They were proud gancheros and they were still willing to fight, despite having lost the war, and despite being imprisoned, condemned to work with a pickaxe, pointlessly swinging it against hard rocks, and hopelessly trying to strike sparks, signs of life and pain that jolted their hands. They were mocked by the surrounding guards. One day, one of the guards, fat and greasy, a pig of a man, was smoking a cigar in front of them and blew the smoke into their faces, as if its smell could make them dream of a better life.

'Would you like to smoke? Would you like a drag?' Without thinking twice, Doroteo stopped making sparks fly from the stone and sank the pick into the face of the German soldier. It penetrated his face like soft butter, in a spurt of blood, from where it did not rebound. Punish one, punish all; all three were sent on a train to an extermination camp in Lille, very close to Belgium, the land of eternal mist, humidity and sorrow. They managed to escape from the train, throwing themselves into the darkness, and rolling down the rocky slopes, between the trees replanted from Les Landes, on to the dunes that smelled of the Atlantic. With the quick and lively pace of peasants they arrived in Agen, where children are born with rugby boots on their feet, they are that hard.

Some years later, Matias was told (just as his family read in the occasional letter) that the three of them managed to escape the extermination camp and joined the Resistance. A new war, but this time it was won. In August 1944 Cándido entered Paris with the firsts units Marshal de Gaulle had managed to form. He entered Paris as a free man, waving the yellow, red and purple republican flag, and so did his friends not long after. In Paris they lived and made love, joyfully walking along the streets, drinking wine that tasted like freedom.

Doroteo, the brilliant bohemian, met an artist and decided to stay in Paris. Pedro and Cándido went back to Agen, in the south, where they could easily smell Spain and Spanish could be heard everywhere in the street; there the defeated exiles could cry or take up arms to reconquer their land. Guided by the communists Enrique Lister and 'El Campesino', who organised the exiles and helped soldiers regroup after the Second World War, Cándido and Pedro volunteered to continue battling in the Valle de Arán. There they waited confidently for the help of western powers in getting rid of Franquismo, now that fascism had been defeated in Italy, Germany and all the occupied countries. After conquering the Valle de Arán, which gave access to France, and where the waters of the Garonne River are born to end up in Bordeaux, the Spanish communists (Cándido and Pedro among them) were fooling themselves if they thought they could count on military support that would be adequate to confront Franco's army in the open. But Candido and Pedro were blinded by their enthusiasm. Support troops never came. They had to flee as best they could. Franco remained 25 more years in power, the cruel and perpetual dictator he was.

'Pedro Pernia is back. He is there for his father's funeral,' Pernia's mother told Matias one day. He said that Cándido was doing well, but that he was afraid to come back – afraid for us, not for himself.

However, the Soria family was respected in the town of Priego, perhaps because of the occasional intervention by their Carlist son with the authorities. It was the defeated communists to whom nobody spoke, who were not contracted by the landlords to work in the fields, who were not allowed either in bars or in the church in which the imperial eagle, carved in stone, marked the way to the cross of the fallen at the door – but at least they were not killed. In the late 40s death was a real threat to communists in Priego. At night, the Maquis, reduced to scraping out an existence in their isolated encampments in the sierra, came down to the village to steal hens, pigs, chorizos and eggs from the few rich landlords. But it was there where they found the moving solidarity of those who had lost everything, poor people who gave them shelter and protection. The captain of the Guardia

Civíl warned: for every night robbery he would kill a communist in the village square the next day. The man of the sinister three-corned hat kept his word. The dawn in the village was darkened by the sound of three or four deadly shots. The captain's task finally came to an end when one night the Maquis decided to kill him in his office instead of stealing food. Then they left forever, but, isolated in the sierra, they died one by one in ambushes.

Cándido did not come back to Priego, because he knew he would be arrested, sent to another concentration camp, like all communists, or sentenced to death for losing the war. But Pedro Pernia was allowed to attend his father's funeral. Pedro, who had established himself as a shoemaker in Agen, came back but would not stay for long. Before returning to France he spoke to his sister Julia, little more than a girl, but with three children of her own and starving.

'You don't have a future here,' he told his sister. 'Here there's only poverty. You must convince Luis to go up north, at least to the Valle de Arán, where your sister decided to stay after the war. I'll go with him, we'll make it a one way journey.'

Julia was married to Luis Ocaña, one of the poor, communist Ocañas and their first son, named Jesús Luis, was born on 6 July 1945. Two years later Jesús Luis had a sister called Amparo and Antonio, the third one, came early in 1951.

Luis's wages were mostly used to feed them all: a daily kilo of black bread – with its cloying and rancid smell of old and cold fat, of sheep, and of the lanolin extracted from the wool when it was washed with lye, a few items he was given in the factory where he worked carding sheep's fleece from dawn till dusk. He could also complement this with a few vegetables from a small plot, some beans, and a few containers of oil he was allowed to take home from the mill where he helped to press the olives. Its smell made everyone happy. He also had to spend many spring nights sleeping outdoors, next to the small orchard, if he did not want to lose his turn to water his lettuces, planted in the miserly earth. However, the factory closed and Luis was left with nothing, not even work as a day labourer. He had spent months in this situation when Pedro spoke about the Valle de Arán to his sister in the dark, sad kitchen, as cold as the grave, in his house made of lime and poor pebbles, and scorched by the sun.

'It will be hard work. It's going to be a miner's work, swinging a pick-axe and excavating tunnels and underground passages for the big power station under construction in the Pyrenees. But I know Luis. He is not scared of hard work. He is strong, hard, a real fighter, so you'll earn enough to eat.' The words Pedro said to Luisa came deep from his compassionate, communist and tenacious soul. He told her they would also have a chance to leave this village where they were not loved by many, and so they would also have a chance to flee from the misery they seemed to be condemned to in Priego. 'You will be close to both of your sisters and close to me and Candido as well,' said Pedro.

At the frontier, in Les Landes and in Agen, the Soria-Pernia family bond, which the Ocaña branch would eventually join, grew as organised and with as much solidarity as the cell of the Communist party to which they belonged, generous and unsophisticated as they were. Cándido ended up marrying another of Pedro Pernia's sisters and worked as a woodcutter in Magnan. Cándido's big and strong hands held tight to the axe in the days of winter and a waning crescent moon. With these hands Cándido would bring down the tall and straight pines whose frozen resin retreats into the roots, making the tree healthier and ready to dry up once cut. Cándido has been familiar with all this since he was a child, because he worked as a ganchero in the high Tajo, moving tree trunks effortlessly, as if by magic. It was something he would never forget; he was condemned, with a degree of melancholia, to remember it forever.

Jesús Luis Ocaña left Priego before he was six and had no time for nostalgia towards the town and its sierras to take root. Later on, in his visits, he longed for its smell, its dry wind and its hard sun as if they were a part of himself, a part of his childhood. Others, like his childhood friend Salvador, used to talk to him about the things that scared them most, like the story of el Hierro cave, in Villaconejos, south of the village, on the other side of the cliffs of Puntal del Fraile. This cave was so big nobody had ever managed to cross it entirely. A sinister river of frozen water passed through it and none of those who fell into it came out alive. They also talked about the wonderful things that happened when they got lost in the forest whilst chasing birds whose sounds drove them mad, although they almost never succeeded in hitting them with stones. They were also fascinated by a fountain called la Loca del Desierto, which descended more than 30 yards from the cliff from where it was born, imitating, according to the impulse of the wind, now a heavy dew, now a pleasant rain, now a downpour. Years later they lay down together and Salvador used to tell these stories to Jesús Luis, whose memory failed him. They lay down next to each other and imagined the world as if it were pushed by the wind, wherever la Loca fancied taking them. But Jesús Luis could not remember this either, which hurt him deeply, because he spent all his life in search of something in his childhood which might have brought him some happiness. Nor could he remember the river Trabaque, into which the river Escabas flows, two kilometres beyond the very high lime and stone Allende bridge. From there both of them admired the light ballet of the gancheros, and the docile descent of the tree trunks between rocks and whirlpools in the thaw. In that river they used to bathe and scream to scare the fish and trout, not so abundant there as far above in the sierra. But they were much tastier and salmon coloured. Fishermen around got angry as they also had hopes of catching some exquisite eels, although they knew there were not many left after the numerous crabs had finished with the spawn. They did not remember either the fresh gulps from Matías Soria's water jar that they ripped off from the rag and bone man, imitating the braying of his donkey behind him on the dry and stony path.

2

Luis Ocaña was always Jesús to his family. In fact, his brothers, cousins and friends still call him Jesús, or a French-influenced, unintended pun 'Yesuis', just like the cyclist introduced himself to Josiane, who would become his wife: 'Yesuis Luis Ocaña' ('I am Luis Ocaña'). Ocaña's unwanted dark childhood, the one which Jesús Luis wanted to forget, was in Vila and Vielha, in Arán. This was the childhood he later wanted to get rid of as a cyclist, after he 'killed' Merckx.

Luis Ocaña's father finally left with his brother-in-law, Pedro Pernia, and settled alone in the Valle de Arán in 1951. A few months later he returned to Priego to take all his family with him: his wife Julia, cold and toughened, Jesús Luis, Amparo and Antonio who was still crawling.

They lived in Vila, in a house on the side of a mountain of piled slabs. Even in summer a freezing wind always found a way to seep into it, with a chilling, sad hiss. During the months of snow they had to leave the house through a small window because the door was blocked. Once outside they could unblock it. There, in Vila, where they lived until Jesús Luis turned 12, he and Amparo were wild and free, but hungry. Their father was still a slave and every night their mother washed the few pieces of clothing the children had: a coat, a pair of high collared sweaters, some skirts and trousers, which she dried next to the chimney so that they could go to school with clean, even if smoke-smelling, clothes. Their father was promoted in work. He wouldn't dig in the tunnels anymore; he would make the underground shutterings, which thoroughly suited his artisan soul, the soul of someone who knows how to adapt the materials he finds around him to his needs, like sinking the teeth of a tightly grasped saw into the wood and and sawing off enough wood. But he still earned very little.

'Kids, come in!' shouted Julia. 'Come on, quick!'

'Why mum?' Amparo replied, surprised, from the top of a tree she had managed to climb, her knees, hands and fingers now hurt and bleeding. 'Why mum? It's still daytime, it's sunny, we are playing hide and seek, hunting birds, dreaming among boughs and green leaves that make us happy. Why do you want to take us inside?'

'I told you to come so come. Don't make me come and get you. You can carry on playing later.'

Feeling sad and punished, Luis and Amparo returned to their dark, ugly and bad tempered house, while they watched how other children went inside joyfully and came outside later with a piece of bread and chocolate, or chorizo in their hands. It was the time for an afternoon snack. Julia couldn't punish the children. She just lied to them. There was no afternoon snack in the house. There was no bread in an empty pantry with a floor made of hardened mud. She took the children home because she didn't want them to see other children eating, shouting joyfully and having their afternoon snacks. In this way they would toughen up, suffering poverty almost without noticing it. But they dreamt of making a success in life. Amparo promised herself she would never go hungry again and swore to herself she would marry a chef someday. She would do everything she could to fulfil her dreams as soon as she could. Luis couldn't hide how much he wanted to achieve something better in life, in spite of his sickly body – tubercular lungs bought on by hunger which would afflict him for the rest of his life, and undernourished and sick gums in his toothless mouth. He didn't say what he would be, nor did he know, but he whispered every night to Amparo that he would become something, while she kept dreaming about her chef. Later on, he would describe his school reports as soda bottles because all the zeros were like bubbles, while his ears grew larger every time they were pulled at home and in the school, and his dark eyes sank deeper into his skull.

One day their father decided to take the children out of the village school, where they fought, shouted, insulted and were insulted. That day Luis arrived home with swollen face and cheeks, crying rivers, and with the unmistakable mark of the teacher's hand on his face. Although he didn't trust priests (always close to power, always defending the interests of the powerful), the father who never smiled decided that what their children needed was real discipline, a hard life, humility. He enrolled them in San Juan Bautista de La Salle School in Vielha.

When Amparo and Luis used to wake up in winter, silent and hungry, it was still dark. They jumped through the window into the street and ran downhill through the field towards the school. They walked seven kilometres to Vielha and back, always in the dark, splashing in frozen, dirty puddles, and in dirty snow that never seemed to melt. One day, however, they were surprised by distant headlamps and the coarse cough of an engine. It was an invitingly open lorry going down the road to Vielha. They ran as fast as they could, reaching the kerb before the lorry and managed to stop it. They convinced the driver to take them and so they made themselves comfortable among the sacks of cement and bricks and wrap themselves up with their non-existent coat. But for the lorry, the distance to the school was nothing, and in the blink of an eye they crossed the square of the prison from which, it was said, some prisoners had managed to escape by excavating a hole in the soft mud walls with a spoon. In the school, where the rich boarders skied and became champions, the best moment of the day was waiting for them, when they could have a glass of hot milk and a biscuit, which was their only breakfast.

In their own particular hell of Vila, one day Amparo began to believe in the paradise the priests used to tell her about. This was repeated in the religion class that Luis also suffered before his first communion, when he was only nine. The first communion was not paradise at all, and judging by the picture portraying it, the oldest existing picture of his childhood without pictures, it really must have been a torment. Baggy-eyed Luis was in the centre of the picture, showing his new suit, his hair parted straight on the left, a faint smile in his thin lips, short trousers and a denim jacket, white socks just a bit above the ankle, white like the ones he would be wearing later on as a cyclist. He was also wearing white gloves and holding a pearl white missal in his right hand, a rosary of white beads, a white tie, a shirt with splendid collars over the jacket's lapel, and a white handkerchief sticking out like a triangle from the breast pocket. On his left Amparo was sobbing, dressed in black up to her neck and with a black skirt, white sandals with white socks and a great white ribbon with a bobble in her black hair and a straight fringe in the middle of her forehead. On the right of Luis was Antonio, who was rubbing his left eye with his left hand as if he were not sure whether to stop crying once and for all and pay attention to the photographer's birdie. Antonio was the third child, blonde, and he was wearing light-coloured short trousers with a bib. Their parents, hard-faced, were behind them. On the left, Julia, their mother, was dressed in black, with stretched and tightened hair, with a parting, upswept behind leaving a loose ponytail. In her arms and wrapped in a baby blanket was Marino, their fourth child, like the one they lost some years earlier. Marino had just been born. He had a thick head, chubby cheeks from his mother's good milk, and a black lock of hair on his forehead. On the right was Luis, the father, furrowing his brow, looking at the photographer while calculating how much the photograph would cost. His fine mouth was a straight line, as if drawn with a ruler. It was right in the middle of a face with marked, strong cheekbones, sunken eyes and an ample forehead, with very short, receding hair. He was 39 but he looked like he was 50 at least, a worn out 50, with those enormous hands holding Amparo, hands that stuck out of the sleeve of an oversized, unbuttoned, sloppy jacket, as if he were not used to wearing it. He also wore a nice tie with a minute knot, all on the white shirt, with one collar above the jacket and another below it. Luis's head did not reach his father's shoulders but he was trying to maintain the same rigid position. He tried to be like his father and later he confessed that some days, just to imitate his strength and powerful will, he would go without eating, like him.

The day of Luis's first communion was a special day, but certainly not the happiest for any of the children. Luis clearly remembered one day, the day on which he saw a bicycle for the first time. He remembered all his life the name of the person who could follow effortlessly the lorry that was taking Luis to school. How he admired that. His name was Fenoy he would say many times later on. He was an amateur cyclist whose training method consisted in chasing trucks every day.

He was a young lad who used to pedal with mad audacity a beautiful pearl grey bicycle with chrome forks, as elegant and light as Fenoy's pedalling. Luis became immediately jealous of him; he was jealous of his freedom and his freshness and started to dream about being like him one day.

A few days later, at the entrance of a bar in Vielha, Luis noticed a red bicycle without owner and without padlock. He saw it there again for several days. One day, at a crossroads, Luis jumped off the lorry and ran towards the bicycle. Then he jumped on it and began to pedal. That was the first time he had ever been on a bicycle, but he managed to keep his balance remarkably for a few metres. Then he ended up running into a passer-by who was crossing the street. After his first bicycle ride and his first fall, he quickly took the bicycle back to the bar and ran to the school. That moment he felt his life had changed forever.

For Amparo, her dream of earthly paradise came true on the day when her happy, communist uncle, Pedro Pernia, announced his arrival at Vila with the joyful honk of his car. There, before her astonished eyes were endless quantities of unknown fruits, such as apricots, watermelons, cherries and pears, and chocolate. This was not Adam and Eve's sinful apple; it was a true and tasty one. He arrived from Agen with his car packed with food and with a message: 'You can't continue to starve here anymore, you must come to France. I have spoken with Candido. He has found Luis a job as a woodcutter in his group. You can stay in his house until you find one for yourselves.'

Luis left first, before the rest of his family, just as he did when he left Priego with a cardboard suitcase, following his brother-in-law Pedro to the Valley of Arán. In the meantime, he would send sticky franc notes to his family in Vila, earned with hands hardened by the axe and in a proper job, not just hired by the day. A few months later he came back to take his family with him in what would be their final exodus.

3

In 1957 the six members of the Ocaña family abandoned poverty and left Spain for good. Shortly after, Luis, the son, already 12 years old, would start to think in French. First they settled in Magnac, in the department of Gers, home of foie and Armagnac, bordering Les Landes. It was the centre of a circle of 20 kilometres radius that would contain all the important places in the life of Luis Ocaña and his family: Le Houga, Aire-sur-Adour, Mont-de-Marsan, Bretagne-de-Marsan, Nogaro, Caupenne d'Armagnac, Labastide d'Armagnac…

France, the paradise, was only ten kilometres away from Vila, but it felt like a different world. All you had to do was follow the river Garonne which marked the frontier; then just cross the Portillón and carry on beyond Luchon towards the plain on which the Pyrenees abruptly ended, through crisp valleys where you could see bears; and then simply carry on a few kilomteres north of Pau to Gers to get to Magnan, where Candido Soria lived with Julia's sister and with his daughters, and where the well-lit school had hedges, purple, sweet smelling flowers and mimosas.

The family arrived in the spring to a place where there was food, but where life was also hard to begin with. In Candido's house, with a garden full of singing birds and little chicks running around, Luis felt free to run wild and to enjoy himself. There he also discovered the real meaning of the word 'feast' as, for the first time in his life, he ate his fill, only stopping out of sheer boredom. Little Luis did not think of himself as the sickly, weak boy anymore, looked down upon by his father. He felt strong and healthy and grown up, and he wanted to be as strong as his father, and also as hard and as stubborn. But he also wanted to feel free, to take control of his life in order to be successful.

The six Ocañas and the four Sorias lived in the same house, the two couples and their two daughters, Angela and Maria, Luis's younger cousins, who had bicycles like their parents. Luis did not learn to ride the bicycle until the family spent a weekend in the house of shoemaker, uncle Pedro, in Agen. He was certainly the most beloved by everyone, the axis around which the whole family revolved. In the blink of an eye, Luis saw his cousin's bicycle and he did not stop until he learnt how to ride it properly, without anyone's help, just like his father would have done.

Luis was a shy boy who wouldn't talk much except for cursing. His childhood hurt. He was only a Spaniard, just a poor hick, almost African, who couldn't even speak French. He was bullied and despised by his schoolmates: they insulted him, spat at him, and threw stones at him. But he had to be stronger, braver, hit harder and be more French than those who insulted him, both at school and at home.

One day Luis was woken up by his father before dawn, when its rosy tint was still the colour of grey milk. Both had a good breakfast and filled the pouch with a razor, salami, bread, and a couple of bottles of wine. It was spring and it was time to strip the bark from the trees, prune and split the pine trees felled in the cold winter days of January, before the sapwood spoiled. It was Thursday, there was no school, and Luis was beginning to earn his first bits of money helping his father. In silence, both of them left for the forest, riding their bicycles, each in his own world. Luis looked at a clearing sky beautifully woven between the abundance of poplar leaves, and the dew bordering the road. He listened to the birds, their music, and smelt the perfumes. For the first time in his childhood he felt happy, flying on his cousin's bicycle. In the wood his father made a clearing and put a whip-saw in his hands with a handle of rough wood softened by years of sweat from calloused hands. But little Luis was still too sickly, too weak to hold it strongly, and neither could he move it as the teeth sunk into the wood, without crying in pain despite his hands being as big as his father's, like the hands of all the great cyclists. His father jeered at him calling him weak, although he really was insulting himself for having such a weak son. Years later Luis Ocaña began to understand, to forgive and excuse his father, when he himself had to confront the stubbornness, rebelliousness, and the wild free spirit of his own son. He came to understand his father when he had thought a 12 year old, his own son what's more, ought to be capable of doing that kind of work. He thought it was only too easy. For him it was. He was a man unafraid of anything, who showed the hardened skin on his back when he took off his shirt; it was so hard that, like a fakir, he could not feel the thorns when he walked through brambles. Luis the son could not help but be carried along by the need to love the man who lived without love and affection. He concluded that, in essence, his father was a martyr, driven to torture his own body by his own self-sacrifice and self-rejection. In this way Luis could also justify himself, and with the passing of time he would also despise pain and those who showed it, like his father. But this is a feeling that goes against nature. Sons should never be like this. If sons want to do something good for society then they should see in their parents' eyes the desperate sadness of being old, like Fenoglio sang; old, grey-haired and rusty, against the debauchery of agile, fierce and proud youth. A few years later Luis discovered the fierce youth of his father when he saw himself in the mirror as an old, grey-haired, rusty and desperate man, when he felt he did not want to live anymore.

Luis became fond of the wood that hurt so much and would end up mastering it like a sculptor, shaping his imagination with it. Thursdays and Sundays when there was no school, were like this, from dawn till dusk, over the next two years. But summer days were destined for helping in the fields, and doing the grape harvest in September, until Luis started as a cabinetmaker apprentice in Ducos's furniture shop, in Aire-sur-l'Adour. He was 14, and to get there and back from the house where the family now lived, some 15 kilometres away, he needed his own bicycle. The village, more a hamlet than a village, was called Le Houga and was a step forward for Luis's father, who changed his job, from woodcutter to an employee in the village farming cooperative. He did not cut trees anymore, but he kept on working as if there was nothing else worthwhile in life. He used to wake up at 4am and leave for work with his bicycle. He collected a few eggs, cleaned the henhouse, attended to the irrigation in the fields... And when he came back home at dusk he still had time to look after the tiny plot that he had always wanted to have, his own true vital space.

With the few francs he was able to save from working on the grape-harvest and with all the sawing and bark-stripping with his father, and with helping muleteers dragging the trunks towards the lorries waiting to transport them, young Luis was able to run to the shop in a nearby village, Barcelonne-du-Gers, next to al Adour, to take the road to Le Houga and buy his first bicycle. It was no less than an Automoto: the brand used by the early winners of the Tour; the brand of the pre-World War I champions, the bicycle of Petit Breton, Trousselier and Girardengo, the first *campionissimo*; the bicycle of Henri Pelissier, the 'convict of the road', and Ottavio Bottecchia, the communist bricklayer from El Friuli; the brand of Lucien Buysse, as the poets sang of his life many years later. A cream coloured Automoto with red lug-lining, Luis later remembered.

Luis Ocaña, condemned to be a French cyclist in France, and to write his life on the roads of the Tour, in the shadowy Pyrenees, or in the Alps where the heat would burn the cyclists' necks, discovered the Tour in the Santiago Bernabeu stadium. Luis was 14 years old when, one really hot summer, the whole family came back from their exile to Priego.

His father, like a *noveau riche* arriving from the Americas, visited his old mother, the ruins of the house and the village he had abandoned, a place with only a few buzzing flies and bad memories left. That was in August 1959. A month earlier Bahamontes had won the Tour and he was back in Toledo after riding the criteriums. Newspapers were full of it, with the Eagle's imperial entrance in a convertible car, going up through the gate of La Bisagra up to the Zocodover, just next to the Alcazar, to end up bowing to the Cardenal Primate in front of his cathedral, among a delirious crowd, some fainting from the heat and the emotion in those steep streets. Men were wearing yellow bow ties at their necks, over their work shirts; in the market, porters (one of Bahamontes's jobs before he decided to pedal to harden his legs like stones) were also wearing yellow shirts. Bahamontes had enjoyed 28 different celebrations and homages in the 30 days since his triumphant parade in the Parc des Princes velodrome in Paris. In Mataro sports centre, Barcelona's goalkeeper, Antoni Ramallets, gave him a present. A week later in the Bernabeu, a homage was organised to Bahamontes and Guillermo Timoner, the motor-paced world champion. More than 40,000 people admired the skills and speed of cyclists going round a narrow wooden track placed haphazardly around the field, with banked bends at the right-angled corners. There were also some prominent sportsmen applauding when the champions were given two great golden watches by the authorities: their white teeth shining with the golden reflection from the light beams. Among the 40.000 fans were the Ocañas, father and son, who could afford the treat of taking a slow and tortuous bus from Priego to Guadalajara, and another one from the capital of the Alcarria to Madrid. Luis, already in love with his bike, was impressed at the sight of the champions: a young Anquetil with his sad smile and blonde hair, old Geminiani, Rivière, who one year later would end up in a wheelchair after falling down the cliff face of what could barely be called a mountain pass, Bahamontes and Gaul in yellow, Antonio Suarez, (with a big face like a runaway horse), who beat Van Looy in the Spanish Vuelta, and Poblet, who arrived from San Remo only to crash on the second curve, the most dangerous of the four, a criminal curve that the riders took very fast, unaware that it took them into the barriers. Although the fear of falling might have deterred Luis, the sight he had witnessed of what a champion's life might be, the wealth, the adoration of the masses and the gold were more powerful. Without doubt he was going to be a cyclist. He was going to be great. His father would find out just what he was capable of.

After two years working as an apprentice cabinetmaker, handling the saw, the jack plane, the brush, sweeping up the wood shavings, and breathing the disgusting smell of sawdust, with glue sticking to the sad lightbulbs that emitted a dark and yellow light, he still had not seen a franc. That was the contract. He attached a portrait of Bahamontes to the handlebars of his Automoto. It was a caricature of Bahamontes taken from an old back number of the newspaper *Marca* which he used to encourage him on the climbs. Soon he gained notoriety among the boys in the village, who knew very well it was enough to say to him, 'Hey, you don't have the guts to do this,' and however insane or dangerous it was, Luis would do it. Luis was challenged every day by other children, but he was also feared and respected. In the springtime the boys used to race in the afternoons, after 6 o'clock, just when Luis used to leave the workshop; his hours were from eight to midday and from two to six, although sometimes it was altered with a few lost hours here and there. They raced through narrow and deserted roads leading to Les Lande, through the pine forest. Short slopes were enough to have fun and to challenge themselves. They used to go from Aire westwards, when the A65 that split the region and the landscape had not yet been built, making for the hill at Duhort. When a newcomer joined the group they used to tell him, 'Watch out for the Spaniard, he is a very good climber,' and when the newcomer underestimated him, Luis, on his 14 kilo Automoto, appeared like an arrow and climbed like nobody.

4

Luis arrived at Le Houga on a dark night, sweating and panting, just when he had turned 16. He carefully leaned his bicycle against a street wall, between pots of geraniums as red as life, and went into his house. In one of his sweaty hands he held a yellow card the size of a leaflet.

'I have been to the Cheval Cycling Club in Aire and they say your signature is required to enrol,' he told his father, who was looking melancholically at a bottle of red wine as if love was dying. Luis handed his father the application form for a juvenile cycling license. His father did not look at the paper; he only stared at his son, fully in the face, and with a look of contempt that scared him.

'You, a cyclist? You, who spends the whole night spitting blood from your tuberculous lungs? You, who are so afraid of everything, with your crying? Cycling is for men, not for you. Your future is to suffer like I have suffered, to starve and be poor like me. Only work will keep you out of poverty. Make the most of the workshop, stop being a carpenter and become a cabinetmaker and be better than me. Make chairs; make a cupboard for your sister and a cradle for Marie-France. You, a cyclist?'

That night, while his father was sleeping, Luis filled in the license application, with a shaking hand and a pen that tore the paper. He signed it, in the space for parental permission, with his name, Luis Ocaña, the same name as his father. He was already a member of the Avenir Aturin, the first club in his life. When he went to bed he whispered the news to his sister and got her on his side. She, like him, was strong and wild, and determined to be free and to free herself from the hell of her mother, who was cold as ice.

When Amparo was 12 she was taken out of school. Her mother, who had just given birth to the fifth baby, did not allow her to finish even primary school. The baby was the first to be born in France and was called Marie-France. 'You won't go to school anymore,' her mother told her. 'Now it's more important that you raise Marie-France. School is of no use for you anyway; you won't do your homework, you are bottom of the class, you do nothing well.'

Amparo did not confront her mother's cruelty; she didn't even dare to reply that if she couldn't do her homework it was because she didn't not have time for anything, because she was a slave in the house, a servant, a babysitter, a seamstress and cook. 'Now you have to look after the baby,' Julia said to Amparo. She did not even know that mothers kiss their children, because she herself had never been kissed by her mother in the difficult years of her youth and could not believe such gestures of affection were possible. Amparo ended up getting up at night to prepare porridge with water and sugar for Marie-France. She was feeling like a mother and continued to dream about marrying a cook who would take her out of her misery, of hunger, into freedom.

Amparo admired Luis and she heard his dreams in the night. She felt for him and was moved by his courageousness and his will to escape from that grim reality. She hated their father's contempt for him. Luis promised her: 'I am going to succeed in life.' She was convinced that he certainly would because she knew his strength of will. But she cried for the lack of affection in the family, which would curse Luis until the end of his life.

Forced by law, the exploitative employer Decos sent the first wage to the Spanish apprentice Ocaña. Luis calculated the amount in Spanish pesetas: 600 a month, which was equivalent to 30 francs at that time. That amounted to only a fifth of what he needed to buy a second-hand racing bicycle that he had to buy if he wanted to be part of the team. Ocaña was not paid for five months, precisely the five months advanced by Ducos to buy a 12-kilo bike for 3.000 pesetas. Before, he had spent his wages on black cycling shorts, a pair of black cycling shoes and light gloves made of leather on the palm side and crochet on the upper side. Cheval, the man in charge of the club, gave him the maillot, and his mother gave him a pair of white, short socks. This was the only contribution the family made to Luis' inevitable and unstoppable cycling adventure.

Young Ocaña came 10th in his first race, 68 kilometres in Captieux, a village further north from Aire in Les Landes. A few weeks later he won his second race for his club: 70 kilometres in Bretagne-de-Marsan. He won it as only he could, in a solo escape. In 1961, when he was only 16, he won six races in the villages around the region, and many others in 1962 and 1963. His victories earned him enough money to travel to the next race and to have some fun at weekends. He did not think about anything else. Although Ducos (now his number one supporter) let him have Thursday afternoons off, to train, and although his father had stopped throwing stones at him every time he saw him cycling instead of working, Ocaña did not feel like a cyclist yet. He felt like a young boy with a few privileges, free to go to the discotheque, to cinemas, or to enter in bars to smoke and drink. He felt like a cheerful, small town boy who become a different person when he got on his bicycle.

At that time Ocaña was already the kind of cyclist he would become, different from the rest. Ocaña had a kind of fixed, immobile shape, firmly fixed to the bicycle. Man and bicycle were one: his right shoulder was like a prow, a keel, like Coppi's breast, which allowed him to cut the air like a knife, a balloon, an inflated spinnaker pushed by all the winds that only blew in his favour, that were at his mercy. His distinctive hunchbacked time trial position was the same rounded arch that only Anquetil had previously had, and no one else after him. His head was sunk between the shoulders, as if he were a hare; his useless neck retracted to avoid spoiling the natural aerodynamic perfection of creatures designed to fly. His dark eyes and dark look never wavered, always fixed on the tarmac ahead and on the horizon at the same time. Like his strength of will, like his temperament, they never shifted. His big hands, like those of his father, held the lower part of the handle bar tight as if he did not want to let it go, as if his survival depended on holding on to it. Indeed, he only let it go when he fell from the bicycle, so painfully, so often. His legs were strong and muscular; his height, 1.78, was ideal for a cyclist; and he had the tenacity, the distrust of others, and the competitive, insatiable hunger of someone who had known hunger all his life.

One day in autumn he had a visit just as he was leaving Pierre Cescutti's workshop. Ocaña had just won the Lesseube, in the Pyrenees, the great prize for *grimpeurs*, a race only reserved for the first category elite. Cescutti was 43, only one year younger than Ocaña's father, and the president of Stade Montois, the most important cycling club in the region and, with its history, one of the most important in France. Its jersey was yellow with black shoulders, and a squirrel as the emblem. This visit would change Luis's life forever. Cescutti asked Luis to go and live in Mont-de-Marsan, the capital of the region and also the site of the club's main offices; that was where the team's riders lived and trained. He tried to convince him, promising they would find him a job in the carpentry shop owned by Marius Dupeyron, Cescutti's friend and also manager of the club, who would grant Luis all the time he needed to train.

'I will be your trainer, and I will teach you everything you don't know yet. I will look after you.' He also promised him a room in L'Escale, a friend's hostel in la rue Lagrange, all paid for, full board.

'Ok, ok,' replied Ocaña, who, for the first time in his life. was being treated with fondness instead of threats. 'But I am not free. I can't decide on my own. I can't tell my club now that I am leaving and nor can I say to my father, "Goodbye, I am going to become a cyclist in Mont-de-Marsan." He'd give me a box round the ears, and my mother would feel as if I'd sunk a knife in her heart.'

'You speak to the club and I will speak to your dad.'

But Ocaña did not speak to the club; he sent a letter to its President instead, telling him either to let him move to a real club to become a better cyclist, or he would never race again. Then, to make it known to Cescutti, he wrote to him: 'I am leaving my club. I think I have done things right. I don't think they will have any objection to me riding for your team.' A few weeks later, before the end of 1963, the regional federation of Aquitaine gave him their blessing and confirmed that the Avenir Taurin would not interfere in the transfer. Ocaña could finally join the Mont-de-Marsan team.

But his father still had to give his permission.

Cescutti was tall and slim. He took after Joseph Cotten, with his short, curly, slightly receding hair, his look of compassion and patience, his cheerful smile. The actor Joseph Cotten always had to put up with Orson Welles's maliciousness, his contempt and mind games that relied on an expression of innocent kindness, and a disarming smile that made villains feel guilty. He only recognised what he had done when it was too late, when Cotten was dead.

Cescutti, like the characters played by Cotten, was a master in the art of persuasion. One spring night in 1964, when Luis was about to turn 19, he visited Ocaña's house in Le Houga to tell Luis's parents that he would be taking charge of Luis's education; he would teach him how to be a cyclist, not a cabinetmaker. He would teach him how to train and eat, the proper standards of personal hygiene to compete in races; the basic tactics and techniques to do well in races, to know where the wind is blowing; how to put himself on somebody's wheel, to pedal without wasting his energy.

'Your son is very talented,' Cescutti told his parents with sincerity. 'Your son is unique. Your son is Anquetil and Bahamontes. And remember, Jacques was the son of a countryman and used to help his father collect strawberries on the clean banks of the Seine in Quincampoix, next to Rouen, and Bahamontes loaded boxes in the central market in Toledo, and also delivered goods with his bicycle...' Luis, their son, came from the same breed. One day he would win the Tour and would make them millionaires, but first Luis had to leave his family; he had to live his life alone.

In 1964, Ocaña settled in Mont-de-Marsan. Cescutti, conscious of the hard life they had led, looked after a number of exiled Spanish cyclist who lived there. One of those was Manuel Manzano, who, once he had got to know him, used to tell Luis about other Spaniards who had been there before, like Adolfo Bello, from Sanguesa, Luis Goya, from Guipuzcoa, who died in 1962, and the Lopez brothers. Two years earlier, in 1963, when he was only 21, Manzano had obtained French nationality. He admired France, he even thought in French, but above all he admired the democracy Spain did not enjoy. His mind was French, but his heart and memories were Spanish. Manzano, four years older than Luis and already respected by many as a leading figure in cycling, tried to persuade Ocaña that he was not unique, that all of them could complain about their lives, but they preferred to fight. He tried, but he soon realised that it was of no use. He would never manage to convince Luis about anything. It did not make sense to try. Luis had a singular temperament, which could become unbearable if you did not truly love him. But that was the way he was. It was his temperament more than his legs that would eventually turn him into the great cyclist he became.

It was two hours after sunrise, but the cold sun of February was deceptive, offering little beyond the suggestion of warmth that you could feel behind the window. It was Thursday and the carpentry was closed. Ocaña was meeting his regular team mates for training where they usually met – in the entrance of Vincent Labadie's bicycle repair shop, at the enormous wooden back doors which they called the confessional because of its little half door that served as an entrance to the dark grotto where his favourite mechanic, Bernanrd Ocariz, worked on the Mercier bicycles. Wearing a thick woollen jersey with flashy horizontal stripes and a thick and velvety winter tracksuit tight to his slender legs, Ocaña met his friends in the workshop: Manzano, Christian Leduc and Guy Glize, young like Luis and his friend. Ocaña was very happy because the day before he got his new false teeth from the dental mechanic. He opened his mouth and posed for a photograph with a fixed smile, with his permanently sunken eyes. He leaned on the crossbar of a bicycle while Ocariz was adjusting the front brake. A bit later the group of cyclists was ready to go. Once on the road, Manzano, the leader, noticed a group of clouds gathering on the right, so he ordered his team mates to turn left at the first crossing. Everybody followed him, except Ocaña, who stopped there.

'Why don't we turn right as usual?' he shouted. Manzano got off the bicycle and replied authoritatively: 'Because you see where the wind is blowing from. Can you see where the clouds are gathering? Do you want to get soaked?'

He got back on his bike and started riding again. But Ocaña did not follow him. Ocaña, the youngest of all (only 19 years old), turned round and started cycling towards the rain. 'We agreed to go that way,' he shouted behind him. 'And that's where I'm going. You do what you want!'

A few hours later, Ocaña was soaking wet and proud of himself in the café where they used to meet after each training session. There they used to have some crème de banane, they chatted or simply enjoyed the best part of the day. But Manolo Manzano took his fellow Spaniard aside.

'Luis, come over here, please; I am going to tell you my story. You must know that we both come from the same place, and you must also know that you are not here in Mont-de-Marsan becoming a professional cyclist by chance. All my family was Republican. My grandad was executed, my father imprisoned, my uncle killed, that's what we all believed. My grandparents were from Granada and they migrated to Morocco when it was still a French protectorate. When the war broke out, his sons, that's to say my father and my uncle, went to France from Morocco to join the army and fight Franco. But they were separated and made prisoners, and they never saw each other again: both ended up believing the other had died. A year after the war, my father was still a prisoner in one of Franco's concentration camps in Miranda de Ebro, but my mother managed to get him out of there. I was born in 1941, in Medina de Rioseco, a dry land of fields, of poor day labourers and reapers. But eventually my father took us all to Santander, following the towpath beside the Canal de Castilla. At 15, I was already a cyclist; at least I had already ridden two races. I came last in one of them but won the other. In Santander there were very good cyclists: I rode against San Emeterio, Emilio Cruz and Ventura Diaz. It was then when I met Cescutti.

'Luis, has anybody told you about Cescutti's life? You should also know about that too. Before you were born, only a month before, in May 1945, Cescutti was a soldier in the Leclerc Division, the 2nd Armoured Division, which was part of the allied army that entered Berlin after it surrendered.' Manzano had never seen Luis so interested in a story, so much that his banana was untouched in the glass. 'You know what? Cescutti was one of the few French soldiers who entered Hitler's bunker after it had been bombed. Then he came back to his home in Mont-de-Marsan, where he continued his love affair with cycling. He also fell in love with a female cyclist, Rolande Danne, whom he used to train and twice he prepared her to beat the hour record (once solo and then motor-paced) in the Bordeaux velodrome. Then he married Rolande, and continued to be in love with cycling and cyclists. He used to insist that it was more important that they were honest and honourable rather than good cyclists. Cescutti had money because he had worked a lot as a bricklayer and as a builder. This is why I know him since before he was a cyclist. Luis, I told you that I met Cescutti in Santander, when I was only 15, when my parents were young and were looking for a job. One day in 1956 Cescutti went to the harbour, a meeting point for hopeful workers, offering work as bricklayers in his building company in France. My father joined without hesitation and soon after, my family and I were living here in Mont-de-Marsan, and we are still here because I have become a cyclist; otherwise, we would have gone back. If it had been up to my parents, we would have gone back immediately, because of all these boring Sunday afternoons in France. They could remember how good it felt to be on the Sardinero beach near Santander. Have another couple of banana creams, Luis, I still have a lot to tell you.'

Ocaña listened to Manzano while he noticed out of the corner of his eye that the seats which, only a minute before had been occupied by his friends, were now empty.

'Do you remember Luis that I told you that I assumed my uncle (my father's brother) had died in the war, because we never had any news about him? Well, I was wrong. My uncle is alive. I found that out a couple of years ago, in 1963. It was the third year I went to Toulon to ride the Mont Faron hill climb, which was done both *en ligne* and as a time trial. Because I came third and second the first two times (I was always defeated by Bahamontes or by Poulidor, my team mate, or both), the *Nice-Matin*, a newspaper of the Côte d'Azur, counted me among the favourites to win the race. There I was, in the newspaper preview, so young and elegant, proud yet serious, with my purple Mercier jersey and its yellow letters. The day of the race, before my turn in the time trial, I was told someone wanted to see me. I did not know who he was, but I immediately felt something special when I met him. I recalled an old picture of my uncle that I saw when I was 20. "Are you my uncle?" I asked, unable to restrain myself. He nodded. He could not deny it. It turned out he lived there, in Toulon, where he'd managed to settle when he fled Spain after the war, and without knowing that his brother lived a few hundred kilometres away. But when he saw my picture in the newspaper, his heart jumped. His brother and I were like two peas in a pod. But all doubt disappeared when he read a piece of news about me, the Spanish Manzano. And there we were, him and me, happy together, leaving behind the sad memories of the past, while the Mediterranean breeze was picking up from the coast. And that's how my father and his brother met again after a long time, Luis. We were also scarred by war.'

'Ok,' replied Ocaña when Manzano finished his story, 'but the only true man here is my father. To be a real man, you have to be like him.'

Manzano and Ocaña lived some 200 metres away from each other in Mont-de-Marsan, but they only met in training sessions and during races. Manzano never went with Ocaña on his crazy nights, when, in the company of his gang, he headed straight to the dark area around the bull ring where the homosexuals used to hang out. To scare them, Ocaña and his gang used to shout: 'Fags, we are going to cut your balls off.' But, on the other hand, Manzano would ride alongside him in at least 150 races over a period of a couple of years.

5

In 1964 Ocaña won the GP Martini in Mont-de-Marsan, wearing the Stade Montois jersey, the one with a squirrel. This was the race of Saint-Roman-le-Noble, Nérac, Bagnères-de-Bigorre, in the far edge of the Pyrenees, in Saint Pierre-du-Mont, in Hasparren, in Langoiran and in Saint-Aulaye. By then Ocaña had already become feared throughout the region for his impulsive attacks. Every victory by his fellow countryman, every cross on the endless map of French villages confirmed in Manzano's mind that Ocaña's defects were in fact his greatest virtues. Manzano regarded this as the result of Ocaña's strong temper, the temper displayed by those who believed that having a strong personality meant contradicting the decisions of both coach and team mates. He was untameable, but for that very reason, for going against what appeared the logical thing to do, he so often ended up winning

One day in that year 1964, one freezing cold day, three degrees below zero, a day that made you grind your teeth, Ocaña won in Bagneres-de-Bigorre. Cescutti was waiting on the finishing line with a blanket with which he quickly wrapped him. He was visibly suffering much from the cold, his hands shaking. Suddenly, he heard a French voice with a distinctive accent, unmistakably Spanish, in its directness and in the pronunciation of every syllable. 'Luis is made of the same stuff as me; he is the blood of my blood.' The person speaking so proudly was Ocaña's father, who had come to see him riding for the first time. He saw him hard and strong, magnificent, like himself, and he saw himself reflected in his son. In another race, Luis's father took some photographs, photographs of him and of his pride at being the father of the champion. The picture must have been taken in summer because little Marie-France was wearing a short-sleeved jersey made of white cotton, a white pleated skirt and white socks. She was smiling with a mixture of sadness and happiness, without knowing where to look; she was standing next to her elder brother, who was naked from the waist up, showing the medal hanging around his neck, with the braces of the shorts hanging loose, washing his face in the fountain. His father was behind him, wearing a white shirt with the sleeves rolled up, and seemed to be congratulating his son, judging by his kind and hard face. From that moment on, Luis's father would be waiting for his son's result every weekend, although he couldn't get to all the races. And when Luis won a race, his father would get drunk and go to the bar to toast the health of the untameable Spanird. Some nights, on his way back home after a race, Luis Ocaña, the prodigal son, used to stop in Le Houga on his way to Mont-de-Marsan to hug his father in the bar where he knew he would be. Luis would always associate the wine on his father's breath and his happiness with his victories. If he'd abandoned the race, his father's reprimand would be hard. 'You are not my son,' he would say. 'A son of mine never surrenders. You must never give up,' he said one day, when Luis noticed he had a bandaged hand.

'What happened?' Luis was worried for his father.

'Nothing, only a hammer blow; it slipped out of my hands.' And, as if he were immune to the pain he must have been feeling, he removed the bandage and the gauze and revealed his two smashed, swollen, fingers with their nails missing. 'It's nothing,' he insisted.

But Luis's strict and stoical father would have many more excuses to get drunk and celebrate. In 1965, when he was 20, Luis Ocaña won again in Saint Aulaye, and in Saint-Pierre-du-Mont, in Hasparren, in Bayonne, where he felt like he was at home and where he attracted the admiration of another cyclist patron, Henri Labadie. He also won in Villandraut, Estang, Houeilles, Lagor, Aillas, and Artix. In one of them Cescutti was taken by surprise. Ocaña was flying to victory, as usual, as if the peloton were a curse, and disposing of it an irritating duty, when, just two kilometres away from the finishing line, Cescutti saw him suddenly stop, got off his bicycle and start looking at the tarmac, as if he had lost something. Cescutti accelerated and got near him. Is it a puncture? Has something broken? Is he hurt? But Luis would immediately resolved Cescutti's concerns. 'I dropped my false teeth when I was about to have a bite of spring onion; it was getting warm in my pocket.' As proof that he had recovered it, Luis breathed out at him. 'But I have found it, so I can continue now.'

With his denture back in his mouth, and with the spring onion in his stomach, two constant reminders of hardship, and of the origins of his strength and appetite, Luis Ocaña crossed the finishing line alone and victorious. Cescutti admired him and felt like an old philosopher, aware of his wisdom yet aware also of his increasing ignorance, and he began to understand that the more he thought he knew Luis, the more he was surprised by what he got to know about him. He concluded that this was another sign of Luis's exceptional nature, of the exceptional class of the boy who had come from the Arán Valley, weak and sickly, to sunny Gers. That boy, who had not even turned twenty, was already competing with Anquetil, about whom Cescutti spoke so much. Luis admired Anquetil for his style and for his solitude, his fierce individualism and his happiness with Jeanine and Geminiani. Being a foreigner and becoming an *hors categorie* amateur allowed him to participate in professional races as an Independent. So it was that Cescutti decided to take him to Mont Faron, on 2 May, to the spring hillclimb with all the top riders, the same place where Manzano told him he had met the uncle he thought was dead. It was a race of 28.5 kilometres, in which Anquetil beat the record with 47 minutes and 45 seconds. Ocaña came fifth, 2'–2" after Anquetil. He was the first Independent and the first Spaniard, so he could not let this opportunity pass. When Anquetil's masseur was rubbing him down and soaking him with cologne to calm down the pain and take off the sweat, Ocaña got a biro and a piece of paper and asked Anquetil for his autograph. He had been the first cyclist to win five Tours and the man who defeated Poulidor, whom Ocaña found unbearable.

Some weeks later Ocaña came second in the Grand Prix de France time trial, behind the Englishman Peter Hill, despite being troubled by breathing problems from his stained lungs, a constant reminder of the hunger he suffered during his childhood. Then he was seventh in the amateur Grand Prix des Nations in the valley of La Chevreuse, on the steep slopes so loved by Anquetil.

In 1966 Ocaña's fame crossed regional boundaries, and even went beyond the French borders. He won a stage of the Tour de Gard, another in the Tour de Bearn and another in the Rosellon Tour, and he also won the criteriums of Saint-Pierre-du-Mont, again, Auch, Lembeye, Pontacq, Cambo-les-Bains, Lamonzie, Vieux-Boucau and Poitiers, all the time wearing Mercier's purple and yellow-sleeved jersey.

However, his name was still a mystery to many Spaniards. Ocaña was quite an evocative and resonant surname, which sparked the imagination, but in Spain it was known only to a few connoisseurs of cycling and mentioned in conversations surrounded by the mist of the legend, and exaggerated by stories of almost magical feats in races from over the frontier. Henri Labadie, whose elder brother was a cyclist, was the man who narrated these feats from France. It was this elder brother who, seeing Henri's early passion for cycling, told him one day: 'Dear Henri, don't be a cyclist, because to become one you have to poison yourself. Look how many cyclists die of unexplained causes, how many of them fall ill without knowing why. Look after yourself, brother, and never become a cyclist.'

Henri was a clever boy and he went into business, despite his continuous love affair with the mystical aura of cycling, with those larger than life figures, who risked their lives every day and who lived beyond the strictures of reality. When he came to do business in Durango or Mondragón, those corners of Basque cycling, Labadie would begin to talk over a glass of wine to celebrate the closing of a deal. Labadie used to sell bicycles in Anglet, between Biarritz and Bayonne, and he was the sales representative of Zeus bicycles on the other side of the Pyrenees. He also looked after and managed a number of Spanish cyclists in France, like Jesús Aranzabal, who lived in his house. Jesús knew everything about the cycling of that time, the time he loved, when cyclists rode for money, not for the sake of sport, as it happened later, unfortunately. 'I know a Spaniard,' he used to say, clicking his tongue, keeping the tension up while he sipped a bit more wine. 'I know a Spanish cyclist who lives in Les Landes; he rides like thunder; he is impossible to tame, but he is great. His name is Ocaña and he works as a carpenter in Mont-de-Marsan. In his verve he resembles Anquetil. The only way to prevent him from attacking is to hang on to him, which is impossible. When he was 18, I saw him in a race where he rode Poulidor off his wheel. What else can you say? He always wanted and he will always want to drop everyone. He was not born to be a *gregario* and he never will be; he was born to be a champion.' And knowing that his friends were beginning to dream and fantasise about his stories, Henri, who was no fool, ordered another wine on their account.

All those stories were summarised by the press with phrases like 'everybody is talking about that Ocaña, a Spanish carpenter who lives in Mont-de-Marsan and who someday will win the Tour, or so people say.' They had been able to see him once in the flesh in the Tour of Bidasoa in 1965 as part of a team created by Labadie himself. The following year he would be seen again in the same race, with the same team, and that would be impossible to forget. Ocaña escaped on the third stage and not even the best Spanish amateurs, including the Olympic team of Gabriel Saura, with López Carril, Tamames and Gómez Lucas, managed to catch him. Despite their best efforts, despite working well together, Ocaña entered San Sebastian's Anoeta velodrome alone to win the Tour of Bidasoa, his first victory in Spain.

'What did I tell you?' hailed Labadie triumphantly from the middle of the track, looking all around, searching for the admiration that his prescient wisdom deserved.

More modestly, softly, almost inaudibly, Cescutti inwardly enjoyed the victory of his boy, but he couldn't help telling him: 'Well done, Luis, but a bit more and you wouldn't have done it. You attacked too early and by the end you were finished. You must think carefully next time. You must be better at anticipating your strength. This time you were fine, but there will be days when you will be defeated even if you are the strongest.'

Ocaña dropped his head, letting a few drops of sweat bounce on the saddle, and he nodded: 'Yes, you are right Cescutti. I am aware of this when I am in the race. My head tells me what to do, but it's not my head that rules me, it's my passion. I can't help it.'

When he won the Tour of Bidasoa, Ocaña was two weeks away from turning 21. But, like his father, he was prematurely old. He felt old beyond his years, overwhelmed by responsibilities, with few people he could trust. On his way back home, on the endless straight roads of Les Landes, he rolled down the window of his first car, a Citroen DS, and put his foot down on the accelerator. Drivinge flat out, he was calmed by the wind blowing from the sea and the smell of the pine trees. He noticed how velocity helped him relax and allowed him to think more clearly. That day he began to chase speed, as his only wish was to escape as fast as he could from the mediocrity that he felt all around him. From that moment on, he would always feel like a lost man.

6

Ocaña's fifth sibling, Michel, was born in his parents' house a year before that and five years after Marie-France. But the eldest sister, Amparo, was not there anymore to prepare porridge with sugar as she had done for Marie-France since the day her mother told her she would not go to school anymore, when she had just turned 12 years old. Amparo had been an all-purpose servant, but her dream, like that of her brother, had been fulfilled: she had married a cook. But she also discovered the terrifying truth, that dreams can turn into nightmares, that her life could descend into helplessness.

Amparo had always proudly fought for her life. Some of her friends wanted to take her to Paris to work as a seamstress, but her parents would not let her go. She ended up marrying a greedy, jealous, alcoholic Spanish cook in Lourdes, who was the son of some neighbours from Le Houga. Jealousy of the sort he had was not bred by tenderness but by utter contempt and possessiveness. She soon discovered that the virgin doesn't only protect the worthy. She was pregnant when she got married. She was looking for love and found how hard life could be. She was only 17.

'But my mother-in-law is far worse; she's from Toledo, Jesús,' she told Luis one day (for her, Luis was always Jesús) when he stopped by her house in Lourdes, with a bunch of flowers from another victory in his hand. 'Do you remember the wedding day when she did not even come to our house to celebrate it? Do you remember that she stayed in her house with her guests while her son was with us? I should have realised what was waiting for me, Jesús.' Jesús was her brother who could do everything, her only accomplice in life. 'Don't worry about me, Jesús, if he abuses me one day, I'll leave him. Don't forget that, my dear brother. Have another doughnut, you look hungry. Don't forget the same pride runs through my veins like it does through yours. We both know that only anger will set us free. You remember that, Jesús? And please, go on and eat some more. Would you like some watermelon, melon or onion? Have some more, little brother. Do you remember that day when I got away from home and went with some friends to a dance in Mont-de-Marsan? Do you remember how you hit me when you saw your little sister there? You were there with your friends. That dance was the dream of my life; to meet boys from the city, because Mont-de-Marsan was like New York or Paris compared to Le Houga, and the first thing you did when you saw me was to hit me and shout at me with that rough Spanish accent of yours, stressing each individual syllable. "What-are-you-do-ing-here?, Who-has-gi-ven-you-per-miss-ion-to-be-here?" But I didn't cry because I know you, and I know that you have the same pride and anger as me, because I knew you did not want to hurt me, I knew you only wanted to protect me from life's mistakes. You are my brother, you are my protector.'

'I also have something to tell you, little Amparo,' Luis said to her with an unusually soft voice, and with an undeniably French accent. 'Come here and sit by my side. I have a girlfriend, Amparo, in fact I have a fiancée, and I am surely going to get married before the end of the year. Her name is Josiane and she is a long haired blonde girl, daughter of Amadeo, a lorry driver from Mont-de-Marsan, perhaps you know him. He is divorced and I have only met her recently because she lives with her mom and studies in Saint-Germaine-en-Laye, in the outskirts of Paris. This summer she came with her sister to spend the holidays with her father. Josiane is a delicate girl; she smells like the perfume of Paris, she is Paris and wants to be Paris. And I will be her Paris. But we will stay here all our life, in the country, because, Amparo, you know very well that I am from the land. I am like father, and it is work and wood and raw materials that give me life. And Josiane. And she will be Paris here.

Josiane's friends asked her, 'Aren't you worried about marrying a Spaniard?' and she replied, 'I am marrying a person, not a country.'

'Look what France is like,' Josiane said to Luis while they were strolling in the narrow streets of Mont-de-Marsan. 'Look what they ask me – how could I marry a Spaniard, and a poor Spaniard as well as that?'

And Luis replied with a question: 'And why are you marrying a poor Spaniard?'

'Because,' and she looked with her turquoise eyes straight into his black, sunken eyes, holding his face with her two hands to prevent him from looking away, 'because I am not France. I am Josiane and I love Luis, and I don't care what society thinks; I don't care about the shopkeeper or the bureaucrat feeling uncomfortable. They will only ever be jealous. I love you because you are strong and beautiful, because you will be great, because I fear and shake with your temperament. I have fallen in love with you, because you are just a man, a carpenter with dreams of greatness. You are ambitious and complete success will not be enough for you; I am in love with a tender boy who works in a workshop and goes out for a ride on his bicycle on Sundays. I am in love with a man like all other men, but different from all the others. A man who can't cope with discipline or bosses, a poor man with a mission, to help his family, his poor parents and his five brothers and sisters and to get ahead, and I want to be a part of this family.'

In a passionate declaration of love, she promised him: 'In life, I want to climb the same stairs as you climb. I know that your cycling career will make us live very special, fabulous moments, which I will not enjoy if I am not with you, I will not be happy otherwise.'

Josiane said these words to Luis, who was a person of few words, shortly after 15 June 1965, the feast day at Saint-Michel-du-Mont, a district in Mont-de-Marsan in which he had won the main race for the third time. Josiane, an 18 year old girl, was walking around with her little sister Nicole. She told her to be quiet, to behave like a woman. 'We are at a dance, so be quiet'. Luis looked at Josiane, her blue dress and her clear blue eyes, her little mane of hair, her smile. Luis immediately realised she was a girl with style and class, definitely not a village girl, and after getting rid of his shy and dull friend Glize, who was liable to put off any woman at a dance, he approached her with total self-confidence and the Don Juan skills that he'd always had, and which made the shy women he liked blush. 'My name is Luis Ocaña,' he introduced himself. 'I am a cyclist. I have won the race and I like you.'

'My name is Josiane,' she replied, already blushing, which pleased the ladies' man, even though her blush was caused by the effort to speak loud enough to be heard above the music of a tireless accordion. 'I haven't seen the race…'

Cescutti accosted Luis a few months later. 'Luis, are you crazy? I've heard you have a girlfriend, is that true? You are only 21 years old; you have all the time in the world to fall in love, and a cycling career to think about. Why? Why now?' Ocaña sensed fear, jealousy and disappointment in the voice of his protector. He was disappointed at not having been told by Luis himself; fearful of losing him as a cyclist; and jealous because now he would have to share Luis with someone else.

Cescutti and Luis were alone in front of the great wooden wall of the confessional, Ocariz's workshop. Summer had just gone and the first cool breezes were shaking the acacia leaves, which, still green and strong, had not fallen. Ocaña was sitting on the crossbar of the bicycle, ready to start a training session and this is how he spoke to his second father, the man to whom he owed everything: 'Don't you trust me, Pierrot? Why are you doubting me? Are you afraid that what has happened to Manzano might happen to me as well? After marrying, Manzano became a lost hope after being considered a young hope; he will never ride the Tour, because his wife is more important than cycling, because he is afraid of falling, because he doesn't dream about glory, but about security. But don't worry Pierrot, I am not like that. I am curt and I don't talk much, but I think. Don't worry Pierrot. I didn't talk to you about it because I was afraid you wouldn't understand it, and I didn't know how to tell you. Don't worry. I will become a great cyclist, and I will train harder than ever. And you must know that if I am with Josiane, my girlfriend, my future wife and the mother of my children, I will train all the harder Pierre. Because she believes in me even more than I do, because she is more ambitious than I am, and she has courage and strength. She will never let me waste this opportunity. She will never let me abandon you.'

Luis was a taciturn Spaniard, not naturally talkative, and the intensity of his speech to Cescutti left him dry and strangely tired, with no wish to train that day. 'Now Pierre, let me invite you to a beer,' Luis insisted. And after the third bottle, Cescutti, more enthusiastic than ever with his cyclist, with his strength of character, offered a toast to his future wedding and made him promise that he would be his best man.

Ocaña was not only stubborn; he also wanted to be innovative: he wanted to be the first man from Mont-de-Marsan to get married on Christmas eve, in a church with Christmas carols and nativity scenes, and loud children on holiday. But the priest of the parish was even louder when he yelled 'Arrogance!' over the black cassock where a fresh drop of wine spilt from the priest's lips was conspicuously shining. The stain was expanding through the whole cassock. 'That is the worst of sins. Arrogance! Do you consider yourself better than Jesus Christ to attempt to obscure in your heart the day of his birth in a poor manger? You, who do not believe in God even though you are baptised, even though you haven't set a foot in a church since your first communion!'

'Well then, if I can't marry on the 24th I won't get married,' Luis told Josiane when they left the parish church, leaving his future wife trying to persuade him to get that date out of his head.

And, of course, he did get married on the 24 December, on Christmas Eve 1966. Josiane was dressed in radiant white like all brides, although the cold and the low winter sun made her screw her eyes up. Her blonde hair was tied back in a bun from where her great veil unfolded in a light descent, falling tenderly on the face of Marie-France, who was also dressed in white, and wearing a miniature bun in her little head of brown hair. The bride carried a bunch of white roses in her gloved hands, or were they orange blossoms? Carnations? The picture was taken from quite a distance by the photographer, who wanted to enlarge the frame to fit four elegant young gentlemen, two on each side of the couple, who were holding in the air a pair of bicycle wheels, aiming to simulate an arch to be crossed by the bride and groom. Luis was standing straight and rigid on the right of Josiane. In his hands he had a pair of grey gloves he had just taken off. From the pocket of his dark jacket there was a white carnation blossom and at the neck of his white shirt a black bow tie, black seeming to imitate the firmly combed hair with its parting on the left, as usual, although a small teasing lock had broken away from the fringe and was dancing freely on his forehead.

From the picture, one can infer the wedding took place on a late winter afternoon as the shadows of the seven people extend into the surrounding ochre fields of fallow land, and the low sky is covered with clouds reaching almost to the far horizon. From the picture one can also identify where the wedding took place: behind the people, on the crossbar of an enormous rectangular arch, like white goalposts, on the path where they stopped to take the picture a sign read: 'Notre Dame des Cyclistes – virgin of cyclists'. The sign lay under a white cross on whose cross piece a couple of wheels were leaning, This was the arch through which you reached this tiny, almost ruined Romanesque chapel in Geou, on the outskirts of Labastide d'Armagnac, which the priest, Joseph Massie, had decided some years earlier to establish as a place of worship to bicycles and cyclists.

'Why would I not marry you on 24th December?' replied the surprised priest when hearing Luis and Josiane's request. 'The needs and wishes of all cyclists are sacred,' the priest told them, 'and it is our duty to fulfil them, even those of the most infidel cyclists, like the infamous Raoul Remy, who complained that the virgin of Lourdes only protected Bartali, the big nose, and the climbers because the priest exhorted cyclists to advance and "climb" in life. What about the *rouleurs*, the all-rounders? And what about the poor *domestiques* who put their life and soul into it?'

The priest had been a keen cyclist since he was a child. One day he was inspired by a sacred story, the visit of the Virgin Mary to her cousin Isabel, and thought how much better things would have been better for the virgin if she had had a bicycle and arrived even before her cousin. After a few letters his idea reached Pope John XXIII through the Bishop of Dax, who happily agreed. And one Pentecostal morning in 1959 the abandoned XIth century shrine was consecrated as a sanctuary of the Virgin of la Visitation, or Virgin of Cyclists, to clarify things.

'I only ask in exchange, my dear and holy cyclist, that you promise to bring me the victorious jerseys you win so I can put them on the wall next to those of other cyclists.' Ocaña was moved by the priest's words, and promised he would fulfil his duty, and on top of his religious wedding (the civil ceremony took place in Le Houga town hall) Luis got the priest to celebrate another sacrament, the baptism of his first nephew. When she was 18 Amparo became the mother of a baby her mother-in-law did not want to see. The mother-in-law from Toledo did not go to the house to meet her newly born grandson, nor to the baptism in the beautiful baptistery in Notre-Dame-des-Cyclistes and the wedding where many Ocañas and Josiane happily joined together on Christmas Eve.

One early afternoon in May, Ocaña went to Doctor Blum's practice where Josiane (now Josiane Ocaña) worked as a secretary. 'What are you doing here?' she asked anxiously. 'Do you have a pain? Why did you leave work so early?'

'No, everything is ok,' Ocaña replied agitatedly. 'Come with me. Apologise to the doctor and tell him something has come up; come home with me and I'll tell you there.' Although Ocaña's cycling career was taking more of his free time for training, Ocaña continued to work as a carpenter. A few weeks earlier he had left Dupeyron's carpentry workshop because Cescutti's friend could not give him more free days, so he ended up working for George Nicou. 'You know what that swine is like, don't you?' he said to Josiane with his heart thumping once they were in the kitchen of their house, while he sipped from a glass of water. 'This afternoon I was in the furniture shop up on the ladder trying to nail the board of a wardrobe; I was hitting hard with the hammer while he was down there, with a cigar in his mouth, the smell was making me feel sick. With his hands in his pockets he was shouting at me: "Be careful, you are going to break the light bulb. Be careful you are going to break it." You know Josiane, it's that bloody light bulb covered in flies' shit which does not even give any light and hangs from a bare cable. He was getting on my nerves, over there with his hands in his pockets, the bastard. And the fourth time he said that, I got tired of him and I broke the light bulb. Boom! What an explosion! He got really mad. "What are you doing? How can you be such a brute, fucking Spaniard?" Then I got the hammer and without thinking twice threw it at his head, but I missed him. He got pale and speechless. Then I went calmly down and took off my dirty overall and I left shouting: "Go and fuck off you son of a bitch!" and I slammed the door.'

This time it was Josiane who did not say a word. She admired and feared Luis at the same time, his temper, the temper of a man who she loved more than anything else in the world at that moment. She really needed him and she wanted him to need her.

'Don't worry, my love,' she said to him, pretending contempt against his carpenter patron. 'He deserved it, the swine just exploits you.' At the same time she began to caress him, unbuttoning his shirt, laying her hand over his chest and his strong and soft back.

'Don't worry my love, my salary with Doctor Blum and the 1,000 francs a month you earn from Cescutti for riding in Mercier's jersey is enough to keep us going. Come here darling.'

They went to their bedroom and they made love like they had never made love before. Luis gave himself with more tenderness and generosity than she imagined he could possibly have, like an abandoned dog that had found someone who licked his wounds. She would never feel such generosity again. Once the afternoon of rage and love had passed, when the sun had given way to a tiny, distant sliver of moon, Josiane expressed her hopes, which, in reality, were her fears.

'We only have each other and the bicycle now, Luis,' she told him. 'After your missed hammer blow, you know it will be impossible for you to find another job; you will have to take whatever you can. There is no way back.' At that moment Josiane was 19, Luis 21.

Luis was aware of all that; and he was also aware that, in essence, the only thing he had left was his bicycle, his only salvation, for which he would sacrifice everything, even the temptation of friendship. In 1967 he rode like never before, and at the same time like he always had ridden and always would ride, like a solitary, mad dog, driven by his wild instinct; and his life ran as wildly as the brook in Priego. 1967 was the year of his 19 victories, the year of the Sarlat Grand Prix, of Pierre-Benite, of a stage in the Tour of the Alps of Provence, of Saint-Geours-de-Marenne, of Nersac, of the Bigorre en Tarbes circuit, Figeac, Champolion, Saint-Julien-d'Armagnac, the Tour of Roussillon plus one stage, and a stage in the Ronda de Muro in Mallorca, the Tour of Bearn, Tartas, Meymac, the hill climb at Massiac, Reignac-de-Blaye, Premio Azur, the amateur Grand Prix des Nations, and even an exhibition 'American' with his idol, Jacques Anquetil, in Palma de Mallorca.

He raced and won in the purple jersey of Mercier, the same jersey as the despised Poulidor, because in Autumn 1966 Cescutti, Luis' benefactor, had managed to secure a small salary for Luis from the head of the team, the revered Antonin Magne. In exchange, Magne would have first preference to sign him if he was good enough to be a professional. Ocaña was the only *stagiare* to have a salary; he also had use of a couple of bicycles and two purple jerseys with yellow sleeves and the BP emblem. The neck was also yellow and on the front, the inscription – MERCIER HUTCHINSON – which sounded like a long sneeze. He also got cycling shorts and a tracksuit, an official portrait, and he featured in the list of team cyclists that appeared in the newspapers. All young talents raised by Cescutti ended up in Mercier, like Manzano, who had become a professional with Magne a few years before.

As a trainee, and with Manzano as a team mate, he took part in and won races throughout part of the '66 season and the whole of '67. Most of these races were for amateurs. In all of them, Manzano tried to drill into Luis's stubborn, Cuenca head some understanding of the reality of cycling. He worked hard to teach Luis all the basic lessons and all the unwritten laws.

Every August in Ussel there was a very famous criterium, which brought together the most important riders from the Tour. The itinerary was hard, a continuous rollercoaster between Limousin and the Auverne. At night, in the room they shared, Manzano spread out a map on the double bed, moved aside the uncomfortable pillow – it hurt his neck just to look at it – and asked Ocaña to listen.

'It's a very hard *parcours*, Luis, very hard, so you stay calm. Don't even move a finger, let them make the moves, study what Poulidor, Gimondi and Anquetil do. Keep an eye on them and stay on their wheels, and when you see the strongest is making a move, follow him. But don't move beforehand, that's very important because that would mean death for you over such a hard route. The following day, even before the town mayor had waved the starting flag, Ocaña attacked. Poulidor won the race; he was clever and a *puncheur*, like a player who reserves his best cards till the end and becomes unbeatable. While they were having a shower to wash away the dust and sweat before having a quick snack to arrive on time for the next race, Manzano swallowed his almost inevitable, 'What did I tell you?' Instead, he was just happy to tell him in a clear and plain Spanish: 'At least in Mallorca you won a stage.'

In Mallorca Manzano and Ocaña took part in the four-stage Ronda de Muro, against the best Spanish amateur cyclists (Rafa Carrasco, González Linares, Gómez Lucas, Mascaró, Bertrán…). They were part of a mixed team, put together for the occasion and called Humus-Regidor.

Given the toughness of the *parcours* (although every day ended on the Muro beach), Ocaña found the third stage the hardest because of its steep climbs to Soller and Puigmajor. The team agreed that given the circumstances, Manzano should be the leader because he was a great climber. Manzano explained the tactics the night before: 'Try to get into an escape, Luis, but if there are more than five of you, don't ride; let them give up and wait for another group of two or three to form. I will be further back waiting to jump and connect up with you.' The next day a group of seven escaped and Ocaña was among them; driven by his instinct he made the longest relays on the front. Manzano had to make a huge effort to catch them and Ocaña stopped pulling only when Manzano was just ten seconds away. Yet, he still had enough strength left to win the stage. The day after Ocaña had a puncture right on the start. A group ahead formed by Ocaña's French team mates was delighted to take advantage of Ocaña's misfortune to escape, and Ocaña ended up losing the yellow jersey to the French Mazeaud. At night, feeling betrayed by his team mates, Ocaña insulted and threatened them: 'I'm buggered if I'm going to race tomorrow, so you can go and fuck off.' Ocaña's multifarious team mates played the victim and told him a whopper while they were having dinner, when those issues were discussed: 'Luis, it is not what you think. We were ahead when you had the puncture and we let ourselves be carried along, but you know González Linares, that big thug with those huge hands and deep voice, he threatened he'd knock us into the kerb one by one if we did not collaborate in the escape. I always keep my word, but he really scared us,' they told Ocaña.

'What the fuck are you talking about?' Manzano could not believe what he was hearing. 'Linares? You joined the escape because you didn't care about Ocaña. You left him hanging like a dog run over in the road.'

'I have changed my mind: tomorrow I will race,' Ocaña firmly stated. He raced and sacrificed himself for Mazeaud, but the Frenchman did not have much to give and Mascaro (Kas) and Bertran (Picadero) managed to break away between the Soller and the Puigmajor. Mascaro, who was from Mallorca, took the stage, and Bertran won the race overall. Mazeaud came third, 25 minutes down.

Ocaña was just one more member of the team, but you could only tell it by his maillot and his shiny Mercier. Months passed by and riding amateur races was not enough for him; he was impatient. He complained to Cescutti.

'Pierrot,' he said to his friend and patron after every easy amateur victory, 'When do you think Magne will let me race in the professional team? I want Poulidor to see my face so he finds out what he's up against.'

Cescutti was an old fighter; it had taken him six years to see Hitler's tomb, but he'd managed it, and rejoiced in it. He tried to calm him down: 'You have to be patient, my friend; life is a long-distance race.' Cescutti pronounced these words lamely as he knew they would be utterly meaningless to the young Ocaña, to whom life was one perpetual sprint, a race of nonstop attacking. But Cescutti, too, was worried and he wouldn't calm down until a telephone call woke him up at home, one Monday at 8 o'clock.

'Hello, hello, is there anybody there?' he managed to hear when he picked up the phone. Cescutti was half asleep; he'd not gone to bed until nearly 4 o'clock, after taking Ocaña home. That was the time when they'd arrived at Mont-de-Marsan after an exhausting journey from Perpignan, where Ocaña had won his most important victory so far, the Tour of Rosellon. Even before Cescutti opened his mouth, the voice on the other end of the line carried on talking, although Cescutti had already managed to identify those dark grey consonants: the voice belonged to Antonin Magne.

'I have heard your little colt has won the Tour of Rosellon.'

'Are you waking me up to tell me something I already know? I'd like to inform you, Mr. Magne, that I have spent every day with him in Perpignan, and he honoured your jersey and your bicycles, Sir,' replied Cescutti with his clear, musical voice of brilliant vowels.

'No, no,' replied Magne. 'I am calling you because your boy has aroused my curiosity and I would like to try him in a real race with real cyclists, in the Midi Libre; I'd like to see how he works for Poulidor.'

The Midi Libre was the race where top riders trained for the Tour, but they also challenged and tried to deceive each other. In this race, Ocaña worked for Poulidor, but even more to enhance his own reputation. On the second stage, which started next to the walls of Carcassonne and ran along the line of the gorge excavated by the River Aude, Ocaña followed his instinct and joined the escape organised by Bic's Michel Grain, although he was pursued, albeit only briefly, by Fagor's Gines Garcia – a giant of a man, born in El Esparragal in Murcia, built like a tractor but somewhat faster. Ocaña, an untameable trainee who did not understand that one could be a cyclist without necessarily attacking, had just turned 22. On the descent of the Col de la Salette in Valras-Plage, on the way to the Mediterranean, near Narbonne, the trio of big names, Pingeon, Poulidor as ever, and Guyot, who in 1967 was considered the new Anquetil, linked up with the escape. Ocaña would always remember his effort and sweat for Poulidor, and the successful escape arrived with an advantage of more than four minutes, which allowed Grain to achieve the most important triumph in his life. Ocaña finished sixth in his first serious professional test, and might have realised what a feat he had accomplished if he had read the passionate report telephoned in by *El Mundo Deportivo*'s correspondent Juan Plans:

> This boy has been the leading figure of the escape; while Poulior was saving energies fearing a surprise attack by Guyot, and Pingeon hesitated between hope and mistrust, Ocaña launched an attack with all his force, tireless, boisterous and obstinate as he was. His true class burst out with all his power. More than once I have thought about the compliments paid by my French colleagues in Perpignan, who considered him a potential Tour winner. A possibility? But today he has made history, and the only confirmation he needs is his victory in the Rosellon Tour. We Spaniards have begun to open our hearts to hope.

The day after he could read in *l'Équipe* the praise made by the director of Guyot's Pelforth-Sauvage, Maurice de Muer:

> Ocaña, with Pingeon, was the strongest in the escape. In the last two kilometres he attacked twice, and he was still strong enough to lead out Poulidor in the sprint (Poulidor came second). It's a pity he hasn't become a French citizen, as then he would have been able to compete in the Tour…

Two days later the Spanish coach, Gabriel Saura, spoke to Ocaña about the possibility of taking part in the Tour, in which only national and French regional teams could compete that year. Saura went to France only to see the star everyone was talking about and he was reading so much about.

'I would like you to ride for our first team, Luis,' Saura told him. 'From what you have shown here I believe you have a real chance of doing very well.'

However, Ocaña had a different idea, an idea he considered better: 'But Mister Gabriel,' he said, 'I am only an amateur, I don't think I am ready for such a hard race. Wouldn't it be better if you took me to the Tour des Porvenir, which I would even have a chance of winning?'

But to Ocaña's surprise, Saura replied, 'No, I don't think you are ready for the Porvenir Tour, but for the big Tour…'

In the end Gómez Lucas managed Saura's team in the Porvenir, where Ocaña came third; it was Gines Garcia, the powerful Murcian, who rode in the Tour itself, and whose help was crucial to Pingeon's final victory, according to Julio Jiménez, who finished second.

From Magne, not a word, however much Ocaña was hoping to hear from him. Not a single word, good or bad. Nothing. Nor from Poulidor.

7

Ocaña had to wait until the end of the season to have news from Mercier's old director again. So, in order to get something out of the mistrustful farmer, he must accomplish yet another feat on his bicycle. Towards the end of September, when autumn begins to resemble winter in Paris, Ocaña won the amateur Grand Prix des Nations, the great time trial that separates the wheat from the chaff. What Mercier did not want to give him, Cescutti did from his own pocket: a new bicycle with a lightweight made-to-measure frame and with the lightest of components that would allow him to compete on an equal footing with his rivals. And he beat them spectacularly. Ocaña went over the sinuous and windy 73.2 kilometres in 1–42'–2" at an average speed of 43.044 kilometres per hour. That very same day, the winner in the professional category, Felice Gimondi, did the same in 1–34'–42" at 46.3 kilometres per hour, with the English specialist, Peter Head, at 48 seconds, Genty at 1'–9", and Cyrille Guimard at 2'–45". It was the first time a Spanish cyclist won that great race and only Julian Gorospe, in 1980, managed to do it again, riding a titanium bicycle, and defeating Stephen Roche in Cannes.

After making the lap of honour around the velodrome in slippers and wearing Mercier's tracksuit and with a huge bunch of flowers, Ocaña and Cescutti returned to the south in Cescutti's car.

'Now I can call myself a cyclist, Pierrot,' he told his coach. 'After this victory I feel ready to run as a professional. Will you call Magne to know what he thinks once we arrive in Mont-de-Marsan?'

'What Magne thinks, what Magne thinks…' a thoughtful Cescutti repeated without taking his eyes off the road. 'I'll tell you what Magne thinks and I'm going to tell you what I think of Magne, Luis…'

And while the night transformed the road into a tunnel from which dazzling furious headlamps emerged, Cescutti told Ocaña a story, another story.

'Look Luis, cycling in France is dominated by two people. No, no, no, I am not talking about Anquetil and Poulidor, but another two: Geminiani and Magne. There would be no Anquetil without Geminiani, and no Poulidor without Magne. You are and will be Anquetil, my friend. You will be Anquetil's hunchback slipping undisturbed through the wind; you will be his gaze fixed on the low horizon, with your head stuck and protected between the shoulders; you will be a natural meteor, Luis. And when spectators see you going past, immobile on your bicycle, immobile like Anquetil, like his profile of a flying Caravelle jet; when they see your brown face and the pain you despise concealed in your guts, when they see you like him, with your eyes of pain and pleasure inflicting upon yourself a torture that only you can resist, when they see you taking the corners on the roads from which engineers will learn road design because you can teach them the ideal curve, all those who see you pass by, like Anquetil passed by, announced by the light touch of the smooth silk tubulars on the uneven tarmac and the whistle of the wind playing between the spokes, all of them will want to become cyclists. They will want to be able to be born again as cyclists, so they can be Anquetil, so they can be Ocaña, so they can be beauty. But Anquetil…Luis, you aren't sleeping, aren't you? Anquetil is Anqeutil for two people, for Geminiani and Jeanine.

'Geminiani has a hotel in the shadows of Puy-de-Dome, wine cellars, and he drinks wine and whisky on long and sleepless nights. He talks and swears, and he befriends the artists with whom he gets drunk and smokes and loves women. Geminiani loves cycling, he loves Anquetil, and he would kill for him. He is a good friend of all cyclists, and all cyclists would kill for him. Some nights he takes his car and burns the kilometres all the way to Normandy to put an idea to Anquetil, Luis, an idea which seems crazy but it is the only idea he knows his own particular Mozart can understand. And Geminiani knows the best way to persuade Anquetil is to provoke him. I have an idea but… No, no, I am sure you're not capable of doing it. Even if it is utterly impossible, like connecting the Dauphiné which, as you know, takes 11 days through the Alps, with the Bordeaux-Paris, which starts the day after, late at night among the vineyards, since it is 557 kilometres, Luis, 15 hours in which they cross the exhausting valley of La Chevreuse that we are going across now, at night, and they do all this behind the motorcycles… but Geminiani could persuade him to take on that madness; he could get Anquetil to jump into an empty swimming pool with his eyes shut, and, like Hercules and his trials, get him to win the race; and to achieve this, Geminiani would go as far as to insult him from the car, guide him, design the strategy for him, love and understand him. He would even call the Air Force to lend him a Mystère to fly him from Grenoble to Bordeaux to be able to start on time. But Luis, you know about this because we have read it on the news and we have seen it in films,' Cescutti told him with his clear voice and his vowels full of light.

'Luis, everything Geminiani knows he has learnt it through pedalling in the hardest of times. Do you know what he told me once about his first Tour, almost twenty years ago? He said it was very hot while they were crossing the newly resurfaced roads of the Midi, and bicycles got stuck in the tar, melted by the heat. It was so hot… In spite of that, Goddet, the new dictator of the Tour, banned cyclists getting water from cars, so all of them were on the look out for springs or streams or anything without worrying about catching typhus or dying from poisoning, while the *domestiques* were sent on ahead to the villages by their leaders. This is what happened until one day, Geminiani, who was really thirsty, realised that another cyclist had a flask full of water and he asked for a sip. He did not have much hope, as water was highly valued in that Tour, but, surprisingly, he said, yes. For several days, Geminiani was allowed to drink from his flask until one day, intrigued by the man's generosity and abundance of water, he asked him: "Why are all our flasks empty but yours always has plenty of water? What is your secret?"

"Ah," he replied with a smile. "It's very simple. I drink from my flask but I never swallow the water; I just rinse my gums and pour the water back again in the flask several times a day."

'Geminiani felt such repugnance that he did not even have the strength to hit that son of a bitch, who got what he deserved anyway when he fell off his bicycle the day after and had to retire. Now go and teach Geminiani something he doesn't know already, go on… You have your Jeanine, who is your Josiane, but you don't have your Geminiani. You don't have a manager who understands you. That's because you think geniuses were not born to be understood, but that's not the reason, Luis. The reason is you don't have a Geminiani. Your Geminiani, Luis, would call Josiane every night to speak about his worries, because he knows you love Josiane and that Josiane knows how to speak to your heart, to your stubborn soul, and he would tell her, "Josiane, we must convince Luis to want to carry on."

'But I do want to carry on Pierrot, I want to be more than Anquetil. I love my blonde Josiane and I want to drive with her in a convertible where our laughter and our hair is caressed by the wind, like Jaques and Jeanine do. I want to have champagne for breakfast and love each other in Paris, and to enjoy our unworried and happy laughter. I want to be what no one else has been before, and I want to twist and squeeze that cyclist that everyone is talking about right now, Merckx. If I can't manage that, then, at least I will have the satisfaction of having tried. And the next day I want to fight again until my last breath … I don't need a Geminiani, Pierrot, I don't need a guide, I need someone to follow me.'

'You don't need Magne, for sure,' said Cescutti. 'Magne is Poulidor, Luis. And like Magne, Poulidor stops when the traffic light is red or this STOP sign is in front of him. Geminiani and Anquetil won't break the rules openly but they will try to find the way to make the rules play in their favour. The other day I was told a nice story, Luis. Anquetil and Poulidor met each other one day near where Jacques lives and they decided to have a race as they did not have anything better to do. The last to arrive at Jacques' house would pay for the lunch. But Poulidor was mistrustful, even though Anquetil had promised he would not cheat, that he would not use any shortcut, that the traffic rules would be followed. They started to drive and were together for a few kilometres until all of a sudden Poulidor realised Anquetil was slowing down. He thought Anquetil was in trouble and decided this was his chance to speed up only to find, coming out of a bend, a traffic light at red. He slowed down and waited for the green light, although it took almost a minute to change colour, as if it had been painted. Poulidor put it in first gear, let the clutch in, and accelerated away on the green light, when suddenly a car flashed past him on his left. It was Anquetil, the blonde Norman, laughing like mad. Anquetil knew the timing of the traffic light, and knew it was useless to accelerate only to find the traffic light at red. He knew it was wiser to calculate the right time to catch the green light and to avoid stopping. I don't know if this story was true, but this is what I have been told, but I have the feeling it might be true, Luis.

'Poulidor loves cars, but he doesn't like speed, although he has a big Mercedes, the sort that Spanish bullfighters and Portuguese taxi drivers have. He drives carefully and he cleans and polishes the car, changes the oil regularly, treats it as if it were his son. There's not a single scratch on it and he claims he will change the car for an exact replica when it reaches 250,000 kilometres, no more no less, because that's the distance this kind of engine has been designed to last for, so he thinks he will have to change the car every four years. He will die old and happy and the inscription on his tomb will read, "I did 4,800,000 kilometres in my car". That is Poulidor, Luis, that is Magne. They are like farmers, Luis, or two small property owners who are more afraid of losing the little they have than of risking it to get a bit more. Old Magne was born at the turn of the century. He is quiet and reserved and serious. To conjure up a smile from him, to make him tell a joke or a funny story is just impossible because he doesn't know any. They don't interest him. Method is his strategy, he says. He means that he is methodical and rational, and imagination scares him. He wears that long, white shirt only to stand out from the rest in the provisioning area and his riders know exactly where they'll find the fresh bidons, the cold chicken breast, the rice pudding or the apple pie. He never takes off his beret. Before the Second World War he won two Tours, two Tours, in the happy times of paid holidays and the Popular Front. Desgrange, the boss of the Tour, did not like Magne at all because he claims he was very dull, that he was not prone to giving headlines to the press, that he went to sleep at 8 o'clock and was not keen to take part in social gatherings or parties. "You have Leducq for that," Magne used to say. "Leducq is a Parisian and a rascal, and all women are captivated by his smile. Leducq tells jokes and smiles. I am Magne." He used to tell Desgrange, proudly, "My name is Antonin Magne. I am a farmer from the outskirts of Paris, the son of a peasant from Cantal. When Leducq is still out partying, I am getting up on cold, winter nights to milk the cows. Then I do some training. I calculate how many kilometres I have to go and how much effort my body will have to cope with. I stop from time to time and count the heartbeats. And when I cycle through the fields I also calculate how many francs I will earn when I win the Tour, because I am going to win two Tours, you know, and how many cows I will be able to buy with that money, and how much milk they will give me. That is me, Mr. Desgrange. In a few days I will go to Nay, at the foot of the Aubisque, and ride the stage you have designed for us fifty times. I will learn it by heart and choose the best gears. That will be the stage of the Tour I will win."'

'Did he win?' asked Luis eagerly, without taking his eyes off Joseph Cotten's profile, accentuated by the shadow that surrounded him, his almost immobile lips, his clear eyes fixed on the road, lit up by the stray headlights crossing from the other carriageway. 'He did win?'

'Yes, he did. He really did win, Luis. He really did. In the '31 Tour he attacked on the Aubisque as he promised, because he was the only one who knew about the newly paved descent, so he could use a gear that nobody else would have. He arrived at the finishing line in Luchon 28 minutes and 40 seconds up on Leducq, the winner of the Tour the year before. Magne also won the Tour of 1934. But listen to this Luis, when he won those Tours everybody had the same yellow bicycles provided by the Tour organisers. In 1939, Magne began to ride for Mercier and he has been the director of that team since 1953 – 15 years. He has never been the manager of any other team, nor will he ever be. But consider this: a Mercier bicycle has never won the Tour and I think it never will. Neither will Poulidor, because he is like

Magne and not like Anquetil, who has won five Tours, the Giro and la Vuelta. You will be Anquetil.

'You know what, Luis?' Cescutti went on after a long silence only broken by the roar of the engine and the coughs on the radio made by static electricity. 'Do you know that Magne only drinks water, despite spending summers in Arcachon, the oyster bay, so close to our beloved Lande and to good white wine? He also toasts with water. And do you know that he only allows the cyclists of his team to drink half a glass of wine diluted with water? Do you know that everybody refers to him as "Mister"? Even Poulidor does so, despite being like a son, after riding for him for ten years. Do you know that he, in turn, refers to everybody as "Mister", even Poulidor, whom he addresses with an affectionate "Mister Poupou"? Even halfway through the stage, when Magne moves closer with the car to remind him of the strategy to follow and the right moment to launch an attack, he even addresses him like this: "Go forward, Mister Poupou and fulfil your duty."

'That is Magne, for you. A man who always signs his letters with the same motto: "There is no glory without virtue." And Poulidor's the same. That's what they were like, two small, proud farmers clinging on to the little plot of land they fought so hard to get hold of. And so proud of it. Supporters love Poulidor because he loses, because he is just like them, just like what they are; they don't dream of what they might become, which is what Anquetil's supporters do. Supporters love Anquetil, that blond, intense Anquetil; they forgive the fact that he hardly ever attacks and they forgive him his accidents, which always happen at the worst moment. But none of them would want to be like Poulidor. They might love him because they see themselves reflected in his cunning: he is the card player who never takes any risks, who saves all his trumps for the end, when he makes the final, inevitable, yet inglorious move. Poulidor loves playing poker; he often wins, but only one cent at a time. That is the only thing at which he beats Anquetil, because Anqueti, like you, Luis, is one of those who are so impatient and even at the second round they're already putting on some miserable bluff which ruins them, or they ruin a good hand by not being able to hide it. You are Anquetil, Luis.'

'And now that you have told me all this, I am not sure what you are hiding from me, Pierrot. What is it you want to tell me? That Magne has confirmed that he'll move me into the professionals and you want to warn me about what I'm getting into? Or..?'

'Last week I received two letters that directly affect your future, Luis,' Cescutti told him. 'One of them is, in effect, from Magne, who writes from the Mercier headquarters in Saint-Étienne. In that letter Antonin admits he doesn't think you are yet ready to become a professional. He says it's better for you to wait one more year; that you are still a bit too imaginative but not disciplined enough. "At present I am not contemplating the possibility of having Luis Ocaña as a professional in Mercier. And I would like to remind him that he is still a trainee and has a renewable contract with us." That is what he writes,' said Cescutti. 'I am afraid you will never be Poulidor.'

'And most importantly, I won't have to work for him, Pierrot, because I am sure that when he says "too imaginative and not disciplined enough" he means that what he really likes is determination and hard work, or that I've got to slog my guts out for his Poupou. He is so ungrateful... He hasn't spoken to me yet, not even a pat on the back to congratulate me for the great Midi I did for them...And what about the other letter?'

'Henri Labadie, our good friend from Anglet, sent me the other letter on behalf of Pedro Matxain, the director of Fagor, the good Spanish team. It's in the back, in the briefcase. If it's ok with you, we could stop in the next village, have something to eat and you have a look at it, and tell me what you think.'

While they gobbled a good magret de canard with local bread and salami, a glass of wine and two coffees, Cescutti and Ocaña read the letter, a real offer for a professional contract, and they discussed it. The offer made by the Society of Arrasate consisted of 5 points. 1. A fixed salary of 15,000 pesetas a month (around 1,200 francs) from 1 January for two years. 2. A long list of clothing items and other material for the bicycle, including a formal suit, bicycles, jerseys, shorts, tracksuits. 3. Funding for all sport-related travelling expenses to and from Mont-de-Marsan. 4. The commitment to start in all the big races in which Fagor takes part in France. 5. The team would double all the prize money won to create a common fund to be shared among all the cyclists of the team.

'Well, these terms are even better than the ones Matxain himself offered me last year after I won the Tour of Bidasoa. He was so keen to get me to sign then that he even offered me 14,000 a month,' concluded Ocaña. Only one problem cast a shadow on his enthusiasm. In his heart he had already accepted the offer and saw himself cycling for Fagor, becoming rich, a property owner, and buying jewels for Josiane.

'The only problem is the condition that you retain your Spanish nationality, so I will have to stop all the paperwork I had already started,' Cescutti admitted.

'Well,' said Ocaña, 'at least I won't have to do the military service in France.'

Cescutti resolved all the bureaucratic obstacles, including a certain stubbornness on the part of Magne and his patron, Émile Mercier, to force Ocaña to remain a trainee in his team for one more year, before having to cope with a bigger and much more painful problem. On 31 December Cescutti's brother-in-law, Guy Boniface, his sister's husband, suffered a serious car accident while he was driving back home from Orthez, where he had taken part in a Christmas charity event. Boniface ('the Mouse') one of the most beloved rugby celebrities in France, died the day after. That was a sad new year entry for Cescutti, another blow to the old fighter along the road of learning to cope with life.

Ocaña was not there to cry at his side. Ocaña was already a young member of Fagor. In November he went to Mondragón with Josiane and Labadie to sign the contract with Agustín Mondragón, the owner, in front of Matxain. After that he wouldn't have a break. In a rushed and belated honeymoon, a year after they got married and with Josiane pregnant, the couple went to Madrid's Palace of Sports velodrome where Ocaña, a national celebrity by then, took part in a meeting together with the greatest cyclists at the time. He enjoyed his time with Julio Jiménez, who was taking advantage of his second position in the Tour, and he was happy to discover that Julio's best friend in the peloton was Anquetil, himself, his Bic team mate. And the magnificent Norman was also there with Jeanine, of course. And so, too, was Poulidor. After they had left the velodrome, and after Poulidor the hick had gone off to sleep (probably dreaming of his cows), everybody went to la Gran Via to enjoy the evening.

From Madrid the young Ocaña couple travelled to Barcelona, from where they took a ferry to Mallorca. There they spent a few days in a house one of their relatives had in Inca. They did not stop in Priego.

'Why are we not going to Priego, Luis?' asked Josiane. 'I would like to see where you come from, to know you better and meet your family again, see where you were born. I want to have and feel everything inside me.'

He replied shyly, 'No, it's better not to, Josiane. You would not like it. Spanish villages are not pretty; they are dirty, sad and poor, and my house is a ruin.'

The couple badly needed those holidays, the journey, the solitude of lovers. Very soon they would not be a mere couple anymore, as they would be starting a family with the birth of their first child. And very shortly, long periods of absence from their council flat in Mont-de-Marsan would start for Josiane and the cyclist, who was already a professional. And that would be the start of long periods of solitude for Josiane as a housewife, and for Luis Ocaña, a solitary cyclist.

Part Two

1968

On 1st December, Ocaña joined his new team mates with whom he spent days in the Alcazar Hotel in Irún, just on the frontier between France and Spain, the frontier of his life. There he was measured for suits, bicycles and shoes. There, Ocaña had an emotional introduction to the great José María Marotías, who arrived from Alegria de Oria with his set-squares to become, from that moment onwards, Ocaña's one and only builder of his made-to-measure bike frames. He was also introduced to Rudy, who arrived from Bera with insoles and pens to draw the soles of the feet of the new team members, to produce the best cycling shoes that could be found, the ones that were longed for by every cyclist in the world. Everyone there was posing for the promotional photographs: Otaño, Errandonea, Perurena, Mendiburu, Aranzábal, Santamarina, Gabika, Momeñe, Vélez, López Rodríguez, Mariano Díaz, Ginés García, Mariné, Alomar and the Galera brothers, Joaquín y Manolo.

'Have you seen this, Luis? I have read in the news that Merckx is getting married today,' Perurena told Ocaña. 'Look, you can read it here, this is the newspaper of three days ago, and it reads exactly like the public announcement displayed in the couple's city council: "Eduardo Luis Joseph Merckx, cyclist, resident in Woluwé-Saint-Pierre, Bouvreils Square, number 4, eldest son of Julian Joseph Merckx and his wife Eugenia Pittomvils, for the one part, and of Claudinc Acou, resident in Anderlecht, Compas street, 75, eldest daughter of Lucien Gustavo Corneille-Acou and his … Oh, there's a line missing in the typesetting…De Boeck, for the other part, are pleased to announce the marriage of their children, Joseph and Corneille in Anderlecht, on December 5th 1967." I think Claudine is the daughter of another cyclist, Lucien Acou; he did a lot of track riding.'

'Well then, Merckx and I have two things in common,' replied Ocaña. 'We are both Gemini, born in June 1945, me on the 6th and him on the 17th, so I am eleven days older. We both got married in December, although I did it one year earlier.'

'And all similarities end there,' said Perurena.

'Yes, they end there; my wedding was not in the newspapers. Only the priest knew about it. And all similarities end there because I have the feeling we are not going to get on well. He may win everything and be the greatest of all times as all newspapers announce. They don't stop talking about him because he has won San Remo and the Flèche, and two stages in the Giro before he turned 22, and because he is already world champion. Eddy may even win five Tours and Giros, the Vuelta, World Championships, and the Classics, but he will never beat me. No, Merckx will never beat me. Do you know why, Peru? Because I will never give up.'

Ocaña and Perurena were both in the cafeteria of the Hotel Candanchu, where they'd arrived that very same morning for the team gathering that was described in the schedule sent by Matxain as a 'process of oxygenation'. They had nothing better to do than sit and contemplate the cold and beautiful ski resort below their feet, where a few tourists were enjoying themselves. For reasons they couldn't understand, because they could only have been profound and sadistic, they were ordered to go up the ski slopes but were emphatically forbidden to ski at all, not only for the risks they'd be running if they fell, but also because the muscles exercised on skis are at odds with the ones needed by cyclists. They were also forbidden to ride a bicycle: they were encouraged to let their bodies have a rest in winter. 'You can take a walk, if you want, or you can go to the gym'. And they could also get bored, wishing they were somewhere else, like Ocaña and Perurena were.

From the moment they looked each other in the eye, when they had shaken hands a couple of days earlier in the hotel in Irún, Ocaña knew Perurena was similar to himself. He was different, exceptional, and he had no time for those who were content with the aura of mediocrity that managers seemed to imbue their teams with. 'Perurena is a non-conformist like me, and so he should be,' Ocaña thought. 'Isn't this village lad the best cyclist in Spain, the one who wins the most races? Isn't he like me – he can't imagine racing without fighting to win because coming second is nothing? The only difference,' he thought.

'is that I am a long-distance rider and he is a sprinter. To win, I need kilometres and mountains; he just needs a few metres and slight slopes. But we are identical. I am Peru and Peru is Luis.'

Peru thought more or less the same. No champion feels envy and certainly not Perurena, who could detect genius and the gene of non-conformism as soon as he smelt it. And he recognised this in Ocaña the moment he shook his big hand, bigger than his own. In that moment it was as if a nervous, electric impulse passed between them, an attack of cramp that for a split second left both of them shocked. Perurena already knew about Ocaña's greatness. He'd become his admirer the year before, watching his victory, and the manner of it, in the Tour of Bidasoa. This was an important race and he admired his temperament, one that he couldn't see in any other cyclist no matter how hard he looked. Peru knew about Ocaña through Labadie, their common friend, the man who recommended him to Fagor. No, Ocaña was not an unknown.

'You have come into cycling at just the right moment,' Perurena told Ocaña while they were cooling their second coffee. 'Until a few years ago, Kas was the only team in Spanish cycling, and they somewhat abused their position. They knew that riding in the yellow and blue of Kas was every rider's dream, and they took advantage of that. But the arrival of Fagor a couple of years ago dignified the profession a bit and increased competition. The Fagor team had strong foundations from its beginning. It had a seriousness about it and was well resourced and so there were changes. As you probably know, some cyclists went from Kas to Fagor in the second year. These were cyclists who had spent all their lives in Kas, such as Vélez, Momeñe, Uriona and Gabika, after winning la Vuelta, and you'll already have met Manolo and Joaquin Galera: they all come from Kas. They all agreed Kas was treating them unfairly. Two years ago, when Fagor was created, cyclists wanted to come to us because of the prizes, because we won a lot of races and because of our great performances in the big Tours. That's why Fagor came at just the right time. That's why I'm saying you are coming at just the right moment, Luis. Just at the moment when it is important to be brave. In Kas, the thing is this: for Dalmacio

Langarica, its boss, the most important things are the team prize and the Mountain prize in the Tour. Dalmacio has no further aspirations, nor does he want his riders to think beyond that. He tells them that the most important thing is to win the team competition and to win a stage, but it doesn't matter who wins it. And all the riders get the same salary. Did you know that, Luis? A couple of years ago Julio Jiménez was in Kas, and after the Tour of '65, in which he'd won a couple of stages and the mountain jersey, he went to Dalmacio and told him he'd had an offer from Geminiani to move to France, but he would prefer to stay at Kas, in Spain, if he had a bit of a pay rise. "You don't need to match Geminiani's offer, which trebles what I earn here, but if you increase my salary a bit I will stay," he said to him. And you know what Dalmacio replied? He told him that in Kas everyone earned the same, no matter who they were and how many prizes they won, and he told him he was sorry for the great Julio, but if he had a pay rise then everyone should have it as well. So Julio called Geminiani and Anquetil and told them he was ready to sign for them. He went to live in Clermont-Ferrand, in the Puy de Dôme, and he was happy there speaking French, drinking cognac, and enjoying young French girls.' And here Perurena gave Ocaña a knowing wink.

'Then, Peru, from what you are telling me, Langarica is a bit like Magne, Poulidor's French manager, who refused to transfer me to his team.'

'Well, yeah, sort of...and Langarica was also a cyclist in the heroic times and he also won a Vuelta. But don't forget that Dalmacio managed to tame none other than Bahamontes, who, from what I know, was as odd and as eccentric as you are. And in order to help the "Eagle" win the Tour, he went as far as to sack Loroño, the Basque hero, from the national team. What about that! Langarica came from Bilbao and the windows of his shop on the Alameda de Rekalde were smashed, but he stood firm: "As regards the Tour, I make all the decisions, and I have decided that Bahamontes will be the leader, whatever Loroño says." But Loroño still kept saying, "He took the Gypsy (because Loroño always considered Bahamontes to be a gypsy) and yes, he won the Tour, but if I had been there I would have beaten the Gypsy." Lorono is a Basque, don't forget that, which means Dalmacio really has got balls.'

'What about our manager Matxain, Peru? Has he got balls?'

'We are from the Basque province of Guipuzcoa, Luis. When our team was formed Matxain went to visit Langarica in his shop in Bilbao. Don Dalmacio told him they were going to kick Fagor's arse, and Matxain, who was even-tempered, took on the challenge and said: "We'll meet on the road." And there is not a single race in Spain without fierce competition between Kas and Fagor. Sometimes we are happy just with preventing one of theirs from winning, even if we don't win either. They are stronger in the mountain, they idealise climbers, but in one-day races we always crush them.

'I am sure Matxain will like you, although he has not been a leading figure in cycling like Langarica, and I am sure he will be impressed when he sees you cycling and he'll give you the freedom you need. But Luis, I am not sure if both of you are what each other really needs. I always think that geniuses need freedom, of course, but cycling demands something more.'

'Don't worry, Peru,' said Ocaña. 'I will know exactly what to do at all times. Don't forget that, Peru. My God, it will be quite a while until supper is ready. What can we do?'

'Shall we stretch our legs?'

'I have a better idea, Peru. Wait a minute; I have left the car keys in the room downstairs.'

They got in Luis's car, and his face showed an air of mystery, like a naughty child who was up to something.

'You'll see now,' he said, and with a sudden, almost violent swerve, he drove the car off the cold tarmac on to the almost freezing snowy slope, among the surprised tourists. There he started skidding and spinning, accelerating and thoroughly enjoying himself. But Perurena was pale and silent while he held on to the handle and prayed. This exhibition of madness did not last long.

'So, did you enjoy that?' Ocaña asked poor Perurena while he burst out laughing. At least Perurena did not throw up like children do in merry-go-rounds.

'Did I enjoy it? Did I enjoy it? I was just thinking one thing,' admitted Perurena. 'I was only thinking: I wish we could have an accident, that would destroy the bodywork of the car with us uninjured, only so I could slap you in the face and tell you: you're an arsehole.'

'You're a real character, with a strong personality,' said Mendiburu very seriously, as seriously as only Mendiburu could be. Mendiburu dragged his words as if to make them endless. Ocaña did not know how to take it, and feared Mendiburu's praise might hide a different meaning. Life has taught Ocaña to be wary. And after two months in Fagor, he had little reason to be either suspicious or trusting, so he interpreted Mendiburu's words about his character positively and waited. He did not understand Mendiburu's use of the word 'character', because Ocaña's Spanish derived from Priego, Cuenca, in the 40s, and had not evolved much since.

After two months as a professional cyclist, Ocaña has seen himself immersed in a process of 'Fagorisation', a journey to the roots of the team and of cycling in the Guipuzcoa region of the Basque Country. It consisted in a visit to the new factory of Mondragón's cooperative, a mass for the Virgin of Dorleta, which included a floral tribute to the patron saint of cyclists, and a prayer for the soul of Valentín Uriona, a member of the team who had died during the Spanish championship the year before, a presentation in the heart of the cooperative, the Bittori junior college, where Fagor trained its refrigerator mechanics, proper traditional home cooking food in Hostal Musakola, and even the Tamborrada[1] in San Sebastian. However, he had not got very acquainted with the rest of the team members, except Peru, with whom the chemistry had been immediate. Ocaña did not speak much and the others saw him as rather a shy person, without understanding that his shyness was more a symptom of introversion than of being timid. Some of the veterans even mocked the hard training he had put in to be ready for the first race of the year, the Tour of Andalucia.

'Yes, yes, of course, man,' they laughed when Ocaña told them that he had spent the whole month of January following Cescutti's strict training plan and diet, while Josiane, who had left her job, stayed at

1. An annual festival of marching drum bands, held in San Sebastián every January.

home preparing the clothing, the cradle and the bottles for the baby they were expecting.

'You take part in these races to slim down and begin to get into good form little by little,' they told him. 'Have you noticed how unfit Gómez del Moral is, the boy from Cabra? He's as fat as a cow, so he is the wheel to follow. You don't have to go mad.'

'I will speak on the road, to let them know who I am,' Ocaña decided, 'and I will get to know them too.'

So it was that on the very first day of the Tour of Andalucia, Saturday, 10 February 1968, when he had barely ridden the first kilometres of his first race wearing Fagor's jersey, Ocaña introduced himself by launching a completely unexpected attack on the way to Nerja. Rinus Wagtmans, the Dutchman with the white lock of hair, the acrobat 'Downhill King', as was unanimously known throughout the peloton, was the first to make a move. He went down the Fuente de la Reina pass on the way to Colmenar on the slopes of the Riogordo and the Alfarnate, where the smell of oil, thyme and firewood smoke coming from the chimneys of the few scattered houses, and the light were not so different from the sierras of Cuenca. It was in there, in his kind of territory, that Wagtmans threw himself downhill, and there, where nobody knew him, that an inspired Ocaña suddenly appeared. This happened only 50 kilometres, halfway through a short and merciless stage. Ocaña swiftly time trialled over the fragrant slopes, slipped past Wagtmans, who tried to follow him, only to give up on the climb to Periana. And Ocaña continued alone as he did in his early races in France, without looking back. Behind him there was chaos, a panicky confusion of swearing. jamming of brakes and threats. In this frantic hunt, Carmelo Morales turned over one of La Casera's team cars, and Bahamontes himself, the team manager, had to take charge of operations. 'Bust your balls,' he yelled at the team. 'Champions prove themselves on the road!' The 'Eagle', still a young at heart manager, sent Sahagún, Sanchidrián and Martínez up the old Almería road after Ocaña, who was already arriving in Nerja. And such was the impetus of Bahamontes' boys, together with three others, that they split the peloton, although they never caught Ocaña. The Frenchman, as some would call him, arrived alone in Nerja with an advantage of 53 seconds, despite puncturing twice.

That was Ocaña. And that was him the following day, too, much to Matxain's despair – he was certainly getting to know him quickly. As the handsome race leader, Ocaña was being attacked on all sides (each attack orchestrated by Bahamontes and Morales from the car they were now having to share, and putting pressure on their own men). Ocaña decided to move clear of the peloton and launched an attack on the ascent to the high Velez de Benaudalla, on the road that goes all the way up from Motril to Granada. That was too much for Matxain's fragile temper; he accelerated, swearing and screeching the wheels to pass the peloton and place his car in front of his rider to force him to stop his long-range attack. Against all the odds, Ocaña seemed to comply with Matxain as he put his hands on the top of the bars and let the pack catch him. But the second time he attacked, climbing the Suspiro pass, no one could stop him. And no one even tried. Ocaña won the stage again, and increased his lead over his main competitor, Flandria's Belgian rider, Tony Houbrechts. And it was the night after that stage in the busy hotel in Granada when Mendiburu must have told him: 'You are quite a character, with lots of personality,' a sentence whose meaning Ocaña did not fully understand until the next day.

The next day was the third stage, between Seville and Jerez de la Frontera, only a hundred kilometres across the plain countryside of the Guadalquivir, rich lands of beetroot fields. It should have been the quietest of days but it was a disaster for Ocaña, and that was the day on which he finally became aware of the meaning of Mendiburu's sentence. This was the day chosen by the Flandria team, managed by 'Brieck' Schotte, redheaded and hard as a brick, whose teams had dominated the Tour of Flanders for decades, to display their superb skills. Taking advantage of a light side wind, the Belgians, crowded around their leader Houbrechts, started to move gently towards the kerb and surreptitiously organise an echelon of riders that gained momentum as the wind increased in strength. Ocaña tried to cope with it, but started to drop further back, 200, 300 metres, kilometres. Many of his team mates had been left behind, although they could have organised themselves to minimise the consequences of this, because, apart from Mariano Diaz, they were all great *rouleurs*. Ginés Garcia, Otaño and Vélez were also there. Ocaña felt nobody was really trying to help him out so he arrived in Jerez nine minutes behind the Flandria with four of the strongest who had resisted the Belgians. In the sprint Ramón Sáez beat Godefroot, but everybody remembered how, the day before, the Valencian rider, nicknamed 'Tarzan' because of his tremendous strength, had climbed the Suspiro pass towed by a tanker truck. He was now penalised three minutes by the judges, although the following day he was as fresh as a daisy and as strong as ever. Houbrechts, a powerful, young *rouleur* who had won the Tour of Portugal the year before, and would eventually develop a career as Gimondi's *domestique* in the Salvarani and Bianchi teams, won the Tour of Andalucia.

Like Gimondi, Ocaña was beginning to develop a significant career. But that night in Jerez, the cheerful city of overlords and streets full of horse poo, Ocaña had his first serious argument with his manager and team mates. Everybody got to know each other really well that night.

After supper Ocaña, feeling aggrieved, complained about the day, the wind, the Belgians, his solitude, and asked Matxain to back him up. He wanted him to tell the team they had not performed like a real team, to give his team mates a dressing down. However, it was he who was on the receiving end of the criticism, delivered not by Matxain but by his own team mates, with Mendiburu their spokesman. And this time he had to take it. Mendiburu, with his serious and impartial tone dismantled Ocaña's arguments. Perurena was not there either to help him with his silent understanding; he was recovering from an injury. Ocaña learned a lesson.

Mendiburu started by saying: 'We liked you because we thought you were a bit shy, Luis, but you immediately got your confidence and now we don't see you as shy but overbearing, too full of yourself, almost arrogant. Some of the things you do are hard for us to understand. You attack without looking or thinking; you don't think about the consequences; you don't think about the following day, you don't even consider you are not alone and that you have an entire team behind you. You don't consider you are just starting and you still have a lot of things to learn in cycling; you don't know how to ride on the flat, you don't know your way around in the echelons; you hardly know how to ride on somebody's wheel; you are stuck to your bicycle and hang on to it like a life jacket. We have to keep an eye on you all the time…And I hope what you understand from us today is that you need us, that when you feel you want to go to the head of the peloton one of us will have to be there, to help you, to bring you water or give a wheel when you have a puncture. Luis.'

Ocaña would have loved to respond to that criticism, saying that real champions don't understand that kind of language and those kind of concepts, and that he was a champion. But that night, after the embarrassing defeat, he realised he had spoiled the day in the Guadalquivir countryside. He saw himself further than ever from being a real champion. He felt dark and lifeless, like the nights in Vila when the wind blew through the slabs, leaving little grey stars of snow on the floor of the house. But he felt he had reasons to yell out what he had learnt since his father insulted him for not being strong enough and being unable to cope with pain. He had learnt that team spirit did not necessarily help a champion because it prevented him from becoming a giant; that one needs to become a giant in order to win, that one needs to learn to be different, that one needs to be a son of a bitch and a bastard to become a champion, that rivals need to be humiliated. He would have liked to have concluded by asking them not to kill his individuality, that that, being different, was the price he needed to pay to become a champion.

And he would have liked to talk to them about Merckx, who was a son of a bitch and a bastard himself, a cyclist with an enormous appetite, despite not having known hunger in his life because he was the son of shopkeepers and there was always bread, chocolate, condensed milk, coffee, jam, ham and butter in his house. So why did Ocaña feel punished and harassed when the only thing he wanted was to forget his hunger, when Merckx was adored for his and his gluttony was forgiven, even if he ate like a horse without being hungry at all? And in that hotel in Granada he would have liked to tell his team mates, if he had had the voice and felt he had the right to do so, the chance to do so, that he, Ocaña, from Priego in Cuenca was going to defeat that arsehole Belgian son of a bitch, that champion of gluttony.

But Luis did not speak that night. Ocaña spoke on the road the following day. He attacked again when the wind changed direction from Tarifa to Algeciras through the Cabrito pass. He attacked again and went clear. Houbrechts did not resist the attack. Ocaña finished alone, just as he liked it. And he won, of course.

Scarcely a month and a half later, Luis met Merckx for the first time.

'I have shaken hands with God,' he told Perurena a few minutes later, while they were waiting for the start of the Setmana Catalana and searching for a fleeting ray of sunshine in the new spring in the Ciudadela park.

'What did he say to you?' asked his Basque friend with irony. 'That you should be good to enter his kingdom?'

'No, nothing special,' replied Ocaña. 'We talked about the weather, health, chance…To be honest, he commands respect; he is my age, 22, but he has quickly become the most feared cyclist in the peloton.'

'Yes, that's true,' replied Perurena. 'He has been around our group before, surrounded by a mass of photographers, shining in his rainbow jersey and a big inscription of Faema. He greeted each one of us, Julito, Tarzan and me, and all that was lacking was us bowing to him, but what an enchanting smile we put on, honoured as we were by his visit. Even Samaranch himself has bowed in front of him.'

Merckx was both admired and feared among the cyclists. He was admired for what he did and for his victories, because he had won two San Remos and a Flèche, and almost won a Liège, all before he was 22. And as soon as he turned 22 he made his debut in the Giro and he won a World Championship. He was admired because he sprinted, he climbed, he performed well on the track and in time trials, because he performed well in everything. He was admired, but he was also pitied because he was seen as being condemned to forced labour in the saddle which, paradoxically, would soon make him rich. Since October Merckx's incomparable racing agenda was passed from mouth to mouth; everyone knew about it: an 'American' in Madrid with Ferdinand Bracke, a mountain race in Lausana, an 'American' in Antwerp with Patrick Sercu, an omnium indoor track and the Six Days of Ghent with Sercu, the Baracchi with Bracke, a wedding on 5 December and a honeymoon in the Canary Islands until the 20th, an omnium in Antwerp with Sercu on the 23 December, the Six Days of Brussels until New Year's Eve, a race in Charleroi on 27 January and another one in Antwerp on the 28 January, another race in Cannes on 18 February, the Sardinia Tour from 24 February to the 1 March, Cagliari on 3 March, the Paris-Nice starting on 10 March (which he ended up quitting because of a knee injury), a victory in the Romano Lombardo on the 18th, the Flèche Brabançone on the 19th, the Milan-San Remo (which he did not win) on 23rd, Harelbeke, the beginning of the Setmana Catalana on Tuesday 26th.

'And I have been told,' concluded Perurena, 'that he has been counting the days to leave on Thursday after the double sector, and catching a plane to Brussels to take part in the Tour of Flanders on the 30th, and has a meeting in the Velodrome with Sercu on Sunday 31st. That is no life at all.'

Merckx was feared among the rest of cyclists because of his insatiable and vicious appetite for winning; and they wouldn't let themselves be fooled by the fact that Merckx allowed a couple of his *domestiques*, Van den Bossche and Reybrouk to win the first two stages of the Setmana Catalana. Significantly, Merckx came second on both days. Then, in the rush to get a plane in Castelldefels, he came third on the fourth stage after the Frenchman Lemeteyer overtook him, although Reybrouck ended up winning. But everybody in the peloton knew that in reality Merckx was reminding his team mates that they owed their victories to him and that he was still God and not to forget it since he might decide that they would never win another race in their lives.

But Ocaña wouldn't be fooled by Merckx's attitude. Ocaña had an untameable pride; he loved to fight and this is precisely why he enjoyed so much the second day of the race. While crossing Olot he escaped with Pinyera and Martinez, and climbing the difficult slopes of Coubet and Santigosa on the way to Sant Joan de les Abadesses, their advantage on the peloton reached two minutes. But that was as far as it stretched. However much he tried (and his effort saw Pinyera dropped, leaving him with no support) Ocaña couldn't increase the gap. His puzzlement at this turned to satisfaction when he heard Matxain yelling at him from his car: 'Stop Luis, slow down, put your hands on the tops and let them catch you because Merckx himself is chasing you behind and he won't stop until he reaches you, and he is going to finish off you and the peloton.'

'Ah Merckx, and you say that he is trying to kill off my escape?' asked Ocaña merrily. 'So, he is keeping an eye on me; he knows who I am. He's afraid of me. Now I am important to him.' For Ocaña, this unsuccessful escape in deepest Cataluña was a statement of intent to the best cyclist in history, who, the following day, at the peak of his art and his hunger, would take two minutes out of him in the 35-kilometre time trial between Terrassa and Manresa.

When Ocaña felt sad and in deep thought, he imagined himself as a toy in the hands of fate, shifted from here to there, like a piece of wood carried by the sea. 'When someone has suffered as much as I have,' he told Josiane on one of his melancholic days, 'it is difficult to hope that everything will turn out right, because there will always be something that screws it up.' Ocaña was speaking of bad luck. On grey days he thought about fatalism; he felt doomed and convinced himself that he would never be in command of his fate. 'But this doesn't mean I am not going to continue fighting against my fate,' he promised Josiane while she was breastfeeding their newborn baby, Jean-Louis, born in Mont-de-Marsan on 23 February 1968. 'I will never give up fighting because I know that there is always a reward for those who fight, no matter if you win or lose. My life will be an all or nothing.' From that moment on his cycling career would swerve between heroism and tragedy. Like his personality, there would be no middle ground.

Fatalism was born with Ocaña, in his poverty and hunger, in his forever affected lungs, in his liver, and it was always there, latent, in spite of things beginning to go well for him, escaping from misery, looking forward to a bright future. It was at that very moment when reality gave him a rude awakening, and the fate he couldn't control began to shape his cycling career. The first two important races he took part in, the Vuelta a España and the Giro d'Italia, proved to be signs of what was in store for him.

He quit his first Spanish Tour on the tenth day, without even reaching Madrid, which in those times marked the mid-point of the race. They crossed La Mancha in May, with the vineyards already announcing their fertility, and the cereal fields showing yellow. But the wind was so strong it swept everything before it, including the peloton, cycling from Almansa to Alcazar de San Juan, which ended up splintered on the long straight roads of La Roda. Thirty cyclists were ahead, with Rudi Altig and his friend Gimondi, and Jan Janssen and finally the Spanish favourites, Pérez Francés among them. There were another thirty at the back, the weakest, the sick and the faithless.

Ocaña was in the middle, lashed by all the winds, but he wasn't sick, neither was he faithless; he was just a clumsy scatterbrain who couldn't manage to perform in an echelon. He was certainly strong, as he had proved the day before when he won the first sprint of his career in Almansa (although it must be admitted that it was for second place behind Pinyera, but even so he was ahead of fast men like Janssen and Adorni). But for his team Ocaña was one of the group, not a leader. Not for one moment did anybody in Fagor believe a young debutant like Ocaña could win the Vuelta. None of his team mates dropped back from the first group, and there were four of them: Errandonea, Otaño, López Rodríguez and Vélez. None of them stayed with him later on (nor would they have wanted to, except his friend Peru, who would gladly have done so) when, after many kilometres out on his own, and with three or four other riders on his wheel, he couldn't hold the pace of the second group and fell further behind, to the very back.

Going through the village of Campo de Criptana, the local boy, Fernando Manzaneque, had been encouraged by a multitude of supporters with their placards at the sides of the road. Minutes later only two dogs were left on the dusty kerb; they attempted to follow the wheels but settled for an apathetic bark. The blades of the mills in the heights, were lifeless. Ocaña came next to last on that stage, 24 minutes and 51 seconds behind his team mate Errandonea, who won the stage.

Next day, Saturday 4 May, an exhausted, humiliated and furious Ocaña quit the Vuelta, which would eventually be won by Gimondi, who joined Anquetil as the only man who had won all three big Tours. If Ocaña had managed to finish the race in Madrid, he would have enjoyed Peru's splendid victory in the Retiro park, with its scented curve in La Rosaleda, ahead of none other than Altig and Janssen. Ocaña had to content himself by reading a newspaper interview the following day with Peru, the lion of Astigarraga. Peru's lethargic answer to the interviewer after he had thrown the bouquet of flowers to his family in Madrid made him crack up with laughter:

'What happened to you between Almansa and Alcázar de San Juan, where you lost more than 10 minutes?'

'Since I had the accident [a year before in the Vuelta of '67, Perurena broke his femur in a fall in the stage Villabona-Zarauz], I suffer incomprehensible ups and downs. One day I feel strong like a bull, the next my legs shake in the first attack.'

'What do doctors say?'

'They say they are the side effects of the bellyful of chloroform I had to take for the surgery.'

'Something temporary?'

'I hope so.'

Ten days after withdrawing from the Vuelta Ocaña was told by Matxain that he would take part in the Giro, which would start on 21 May in Campione, on the banks of Lake Lugano. Ocaña replied with a note from the team doctor, Doctor Zabala.

'I am sick,' he told Matxain. 'Your doctor is very clear about it. I can barely breath, my bronchial tube is not well,' but Matxain ignored it. Ocaña reproached him, saying Matxain would make him ride at night if there were night-time races. What Ocaña didn't fully realise was that the team line-up was decided one day at a time, practically on the eve of the race. Ocaña was called to every possible race and he complained, but he would end up riding his first Giro, where he would meet Merckx again after the Setmana Catalana. It was one more reasons to accept fatalism as a philosophy of life.

Ocaña started with bronchitis, and when he had almost recovered and his cough was not alarming the doctors who were dealing with him, he found himself caught in a massive fall in a downpour on the eighth stage. It happened at the top of Ospitaletto on the way to La Maddalena climb in Brescia, and his chest hit a hard, concrete kilometre stone. His team mate, Momeñe, who was delighted to have won the Alessandria stage in the Piamonte de Coppi three days before, broke a number of ribs and took a hard blow to his hips and another to his head. His race ended in the ambulance that took him to Chiari's hospital, while Ocaña had to ride four stages with a bandaged and still painful chest. Once he was over that, he then suffered from haemorrhoids, which prevented him from sitting comfortably on the saddle for another week (he couldn't even sit down for a few days). The chest doctor cured his pain with 14 injections and a few good words. Despite his morale being so low with all his vicissitudes, pain and accidents, Ocaña kept the promise he made to Josiane: he fought, and he never gave up.

That was his personal, ignorant, involuntary contribution to May '68, to the youth who had turned the feared *pavés* of Roubaix into a weapon of the future in Paris. He finished the Giro in 32nd place. He had managed to complete his first three-week race, which signalled yet another declaration of principle: where his body could not reach his fighting spirit would. He had met the Dolomites and the Three Peaks of Lavaredo, where Merckx, with the help of Adorni, finally smashed Gimondi. Thus, at the age of 22, he had sealed his first Giro victory and the first of the eleven grand Tours he would win. In the state Ocaña was in, the Pale Mountains did not move him enough to make him return: he would never again take part in the *Corsa Rosa*. The Tour and its heat would be his race, but he would have to wait one more year for it.

But before, he needed new statements of principles, new proclamations. When, at the beginning of the season, his friend Peru told him that the only important thing in Spanish cycling was the rivalry between Kas and Fagor, that neither of the teams could stomach each other's victories, this was something Ocaña could not understand. Somehow, his French education had stifled the passionate stream running through the veins of his family. 'Cycling teams are just meant to sell the products they advertise; they advertise refreshments, we advertise fridges,' Ocaña told Peru. 'Do they really care if more sodas than fridges are sold? They are not rivals. And listen to what I tell you Peru: a third party always takes advantage of these silly rivalries.' However, a few months later, Ocaña would understand the full dimension of this rivalry, and the value of forcing the rival team to its knees. Then he was delighted to discover the truth in Peru's words, a truth he did not want to believe initially: defeating Kas was worth double and tasted so much better, even better when the team Ocaña defeated in the Grand Prix of Llodio during that August of fire and melted stones, was as powerful as Kas.

'Hey, Frenchman, you are crazy! Stop the car, right now. I'm getting out.'

'Get out now, Mome, if you have the guts; I am not stopping. Come on, jump! Open the door and jump!'

Ocaña was trying out his brand new Opel, an uncomfortable sports coupé in which he had taken Momeñe by surprise to apply a shock and stress therapy, Ocaña's own particular form of business card, while they were heading to the start of the race in Llodio. On the narrow and twisting Basque roads, Ocaña drove in the only way he knew, like a mad daredevil. Momeñe was frightened every time Ocaña put his foot down on the accelerator; he sat there, pale and silent, until he couldn't put up with it any longer. At first he reacted calmly. 'Frenchman, drive a bit more slowly. It's raining and the roads are wet. You don't want to have an accident on the corners,' pleaded the man who had been seriously injured in the big fall during the Giro, and who had recovered and was back in competition two months later.

'Raining? Raining? I can't see it's raining,' replied Ocaña at the same time that, as if he were in a rally, he drove around a blind bend sticking a leg out of the door, much to Momeñe's shock. 'No, it's not raining at all; look at my feet, they're dry.' The journey was short, and the adrenaline shot caused by Ocaña's frightful driving would eventually have a good influence on the race. The Kas team started strongly, which provoked a response from Ocaña.

'You'll see now,' he yelled, and jumped away by himself. That was at kilometre 10, with 180 more ahead of him. At first, nobody paid any attention to an escape so far from the finish. 'He always does the same,' it was said. 'It's still a long way to go. The heat will kill him.' It was certainly still a long way to go. But when there were 80 kilometres left, Dalmacio began to organise his Kas team, the great Kas team, to set about chasing down the Frenchman to whom fantasy and imagination were simply irresistible. To Dalmacio, common sense dictated that with good team work it wouldn't take long to reel him in. When there were only 50 kilometres of tortuous, constantly undulating terrain to go, with hard steep slopes and abrupt descents, the Kas director started to worry. Instead of decreasing, the gap to Ocaña was widening. And when some of his team began to lose energy whenever they took their turns on the front and others were dropped, and the solid peloton was reduced to a small, splintered group of exhausted lost souls, Dalmacio was beside himself. 'It's not possible!' he shouted, scrunching his cigar in the ashtray and throwing the stub out of the window. With strident, hysterical honks on the horn he made his way through the threadbare peloton in search of the fugitive.

'It's not possible, it's not possible. There's a trick going on here,' he repeatedly told Letona, his quiet mechanic. 'There's something fishy here; the Frenchman is being towed and the *commissaire* is turning a blind eye; maybe he is being pulled by a rope attached to a motorbike, or he may have even got into a car, who knows.'

But when he reached Ocaña he saw nothing, or he saw everything, like a revelation: there was hunchbacked Ocaña, his gaze fixed on the horizon, his hands down on the bottom of the bars, and his will to reach where nobody had ever been before. Mister Dalmacio and the entire, worn-out Kas team now knew who Ocaña really was. Even another Fagor rider, Momeñe, came second, albeit at some distance, while the Frenchman had made a giant step in his quest to conquer cycling.

But there was something far more urgent at that particular moment; his father was dying. In February, when Jean-Louis was born, Luis's father (already a grandfather at 48) told his son about his illness calmly, almost coldly: 'I have been diagnosed with prostate cancer; the doctors think I only have six months to live. I have refused any treatment because it doesn't guarantee anything.' Grandad Luis had continued going to work as if nothing had happened, as if he were not feeling pain, displaying the courage and contempt for weakness that he had shown all his life. But in the final month he couldn't cope any longer. He, the man who was more than a man, was now fallen; he wasn't strong enough to stand up on his own. He lived in bed in a dark, oppressive room that smelled of urine, metasedin and camphorated alcohol, with a glass of water on the bedside table.

Strangely, Ocaña's shining red and yellow jersey as Spanish champion, that he was wearing as a sign of his last conquest, together with his black beret not seem inappropriate in that dark and shadowy room. Rather, it gave a certain sense of achievement to the life of an exile who was dying too young.

'It's not bad at all, kid,' said a weakened father to his son, who had just been proclaimed Champion of Spain, his most symbolic prize so far. 'But I wish the jersey had the colours of the republican flag, not those of Franco. Finally, boy, you have done something important. First they starved us, and then they sent us into exile, but now you are the best Spaniard, and you have made that very clear to them.'

Ocaña made sure everyone knew him with another solitary performance, although in this case there was no alternative because the Spanish championship took place in Mungia in 1968, with a 75-kilometres time trial. It was an overpowering performance by the same Ocaña who had won the amateur Grand Prix des Nations the year before; the same Ocaña who had an advantage of more than two and a half minutes over the second man, Gómez del Moral, the colossus from Cabra. Over an extremely hard route, Ocaña raced at an average speed of 42 kph on his superb Marotias, and made his supporters' jaws drop; they were exultant. After decades and decades of prayer, finally a cyclist had been born in Spain who could make them dream about the time trial. Also, that day in August, Ocaña and the top four finishers had to pass the first antidoping control in their lives. The cyclists urinated in Mungia's town hall, and the samples, properly sealed, were sent to the laboratory of the National Toxicology Service in the Faculty of Medicine in Madrid.

Three days later, in Mondragón, on a *parcours* that included the ascent to Kanpazar, the descent to Elorrio, another ascent to Elgeta, and the descent to Mondragón through Bergara, all of which had to be completed four times, Ocaña might have closed the circle with the title of Spanish mountain champion. However, a puncture near the finish line, while he was away with San Miguel, prevented him from competing for victory against the Kas rider from Biscay, who ended up fourth in Janssen's 1968 Tour de France. Changing wheels was not permitted outside the places established by the organisation.

He was 23 years old. Until that moment he had been no more than a man of the soil whose legs were hard as stone, an incredible physical prodigy, a man who raced with a pocket full of bread and raw garlic and tomato – his favourite foodstuff. And a man who admired his father.

With the death of his father, on 31 August, which occurred while he (already a father and now an orphan) was competing for his first world championship in Imola, Ocaña immediately took responsibility for the family clan. In practice he had already started to take that on as his parents and siblings came to depend more and more on his income. Luis' mother also proclaimed openly that Luis was her favourite son and that any decision he would make would have her blessing. Luis became a new father to Marino, Marie-France and Michel; all of them were minors born in France and they hadn't reached the age of ten when their father died. An invisible, yet very real barrier had been built between them, who had known a comfortable life in France, and the others, Luis, his sister Amparo and brother Antonio, who had known hunger in Spain. Luis would come up against this barrier, just as he would later come up against another barrier, with his own children.

Those Sundays when they went to have lunch in Le Houga, and years later in the big house he managed to buy, Josiane would feel overwhelmed by the whole Ocaña family and those gigantic Spanish meals. She was hardly accustomed to the Spaniards' noise and enjoyment at the table, and Luis's overflowing happiness when he saw all the family together. Josiane always had to remind him about it.

'Please Luis, you have to understand that my parents got divorced, and I only have one sister; and my mother and grandma were only children, I am not accustomed to this racket.'

They all joined together after the great stew their mother cooked, which Luis loved so much, with its soup, chickpeas, meat, stuffing, black pudding, and streaky bacon. The always hungry cyclist (who ate with the knowledge of everything he'd not been able to eat in the past, with that anxiety born of fear) invariably complemented the meal with one or two pieces of hard turron that he managed to devour, biting through it, despite the clicks and cracks made by his false teeth.

Once the table was cleared Luis gathered his brothers like a real godfather and asked them about their problems, gave them money for their projects and particular needs, worried about their courtships and marriages, almost all of them disastrous, almost always cursed by Luis. He could never put up with either of his brothers-in-law, even less with his son-in-law; he gave all his family the best advice he could, always forcefully. In case of doubt, he always stood by the side of his brothers and sisters, his own blood.

1969

In 1969, Merckx won his first Tour, on the same day that man landed on the moon, and it was in 1969 that Ocaña realised his progress was unstoppable and that he was capable of riding three-week races. But he also realised how much Spanish cycling was excessively centred on itself and its small races, fed by provincial debates, small-town disputes and sterile controversies. He couldn't put up with the eternal rivalry between Kas and Fagor, the stingy aspirations of his team mates, the daily recriminations over dinner. Those aspects of Spanish cycling hurt him as much as the pain in his liver that autumn, right after the death of his father. That crisis had left him weak and yellowish, and in need of Josiane's tender care.

However, he had already recovered by January, and the pallor of his skin changed to a bright tan which was the result of long training sessions in search of the form that he showed gloriously a month and a half later in the Setmana Catalana. Merckx was not there, and Luis had still not managed to defeat him, not even in a criterium, but Gimondi and Poulidor were. So, too, was Dino Zamengu, in a state of grace, and winning sprints with seemingly effortless superiority, and González Linares, the beast of the time trial, so strong, and San Miguel. They were all beaten by Luis on the recently constructed Castelldefels main road (24 kilometres from Bellvitge). The gaps were so enormous (1'–5" on Gimondi, and 2'–0" on Poulidor) that the international press suspected a certain carelessness on the part of the judges. Ocaña felt morally ecstatic: 'I have won a time trial, not any time trial and not only against Spaniards as I have done until now,' he reminded everyone. 'I have defeated the best cyclists in the world, such as Gimondi, the new king of the Grand Prix des Nations; Poulidor, who in his career made even the best rider tremble, even Anquetil. Who thinks about Merckx?

However, old Poulidor, who was at the height of his power at 33, never accepted his defeat in Castelldefels; he would let him know that a few days later in the Tour of the Basque Country.

But when a vengeful Poulidor showed him the hands of his watch between Guernica and Bilbao in the Basque race, Ocaña couldn't care less about the small-minded anger of the little Limousin peasant. At that moment he only had eyes for Anquetil, the dazzling blonde, who shone like a sun in the Basque valleys, which in Spring were always covered in a biting fog that penetrated the dark tunnel of Lizarraga, the first to be excavated through rock to make way for a road into Spain. It was there, on the winding descent towards Estella, through Abarzuza, with its bright green valleys, where shepherds search for perretxikos[1] and find hidden Romanesque chapels, where the nomadic soul of Anquetil launched an attack with Gabika, Galera, Diaz, San Miguel and Castellon.

The group arrived with an advantage of more than seven minutes over the Poulidor group. Anquetil decided the fate of the race and became the first great cyclist since 1935, since the Spanish war broke out, who would forever honour the Basque Tour. That was Anquetil's last great victory, and it was there, in the time trial between Guernica and Bilbao, that Ocaña discovered his own true flesh and blood God whom he would adore. Ocaña did adore Anquetil, just like Basque supporters adored him, as only a supernatural entity can be adored, when they saw him race over their dangerous roads with his immobile chest, his gaze fixed on the tarmac, the slightest movement of his hands, which only left the drops of his handlebars to shift the gear levers. The next day journalists, so amazed at his performance, would compete with each other's creativity to find the best words that helped them understand that miracle. They concluded that Anquetil and old Raymond Louviot, the director who followed him in the car through Olabarri, Mungia, Santo Domingo (a hard, wet and dangerous route that ended in the San Ignacio Stadium, in Bocho) used a kind of communication code that only the two of them could understand. The journalist explained it as follows: on the day before, meticulous Louviot examined the route, made notes of it and memorised its main features. On the race day Louviot blew the car's horn to warn Anquetil of what he could

---

1. Perretxikos - a particular kind of mushroom associated with the Basque Country, said to be prolific in April.

expect ahead of him, and to prevent the perfect racing machinery of the Norman from any distraction. Journalists said one blow of the horn meant the road was flat and straight so Anquetil could drop on to the smallest cog and use his favourite 52x13, which allowed him to open up big gaps on his rivals; two blows of the horn meant mixed terrain, so he shifts to a larger cog to avoid losing cadence; and if he heard three, that meant hard climbing, and he should use the small front ring. Anquetil did not win the time trial, because his overall advantage in the general classification was so big that he did not need to take risks on the descents and wet corners. So he allowed Poulidor to enjoy the honour of a partial victory. But Ocaña, who ended up ahead of the Norman in the time trial, did not seem really worried. At night he approached Anquetil in his hotel and praised him: 'I have never seen a cyclist with more class, nor so brimming with health.'

Ocaña was young, but not naïve. The boy from Priego was aware that the perfect result and magnificent way the previous stage had panned out were as much the result of his thirst for revenge as of Anquetil's intelligence – Poulidor and Ocaña, who had both been defeated in Lizarraga the day before, attacked on the Jaizkibel and, despite a great chase headed by Anquetil, in person, they arrived in San Sebastian with a very small lead, and Ocaña won the stage. It excited their followers but did not endanger the final victory of Normandy's blonde star. Anquetil understood that a cycling peloton was a structure formed by a combination of efforts, commitments, agreements, legs, intelligence, tactics, heart, and punctures: that was its greatness. Anquetil was aware of all that and indeed he took part in all that, which was why he was not surprised when he found himself an involuntary witness to a scene in the Gernika Hotel, between the first morning sector and the time trial in the afternoon. A little alcohol camping stove was still burning and its sugary smell pervaded the room. On it there was a small zinc case with bubbling water in which Anquetil had just sterilised a small glass syringe with which he was giving Poulidor a shot. If there existed a photograph that could reproduce this image that exists in the memory of a fourth person in that room, it would really represent the most accurate picture of those years. But more important than anything else was the Tour, and in that race, and that race only, no compromises were possible at all.

And more important even than the Tour was class; and class cannot be invented, manufactured, agreed or traded upon. Class is present from birth, and Anquetil was pure class. That night, Ocaña reminded him of that. 'I bow to class,' he said to him.

'You are also marked by class, Luis,' Anquetil replied. 'You can be great, the greatest, the only one who can force Merckx to his knees, but in order to achieve this you have to leave Spain, Luis. You have to leave these narrow, shadowy and uninspiring valleys, you have to leave this stingy and short-sighted cycling because it is suffocating and taking your future away. Leave Spain, Luis, leave Fagor. Come to France, Luis. Come to Bic. Geminiani is waiting for you; he is the man who has been able to extract all the greatness in me beyond my will. I'll speak to Gem, Luis, and you will take my place, my space in the team. France needs a champion, a leader in the fight against Merckx. I am finished. I am 35 years old. I won't last beyond this season, and Poulidor, without me, will be nothing; he will be nobody. Poulidor will never win the Tour, Luis. You are the leading figure France is waiting for. You are the only one who can prevent Merckx from winning five Tours like I did.'

'Yes Jacques, but I am Spanish and I cannot apply now for French citizenship, because I would have to do the military service and my cycling career would be interrupted for at least a year, and who knows what I would be like after that. Moreover, I feel as Spanish as I do French, and I will never disown my Spanishness.'

'You won't disown your Frenchness either.' replied Anquetil. 'You will have a new nationality, call it Frenchnish or Spafrench, but nobody is asking you to become French, Luis. With that voice, that blood, that accent, you will never pass for a Frenchman. But you will only be a champion if you ride with a French team, á la France. And you are what you are because you have grown up and lived in France, Luis. You feel at home in France, and for the French you will always be French, like Picasso; and for Spaniards you will always be Spanish, and you will always feel Spanish,' Anquetil promised him. He was a true champion, which is why he believed in the innate kindness of people.

Ocaña, because of his origin, was a distrusting person and he soon realised that he was not wrong about his misgivings. He soon realised with the pain that comes from incomprehension that, despite his wishes, as far as the French were concerned, he was always nothing more than a Spanish bullfighter or Quijote, especially when he had a fall. And for Spaniards, he was always a Frenchman, especially when he had a fall, a Fenchman whose French arrogance and accent gave him away. In France he would always be Ocaña, 'the Frenchman from Priego', and in Spain he would be 'the Spaniard from Mont-de-Marsan'.

But in the 1969 Vuelta, his second Vuelta, he was received like the Messiah by the Spanish fans. His fame had grown so much, and so much was expected from him. He was first in the Badajoz prologue, but he would not wear the yellow jeresy the following day because he had recorded the same time as Gómez del Moral, the little boy who started as a coal and wood seller with his bicycle in Lucena. The organisers decided that no one should wear the leader's jersey on the first stage, something unprecedented, and all the more extraordinary because the next day, 24 April, Gómez del Moral did not start. He had received a telegram in his hotel informing him of the death of his mother, and went quickly to Cabra. The whole of Spain was deeply touched by the story, and even more so the next day because the Kas rider's grieving father had also died while mourning his wife. Despite the absence of the Andalusian cyclist, whose life had just received such a hard blow even before he had turned 30, Ocaña didn't end up as a leader at the end of the stage: the English sprinter, Wright, took the stage and became the overall leader because of the bonus seconds awarded for his victory.

Things were not going particularly well for Ocaña, who had problems in the right knee which prevented him from getting any sleep at night. He complained so much of the pain that he had to be given a pain killing injection in Caceres before beginning the stage.

'I feel so good doctor,' he told the chief of medical services who anaesthetised his knee. 'I don't feel any pain, but my leg is numb, as if it weren't mine.'

'Don't worry, Champion,' replied Doctor Ramos Calderon. 'That is precisely what you have to feel, but you'll see how well it works during the stage.'

Ocaña's knee worked properly for the rest of the Vuelta; indeed, it worked well enough for his Fagor team mates, unable to mind their own business, to remind him that, although he might think in French, he undoubtedly dreamed in Spanish, and as it was his dreams and his blood that determined his nationality, he shouldn't be so daft as to imagine that he wasn't Spanish. They were proud to tell him so as they entered Madrid along the Extremadura road, and pointed to the white placards with his name carefully written on them: 'You are Spanish, you are our idol, the future.' Other placards reiterated the same idea with a less friendly tone: 'You are Spanish, you are one of us. Take sides even if you are starving.' Again, on the way to Alcazar de San Juan, like the year before, there was a stupid, bloody-minded echelon aimed at Kas which ended up as a matter of honour and humiliation with Kas getting its revenge. And accompanying and guiding Ocaña's every move was the voice of Mendiburu, his protection against the wind. When an attack was launched in the unpleasant rain just outside Madrid, along the Andalucia road, there he was, directly ahead of him:

'Come on Luis, to the front. Come on, follow me, we'll kick the hornet's nest.' That was how Mendiburu encouraged and demanded.

'What's going on? What's going on?' asked Ocaña, who did not understand the strategy of Fagor attacking on a flat stage, bearing in mind how much of the Vuelta still lay ahead.

'Nothing. It's just that Carlos Echeverría has fallen and we are going to catch Kas off guard.'

'But…but that's not right,' Ocaña tried to say, 'Taking advantage of a rival's fall to launch an attack is not right. That's not what we were taught at school; that's not cycling.' But he never said it, he simply stopped working. Some time later Echeverría and the whole Kas team got back to the peloton, and soon after that the rain was joined by a strong wind blowing from the side. It was the moment of retribution.

Kas organised its own echelon which found Fagor's riders tired and disorganised. It was then that Ocaña heard Mendiburu's voice saying, 'Come on, Luis, come on, Let's move forward or they are going to put us in trouble.' Ocaña continued to pull, hearing the voice of his protector: 'Come on, Luis, move ahead', but nevertheless he went back and back until he disappeared. He lost 47 seconds; he met Pingeon, who was going strongly, and he half smiled when he heard Geminiani giving a dressing down to Pérez Francés, the Spanish star in Bic that year.

'I was so unlucky,' said the Cantabrian, full of self-pity as he reached Ocaña's group. 'Just when I went for my raincoat the echelon was formed.' But far from consoling him, Geminiani merely noted, 'You use a raincoat when you go for a walk; in a race you get your hair wet.' Ocaña had never felt so alone in his team; his only support was Matxain, the only one who believed he had a chance of winning the Vuelta.

'We have been fooling around this entire Vuelta. We're so Spanish, all we've thought about is inflicting damage on Kas, but we haven't realised there was someone else taking advantage of our stupid fight,' Ocaña told his team mates after supper, when the only things left on the table were empty coffee cups and a feeling of loss symbolised by the torn up pieces of paper that the sugar had been wrapped in. At that moment Matxain had left to allow the cyclists to talk about whatever they needed to talk about.

'You'll see tomorrow,' Ocaña warned his disbelieving team mates in the hotel in Sant Feliu de Guixols. 'I am going to win the Vuelta tomorrow, although it's Monday and sports papers will miss it, and the report will come out late. But it doesn't matter. What I am going to do will be remembered for years; it will be sung about on the radio, and the pictures will linger on. And everyone will talk forever about Ocaña on the Moià stage.'

The most important stage in the Vuelta crossed Guilleries, a gentle, slightly mountainous region of evergreen and cork oaks on its southern hillsides, and oaks and chestnuts on the shadowy northern ones, and plenty of springs and rain, with cols like Piedra Larga and La Pullosa, less than 1,000 metres high. 'We'll see, we'll see,' replied his team mates.

They could not have expressed it better since his team mates and the whole peloton(with the exception of Pingeon and Nemesio Jiménez) were spectators to the action that decided the winner of the Vuelta and, at the same time, condemned and glorified Ocaña. Furious and full of adrenaline, he attacked as soon as the day began. He attacked as only he was capable of. He attacked as he always would, with his gaze fixed ahead, aiming towards the low clouds full of chill and damp, hard rain on the horizon. That was the way he attacked, without looking back, until the only rider who could follow his pace was Pingeon. Even with the Frenchman on his wheel, he kept looking ahead and pulling, without asking him to take a turn, without asking for anything. Matxain, excited but nervously aware that he could really win the Vuelta, and lose it as well, came up in the car and instructed him.

'Let the Frenchman pass; slow down a bit; don't do all the work now, make a pact with Pingeon.' But Luis did not even look at his manager. 'I feel strong, Perico,' he replied. 'I feel strong, don't worry.'

On the last Col, the Pullosa, which goes from Vic to Moià through Tona, less than 20 kilometres away from the finish line, Ocaña sprinted like a *gregario* giving one last, all-out effort on the front, and that was it. Pingeon continued on alone, and arrived alone in Moià in the rain, the virtual winner of the Vuelta six stages before the end. In that final section with a bit of a climb and a final descent, Ocaña lost three and a half minutes, and his spirit was crushed by a dozen unconcerned riders who came past him, as if he did not exist.

'You just can't be told; you only do what you want to do.' Matxain's words after the stage were not soft or kind, nor were the looks of his team mates. Ocaña's challenge to them was bold, but now they did not need to speak to tell him that phrase he knew so well and that so many times he had been told: 'You are quite a character, Luis.' To this they added another reproach: 'You are a character, and you're impulsive, and it was the Frenchman who benefitted from it. What are you, Luis? Are you Spanish, or are you French?'

He defended himself with a public humiliation as he preferred to be taken for a fool rather than a traitor.

'I am so gullible,' he admitted humbly. 'So gullible that I have done what an amateur would never have done. You know I can't stand the rain, not for my lungs, which enjoy the sun and the heat, but for my legs. They're thin and muscular without an ounce of fat on them and they get cramp. I felt strong enough; I never lied to you, but my legs didn't cope with the rhythm of my heart. I didn't have a *pájara*. It's just that I am so gullible I told Pingeon not to worry, that I would not attack because I couldn't, that he would win the stage comfortably. And of course, Pingeon hasn't won this Vuelta by making bargains, and he will not win it just by being friendly to me, but by taking advantage of every opportunity: obviously he didn't attack; he simply went to the front, increased the pace a little and dropped me like a fag end. There I was sunk.'

Ocaña spoke with his heart – or so he thought – so that he was sure he had been convincing. But the hard look of his team mates did not change.

If Ocaña lost 3'–27" on the descent towards Moià, Nemesio Jiménez, a Toledan from La Sagra, at the end of the road that started on the puerto which was opened up for Bahamontes on that triumphant and sunny day when he returned from the Tour, lost 48 minutes. When he arrived at the finishing line the control had already been closed and Pingeon had long since gone back to the hotel with a bouquet, the yellow jersey and a piglet in a wicker basket that he did not know what to do with (at least not at first: later on he would give it to the hotel cook who would know). It was late and the news surprised everyone because Jiménez was in good form, and as hard as a block of newly extracted granite, as demonstrated by his stage victory the day before. The last to see him had picked him out in the leading pack, high on the Pullosa. The following day, Dalmacio, his manager, told the story.

'Coming off the puerto Nemesio fell,' said Langarica, 'and plunged into a ravine. He was unconscious for at least 15 minutes due to hitting his head. Doctor Salinas took care of him and, despite him being semi-unconscious, allowed him to carry on racing. Without knowing how, he managed to get on the bicycle and he continued on to Moià in the company of the good doctor. From time to time he questioned the doctor: "I've escaped , haven't I? There's nobody ahead and I am not being followed either."

'In reality, as you know,' Langarica said to a group of bystanders that formed around him, 'he was at least 30 minutes behind, the last to finish. And here he is again, harder than rock and more lively; it would take several falls and a bunch of broken bones to make him withdraw from the race. So I have managed to persuade the *commissaires* to take pity on him and give him a second chance; the doctor has given his approval so Nemesio is still in the Vuelta.'

Later on, the following day in Barbastro, Ocaña told the same story to Josiane during their daily phone conversation, and he did not know what to think; he wasn't sure whether it was right to feel pity for Nemesio, a team mate who had had a fall. Respect? Yes, but further than that…? Ever since he started his career, he had been taught that cycling was no more than a furious fight of oneself against oneself, and he had always believed in it, a fight between the will to hurt oneself and the fear of pain; the more ruthless, the better the cyclist.

And that's where feeling pity for others was out of the equation. Was it different from feeling pity for oneself?

'What kind of a Spaniard are you?' replied Josiane. 'Why do you doubt so much? Are you Unamuno? How can your team mates consider you a Frenchman and call you French?' Ocaña knew this was a prelude to an argument. 'You are a perfect Spaniard,' she continued while Jean-Louis, (around a year and a half) could be heard bawling in the background. 'You have me here, alone at home. I can't go out, always alert for your call; you don't even let me visit you, like the macho jealous Spaniard you are. But let me tell you one thing, Luis Ocaña: I'll be there in Bilbao at the end of the Vuelta because I want to hold you and I want to feel your heartbeat, and I want to applaud you because, despite your suffering with Pingeon, and despite nobody believing in you, I am sure you will win the Vuelta or end up among the best.'

Although he was annoyed at Josiane's way of reminding him of his proud Spanishness, although that would not have helped to clarify his doubts about cycling and compassion, Ocaña couldn't help deeply admiring Josiane's prescience. So he passionately held her in his arms in Bilbao after stepping off the final podium of the Vuelta, in which he came second amidst the enthusiasm of supporters and cycling directors, who insistently acclaimed him: 'You may not have won the Vuelta, but at just 24 you are a champion with a future ahead of you; if it hadn't been for that day with Pingeon...' All this hopeful prediction was enthusiastically expressed as if he hadn't thought about it before, as if it were something new to him: 'You lost more than three minutes that day and it is only thanks to your majestic time trial in Bilbao and San Sebastian that you have ended up less than two minutes behind Pingeon...Just think what would have happened if you hadn't cracked up? You are a champion! You have proved you are great and you will prove it in the Tour; you will know it and you will win it. You only need a bit more experience, learn to race, and learn not to waste your energy.' He was both flattered and advised by cunning old men...if only they knew they were simply asking Ocaña not to be himself.

Before the Tour Ocaña won the Midi Libre by being more Ocaña than ever, launching an attack on the Col de la Quillane on the way to Font Romeu, which left Poulidor and Bracke, both of whom had gained time on him in the time trial, stunned and watching each other.

More than a conquest, the Tour, as he was going to discover, would teach him one more lesson on the theme of compassion, and its cousins – arrogance and humiliation. The Tour would also allow Ocaña to see (or imagine) Merckx from the distance once more, because he was lying flat on his face. How rough was the taste of tarmac on his swollen lips and the taste of blood on his tongue. He was lying flat, immobile and unconscious, and as tall as he was, his arms were folded under his body, like a boxer kissing the canvas, with a broken chin.

That was his first KO in his first Tour, a faithful reminder that the fatalism that afflicted him was deeply rooted: good news did not last beyond a day, Ocaña thought to himself, and submitted.

Sixth round, first in the mountains, Mulhouse to Ballon in Alsace. Before attacking on the Ballon, before descending the small hill of Herrenberg (la Grosse-Pierre in French), on a fast, steep, straight road, the Italian Pierfranco Vianelli, a good rider in Molteni's team, crossed in front of Ocaña. Sitting rigidly on his bike and, as his team mates were inclined to remind him, lacking bike-handling skills, he braked and swerved to the edge of the road to try and avoid him. But his wheels skidded on the gravel and he came off. Like the year before in the Giro, Ocaña crashed into a traffic sign that left him stretched out in the middle of the road.

'I don't know how I could climb the Ballon after that. I was groggy, in a dense fog, my memory is a black hole,' Ocaña later said to his team mates.

They said nothing, but by way of a reply, simply showed him a picture in the newspaper, another picture that will have historical value in the future, one of those pictures that must be enlarged, framed, one of those pictures that in time become icons of an epic poem. Like a passion play, five cyclists from Fagor, from left to right, Perurena, Gabica, López Rodríguez, Manuel Galera and Santamarina in a moving image, are surrounding and pushing and pulling Ocaña, grabbing him by the shoulders of his white and blue jersey. He is dispirited; one can only discern his dense black hair between his head and his shoulders. From the back, one can imagine his gaze fixed on the ground, as if he is counting the slow revolutions of the front wheel of his bicycle. The only one who said something was his friend Peru, the one who really understood him. He told him with affection: 'No wonder you can't remember anything; I think you were unconscious when you got on your bike; you couldn't even pedal; you couldn't move, you couldn't do anything and you were holding the handlebar so tightly that we had to use a lot of strength to separate you from the bicycle, prising your fingers off the bars one by one.'

From the finish at the summit he was carried to a hospital by helicopter, and thereby missed the first enthronement of his despotic enemy: 18 minutes before, Eddy Merckx had surmounted the Ballon of Alsace, securing his first yellow jersey. Again, their paths crossed, their destinies intertwined. Next day on the start line, followed by his usual courtège of photographers, a sunshine yellow Merckx approached the aching Ocaña, stripped off the plaster protecting his chin, looked at the length and depth of the wound on his chin and told him: 'How I envy you; on cold winter nights your loving wife will caress your scar and will make love to you, and you will feel the privilege of being wounded, the privilege of being marked by the Tour forever.' And he told him very loudly, so that everyone could hear: 'You are a hero, Luis; only God knows how you finished the stage, but you endeavoured to continue; here I proclaim my admiration and I ask everyone to admire you like a hero,' concluded Eddy the magnanimous.

Despite all the recommendations to pull out, Ocaña, who could barely eat (only liquids and only with help from his friends), decided to continue. The following day, another picture: Ocaña's left elbow and wrist were bandaged, and on his bicycle he kept looking to the ground with his head lowered; the naked nape of his neck looked like a sacrifice to a ruthlessly sweltering sun, and he kept on pedalling while Ramón Mendiburu, his day carer in Fagor, rode next to him refreshing the back of his neck with a bidon of fresh water, an impossible relief. He could not finish the next stage and he ended up abandoning on the little ascent to Gex, at kilometre 71 on the way to Thonon-les-Bains

That would be one of his last days wearing the Fagor jersey. Every time they bumped into each other, Geminiani would never neglect to remind Ocaña that his future was in Bic, far from Spain, which limited him and obsessed over him like a Freudian castrating father, and far from Fagor, which confined him to Iberian races.

Christophe Morin, Bic's man in Bayonne in charge of the southern market, made Ocaña a good offer: he promised him he would be Anquetil's heir, and Geminiani would continue with Ocaña the work of art he'd started with Anquetil. Ocaña signed the contract and soon after committed himself to buying a plot of land in Bretagne-du-Marsan, where he wanted to build the house of his dreams for Josiane and his future family. He only had to say goodbye to Fagor. Easier said than done.

A few days after Bic's public relations man, Christian Darras, made the official announcement that Ocaña had signed a two-year contract of one million, one hundred thousand pesetas per year, Ocaña got into a fight with Ramón Sáez, 'Tarzan', during the sixth stage of the Volta a Catalunya right in front of of race director, Miguel Poblet, who had no time to intervene. It happened near Miami Playa, by Montroig in Tarragona, with 200 kilometres still to ride to reach Montjuïc. Saez, who could be distinguished by his size and by his splendid Spanish champion's jersey, pushed Ocaña, who answered back with a kick that knocked the Valencian cyclist down. Saez got up, sorted out his bicycle, then sprinted as only he knew how, as he had shown in the 1967 World Championship, where only Merckx and Janssen were faster. Red with anger, Saez caught up with the peloton, reached Ocaña and jumped on him, according to the reports, in the style of a cowboy bringing down a cow. Then he went into a fistfight with Ocaña. Perurena, Ocaña's friend, tried to separate them, but he was pulled back and received a sprain as he fell to the ground. Injured, Peru had to withdraw from the Volta, but Saez was expelled by Poblet, who personally ripped off his race number. The following day, Salvador Botella, the director of Pepsi Cola, Saez' team, refused to let his riders take the start in protest, arguing that Ocaña should also have been excluded from the race. A few days later, Pepsi Cola announced that they would not be sponsoring the team in 1970, which would eventually lead to its disappearance.

That was not the only team whose collapse was indirectly attributed to Ocaña, who, during all these upheavals went as far as thinking that an evil eye was cursing not only him but all those whom he came into contact with.

'Ok Agustin, I accept your offer of a million pesetas to continue riding for Fagor, but the only condition is that Matxain is sacked. I can't stand him.'

'Pedro is untouchable, Luis, you know that. Fagor is him. If your proposal is to have Matxain sacked, perhaps you don't really want to continue in our team,' replied Agustín Mondragón, the president of the fridge manufacturing company. He was very aware he had an impossible task ahead of him: convincing Ocaña to renew his contract with Fagor. He was aware he had little to offer, less money than what he'd heard Geminiani had offered, less expectations of great performances, fewer big words. Moreover, he was not wholly convinced anymore of the value of maintaining the cycling team. Both Agustín and Ocaña knew exactly the game they were playing: they knew that Fagor would disappear and that Bic had already measured Ocaña up for an orange jersey. But Agustin wanted to get at least one face-saving victory from that clear defeat.

'If he is the team, then I am free.'

'You are free now, Luis, but think about your conscience. Let me tell you one thing, my friend. If you don't continue with us, if you, the great star, destined to change the future of cycling, leave us, it does not make sense for our team to continue. Fagor is finished without you. Cyclists who have given everything for you and members of staff will be unemployed. Have you already forgotten what they did for you on the Ballon of Alsace?'

'I haven't forgotten what they did in the Vuelta, Agustin. And please don't talk to me about unemployment; they are good and admired cyclists; they'll find another team. I am pretty sure Manzaneque and Bahamontes have already signed some of them for La Casera and Werner. They won't starve, Agustin…'

Ocaña, a good poker player, stood firm. There were many reasons why he couldn't go back on his economic and sporting decision to ride for a French team, one of them being his contract was signed and part of the 1,100,000 pesetas (a hundred thousand more than Mondragón's offer) had already been invested in a hectare of land in Bretagne-de-Marsan. The press decided to publish only Mondragón's side of the story: 'For 100 thousand pesetas, Ocaña causes the collapse of Fagor' one could read in *El Mundo Deportivo;* however, the riders, Ocaña's team mates, never accused him of being disloyal.

Ironically, Fagor would manage to carry on in cycling, albeit with a smaller investment. Henri Labadie quickly had a brilliant idea. He was a man of action and determination, who was prepared to help young, talented cyclists in the French Basque Country, as he had done with Ocaña. He was selling Zeus bicycles and had collaborated in the setting up of Fagor. Labadie's office was a chaos of documents and unceasing telephone calls, but that autumn morning in his little office in Anglet (a small village next to Bayonne) all the telephones were off-the-hook while seven people sat around the table: Emile Mercier, the old legend and founder of Mercier bicycles, which Poulidor made famous; Antonin Magne, the manager of Mercier team; the young ex-cyclist Robert Cazala, who had just quit cycling and had the intention of becoming Magne's heir; Agustin Mondragón and his second in command, Urrutia; Pedro Matxain and Labadie himself. It was Labadie who made the proposal, referring to the convergent interests of both sides – Fagor's need to expand in France (the Spanish market was almost saturated), and Mercier's need to ally with a non-cycling company like Fagor, since the bicycle factory could not cope with the contemporary challenges. The agreement was sealed a few weeks later in Mercier headquarters in Saint-Etienne. As well as becoming the first sponsor (Poulidor's team would be called Fagor-Mercier), this investment (lower than what would be needed to maintain its own team in Spain) allowed Fagor to place two of its cycling talents in France, Perurena and Errandonea. Matxain would become Louis Caput's assistant, Magne's final heir. From 1972 onwards the team of the stainless steel limousine would be called Gan-Mercier.

1970

In his transfer to Bic, Ocaña took Jesús Aranzabal with him, a friend from Bergara, one of Labadie's protégées, who put him up, together with Ramón Mendiburu, in his own house among the Zeus bicycles and his business documents. Everyone seemed to be happy, except Perurena.

'Sod it, Luis,' said Peru to Ocaña one day in April in Castelldefels on the starting line of the Setmana Catalana. That was the first time they had met again after the incident with Tarzan. 'It's a good thing that you didn't sign with Mercier. You would have had to cope with Poulidor and Wofshohl; they are a real pain, but also stingy. I really liked how we were treated in Fagor. Since we are not nationals, we don't have social security, and on top of that they don't seem to be willing to invest a penny in anything. To see the director, Louis Caput, going up the road, picking up bidones, even those from other teams… that tells you something, doesn't it? I remember our *musettes* were empty in the Tour because he kept everything that he'd been given to provide us with food. But at least Errandonea and I could consider ourselves privileged because Fagor would pay for everything unlike Mercier, for instance. We didn't have to do like the others, who had to pay something towards their shorts when they were replaced. And what's more, I have to ride with Guimard, who is as fast as me and very ambitious.'

Somehow, this was the punishment Perurena had to pay. When he signed for Mercier, Dalmacio Langarica, the most powerful man at Kas, accused him in the press of being a man whose word couldn't be trusted, because apparently he had said he would transfer to Kas, but without any warning he broke the agreement. Langarica's statement was a just a tantrum, because one year later Peru left Mercier and signed for Kas, where Langarica welcomed him with open arms and kept him for nine seasons until he retired from professional cycling.

'Cheers, Gem, glad to see you so well,' Ocaña cheerfully greeted Geminiani, who'd already given him permission to treat him informally…that Gem sounded like an Englishman pronouncing 'James'. 'When shall we meet to talk about our plans, your plans for next season? I am really looking forward to wearing the Bic jersey and starting to work with you. When is the Côte d'Azure meeting? Shall we meet before in Clermont-Ferrand? Shall I have a drink with you in your bistrot, Gem? Will you tell me your secret, your stories? Will you tell me how you convinced Anquetil to jump into that madness of Dauphine and Bordeaux-Paris without a break? You must come to Mont-de-Marsan to have supper with me and Cescutti…'

It was the end of the previous September but only the autumn light seemed to have arrived in Barcelona. It was as hot as in summer, suffocating and humid, and Luis, sweaty, leaned on the bonnet of Gem's car without getting off the bicycle. Gem was careful enough to park it under the shade of a banana tree. He had just finished the ascent to Montjuïc, and the park of the World Fair was full of cyclists with supporters running around with team flags and paper caps, hoping to touch their idols. Motta had won with Gimondi second. Ocaña, who'd come third, was satisfied to end up ahead of old Poulidor. That would be Ocaña's last race wearing the white and blue maillot with the big red letters of Fagor. And that would also be Anquetil's last race. He was finally retiring at the age of 35. That is why Geminiani was there, at the invitation of *Dicen*, the organising newspaper. Some other great winners of the Tour were also there, such as Kübler, Bartali and Gaul. Merckx was also there. He was sad and hurt. Some weeks before, in a motor-paced event in the Blois velodrome, a pacer and his cyclist fell right in front of his pacer Fernande Wabst, and they crashed into them. The Cannibal broke his hip and suffered a vertebral sprain, but Wabst died on the spot.

'I have seen Merckx and I feel really sorry for him,' continued Ocaña, a taciturn man, who sometimes did not stop talking and could change the subject, or tell secrets, all without altering his tone of voice or the look in his eyes. 'I have tried to greet him and he has told me he is really down, especially because of the death of his friend. He said he fears the panic and nervous attack he suffered at the time will mark him for the rest of his life, What's more, the traumatologist warned him he would never ride again like he did before. "It's terrible, Luis," he told me. "To hear that my back would hurt forever and that I would never be able to ride again with my legs parallel because my hips are dislocated. All this after checking my back and trying a thousand postures, they assure me I will be in a lot of pain; it's like a curse." This is what he told me, Gem, and it seems so dramatic I cannot believe it. Why he told all this to me, exactly, when I am not that well acquainted with him, I don't know.'

'Never trust a winner, Luis, never trust a winner. Don't try to understand his reasons. Do you understand yours sometimes?'

'Mendiburu tells me few people can understand me, which is true. He says I have such a strong personality that I do things I shouldn't do, things that are difficult to understand, but that is precisely the reason why I'll be unique. Yes, I am aware I don't know why I do some of the things I do, but it will be different under your guidance, Gem: you will guide me as you guided Anquetil.'

'But didn't you know, Luis? I don't work for Bic anymore. I left the team in the Tour. I was sacked, to be honest. You know it wasn't precisely the best of Tours. Janssen was not the same as the year before, we did not win any stage, and, on top of that, not only did I have to cope with Pérez Francés, I also had to support him, even though he kicked Pingeon and ended up abandoning…The atmosphere in the team was quite unbearable. Darras started to butt in everywhere and I couldn't put up with it. Once I arrived at the Puy de Dôme I said goodbye; why should I go on to Paris? I stayed home.'

'Yes, I knew about that, but I thought it would be temporary, I thought you would be back.'

'It was for good, Luis. If Anquetil is not there, they don't need me anymore.'

'But how stupid is that? What are you going to do now?' said Ocaña.

'I'll wait. I can live off my business, but I know I will return to cycling. I am not even 45 years old. I am young, but I know what this business is about. It's not the first time that I go back home to read *La Montagne* knowing that sooner or later they'll call me back. It happened to me at the beginning. That was in 1962. I had just retired from cycling and Anquetil's Helyett and Darrigade, who had been sponsored by the Leroux chicories and by the businessman Potin, merged with my Saint Raphael, in which Rudi Altig was the leader. I became, together with Raymond Louviot, second director for a good-for-nothing called Paul Wiegant, who had coached Anquetil since he was young. The beginning of 1962 was disastrous. In the Paris-Nice I couldn't stand it anymore and I had to give that inept Wiegant a good talking to. The following day I went back home. It was not long before they called me back. After several new failures in the German Tour, and in the Tour of Var, Max Augier, the owner of Saint Raphael, stopped in Clermont Ferrand. "Come back, Gem," he said to me. "I need you in the Tour. Wiegant has been sacked." And we won the Vuelta. Surprisingly, the winner was Altig and not Anquetil, which caused a bigger problem. In an 87-kilometre time trial the German beat Anquetil by one second, yes one second over Anquetil. My friend Jacques was so jealous that one day before the end of the Vuelta he withdrew. He was second in the general classification and did not get any prize money, which meant that his team mates had even less to share. That night, when Anquetil announced he was withdrawing, I gave him the biggest roasting I've ever given anybody in my life. And do you know what he did, good old Jacques? He called the owner of the team and he told him that it was me or him, that he wanted Wiegant back for the Tour, that he couldn't put up with me. He was behaving like a spoiled child. Luckily, the rest of the team were on my side. They organised a secret ballot and decided I should be the director, by eight votes to two. So we went to the Tour, the first one organised by commercial teams for several years, and we won it with Jacques, his third Tour, and Altig was the green jersey. And from that moment on, Jacques and I have been inseparable. When Saint Raphael left I found Ford as a sponsor and then Bic. But now the whole of De Muer's Pelforth team has come in like a whirlwind. When Louviot died I was left in a minority. Now Darras and Maurice de Muer manage everything. Gerard Morin, the guy from Bayonne who you talked to about the contract, will be with them, so the label on the bicycle will be changed from Geminiani to Motobecane, the brand that Morin sells in the south of France. And when you have problems with your salary or your insurance you'll have to speak to Jacqueline, Maurice's wife, who is in charge of all the accounting issues.

Do you know how Maurice proposed to Jacqueline? Her father was the president of the cycling club where Maurice started to ride and when he withdrew from the Paris-Roubaix in 1946 – it was already raining – he got in the car where Jacqueline and his future father-in-law were following the race. And it was there where Maurice, dirty, sweaty and defeated, told Marcel Hoffman that he wanted to marry his daughter. That's Maurice, Luis, a man who has done everything on a bicycle or in a cyclist's clothing. As a manager he lives the job 24 hours a day. He eats at the same table with cyclists, sleeps thinking about them, he is as responsible as the civil code and sometimes as boring. That is Maurice, don't ever forget him, Luis.'

'And what am I going to do without you, Gem? You are the reason I came to Bic, you know that, don't you? I joined Bic because I want to be like Anquetil, and I want to be him with you. What the hell does a Northerner, a man from Lille, know about all this, a man from a city where the sky is always grey, and you can only smell the smoke of blast furnaces and only hear the sirens of mines? What does he know about the Mediterranean, about our light, our wine, our life? What does he know about cycling? What does he know about the night? How can someone like him understand me?'

'Luis, appearances are deceptive with Maurice. He is not as courageous, as creative or as intuitive as we are, but he likes a straightforward and attacking kind of cycling, so he is like you.'

'That's what I fear most, Gem. I know how to attack at any moment, but this is the only thing I know. I need to learn how to keep guard, how to choose the right moment to launch an attack. I don't need someone who tells me I have to attack all the time; I need someone who tells me I need to attack right now and only now. Moreover, you know very well Gem, De Muer has a clear preference for Janssen because he is his manager. He built Pelforth with Janssen. I will only be second string there…'

'Make no mistake, Luis, make no mistake. Maurice is, first and foremost, a team manager, and he will put his faith in those who give him the best results. And that will be you, Luis. Don't be afraid of Janssen. Alongside you he will be nothing, and because he is old and wise, he will be generous, that's all he's got left. You should only fear Merckx; he will be your only rival. He will be lucky. Merckx, like Coppi and Anquetil, came to cycling to rule, just as he did last year in his first Tour, as he has already done in the Giro and in all the Classics. Like you, he says he wants to be Anquetil, but Jacques has never had Merckx's insatiable appetite. And, despite the fact that the French have insisted that Anquetil's only true rival has been Poulidor, he has never had a true competitor; his only rival was himself, his will, his ambition. He fought against himself, which was a shame. But Merckx will definitely have a competitor, and that will be you.'

Before the end of the year, Christian Darras, the team's engineer summoned all the Bic riders to a winter meeting at the Le Corbier ski station, in Savoy, in the shadows of the mountain bearing the same name, near Saint-Jean-de-Maurienne and La Toussuire. In an almost military atmosphere intensified by De Muer's talks, Darras handed over 2000-francs worth of sports clothing to each member of the team. This luxury pack included thick anoraks, very thin t-shirts, ordinary clothing, trousers with pleats, form-fitting tracksuits, all of them elegantly wearing the Bic badge. They were the envy of the peloton. 'They are dressed like lords,' rival teams commented. 'They are posh.'

'That's why we are called millionaires,' happily shouted Anatole Novak, the veteran giant, the man trusted by all his mates. But De Muer was not there only to make them happy, or that's what he told them.

'Boys, make no mistake,' he began, having got them all together after dinner. His harangue took on an almost martial tone.

'Here in Bic we are neither philanthropic, nor demagogues. We are a sport team whose manager, Monsieur Darras, believes it must be made profitable. If the managing team spares no costs for you it is because you are expected to respond to this generosity by multiplying the advertising benefits by your effort and your victories. Don't be afraid of the future, you have no reason to be afraid, but be careful, I am warning you: I am the sports manager and I am here to give you all the advice you need, but I don't have time to educate you. I trust your professionalism. It's your responsibility to do your job well.'

Ocaña felt strange, like a foreigner in the group, in the snow, in the cold. He enclosed himself with his little group formed by Mendiburu and Aranzabal. He did not feel accepted by a manager and cyclists from another country. He felt looked down upon, as if they did not know who Luis Ocaña was; the man destined to change everything in cycling.

They met again in January on the Côte d'Azur, in the picturesque village of Seillans, in the slopes of a mountain where the sun always shone and the air was clean from the sea, where shadows were clear and old men played petanque in a little square under banana trees while cyclists from more than 20 teams crossed their steep streets, coming and going in intense and sweaty bouts of training. Under the sunshades of a café, you could find Pingeon, Ocaña, Poulidor, Delisle, and even Merckx, because the entire international peloton spent January on the Côte d'Azure. There, one still, moonlit night, at the entrance to the little hotel where André Clerion hosted De Muer's team every year, Ocaña began to get to know Janssen, the Dutchman who commanded respect, for his shortsighted glasses, for his accomplishments, and for his long-standing friendship with De Muer.

'Don't worry Luis,' said the Dutchman, who showed an unexpected capacity to smile with a certain shyness, as he took out a creased packet of Lucky Strike from his splendid tracksuit and lit a cigarette. 'I smoke Lucky Strike because, as Belmondo said, I believe it brings me luck. I am a champion, that's true, but I am not a legend. When I see you I get the sense that you are afraid of me; it's like you think I am the team leader, that I am envious and jealous of you, that I am going to make things difficult for you, Luis. But you are wrong.'

'I am aware none of you Northern cyclists has faith in me. You have been told I am weak, irregular and lacking in perseverance, and that I have more pride than class, but you are all wrong, Jan. Mentally, I am stronger than any of you. My personality helps me cope with suffering more than anyone else. I can go further than anyone. And yes, that's my pride. I do want to be a champion, Jan. I want to be Anquetil; I am Anquetil, and I want to kill Merckx. But I have been condemned by fate to a personal fight with him. Will you help me, Jan? Geminiani says I should trust you because you are finished, because deep down he thinks that when you said it was not possible to have two drivers for the same car you were conspiring with De Muer to push him out of Bic.'

'Do you know my story, Luis? Do you know how I met Maurice? Since its creation in 1960, Maurice has been the director of Pelforth, the beer brand from Lille. I met him in 1962. I was an amateur, 22, and I was riding in the Tour des Porvenir, where I was doing fine. Gómez del Moral, a Spaniard like you, was the winner and I came third. One day Maurice came to our hotel to sign for his team the best two Dutch cyclists, Nijdam and me. Nijdam had had another offer, from Rik van Looy, and turned him down. I had the same offer, 1000 francs a month, and I accepted. One sentence he said was enough to convince me: "With me you'll be a free cyclist. If you are strong you'll be a winner. With Van Looy you'll only be a water carrier for the rest of your life." That's what he said to me, Luis. I believed him and I have not been deceived. How couldn't I be loyal to Maurice, Luis? And when Pelforth abandoned us and Maurice fought to join Bic to give us a space in Geminiani's machinery, I was his main support. Half of the team went to Bic and the other half went to Stablinski. He had convinced André Bazin, a businessman with whom he rode "gentlemen's races", to create Sonolor, with his brand of radios and transistors. And do you know how I returned the favour to Maurice? Winning the 1967 Vuelta. That victory helped him to call the shots in the team. We all owe something to each other; that's what cycling is like.'

'Jan, you are talking to me about intrigues and friendships, but I am not really interested in that. I don't need to befriend the managers. I am Luis Ocaña. You know me, I can look after myself.'

'Take it easy Luis, you are so young. Victories are made by will and patience. Do you have the willpower? I could have given up everything, I could have quit cycling when I broke my hip in Luchon in the Tour of '63. In Holland my primary care physician told me my heartbeat was very slow, and that it could be very dangerous to be a cyclist. Thank goodness the sport doctors told me that that was an advantage. I recovered, and the following year I won the Paris-Roubaix, which nobody expected. And five years later I won the Tour. Luis, do you feel the flame, the passion to win, to be a champion in your heart? I think you do. Your path is already mapped out, like mine was, and it crossed Roubaix, a Vuelta, a Tour, and a World Championship. You were talking to me about your family, your wife Josiane, who is expecting another baby, about Jean-Louis. You were talking to me about your determination to be a champion, which springs out of love for them. I also have a family. I have Cora, my daughter Kareen and my son Jan.

'The day I won the Tour and became the first Dutchman to win the Tour, nobody wanted to believe in my victory, nobody expected I would succeed in the challenge I'd set myself. Everybody had Van Springel in mind, the Buster Keaton of cycling because of his looks, or Ferdinand Bracke, but nobody thought of me – except Cora. Guided by her own intuition, she took a train to Amsterdam the day before and there she was waiting for me in the Cipale velodrome with the children. It was the happiest day of my life when I saw them and hugged them, and heard Kareen saying "Daddy!"…You will also live through that, Luis. The future is yours. To begin with, you'll be the winner of the Vuelta in three months' time. But be patient Luis, you'll never be alone. What do you think about Maurice?'

'I don't know. At first sight he looks sincere and open, a very straightforward person. He speaks directly to you, or so it seems. I don't know if he hides something. Everybody hides something.'

Janssen was not hiding anything. His commitment, if not to Ocaña, certainly to Bic and to his commercial and publicity obligations, was sincere, and he demonstrated it at the first opportunity, in the first confrontation with Merckx a few weeks later in the Paris-Nice.

Both Ocaña and Janssen knew very well that the Belgian would be untouchable in the French spring stage race. Whereas winter had been calm for the Bic riders, with not many kilometres of training, thinking that the year's first objective would be the Vuelta, Merckx had speeded up his training. After the terrible accident at Blois he only stopped his training when it was absolutely necessary for recovering and at Christmas. In the Belgium Six Day winter circuit, he was already standing out above the rest.

He needed to forget the accident and the death of his friend and he calculated there'd be nothing like winning again to help that process. Moreover, the Paris-Nice would be the preface to his spring Classics season that he would later string together with the Giro and then, after a brief pause, the Tour. Everyone at Bic was aware of that, and, in spite of which, they could not but admire, marvel even at the sight of the Cannibal's furious assult on the Paris-Nice. Merckx took the lead after a powerful attack in the third stage, on the road to Saint-Étienne, which he won, coming in alone. After that he only had to be vigilant and defend his lead from the front for the remaining days. He rounded this off with a victory in the final time trial on the Turbie.

'Luis, Merckx is committing suicide,' said Anquetil over coffee one night: since his recent retirement from professional competition, he had started writing pieces about the races for newspapers. 'If I had ridden like that I wouldn't have endured for so many years.'

'That's Merckx.' replied Ocaña. 'Whoever he's riding against, he starts a fight to the death against the whole of the peloton, challenging all his rivals. He is never satisfied.'

Against the Belgian tornado Janssen and Ocaña defended each other, and worked well together. Janssen won a stage and Ocaña came third in the individual time trial, behind Merckx and Poulidor, a specialist in that kind of short hillclimb, who was four seconds quicker. Ocaña performed for the first time with a new ultralight Motobécane with a titanium headset that saved him 100 grams. In the general classification Ocaña ended up second, 2'–14" behind Merckx, with Janssen third, ten seconds further back. A success.

'Your support and experience have helped me enormously, and the passion of your riding every day, Jan,' said Ocaña on the last day. 'Thanks to you I came second, but I also realised in the hillclimb that

I still have a lot of work to do to improve in the time trials. I need to improve my position; yes, I know everybody says it's practically perfect, that that's the way nature has created me, to bend over the bike and become a sail blown by the wind, with the finest of prows. And I also have to learn to manage the gears better. And I have to find better equipment, and check every detail.'

Poulidor's four-second advantage over him in the time trial made Ocaña feel insecure; he only relaxed 20 days later when he beat Poulidor by five seconds in the Montjuïc time trial that closed the Setmana Catalana. This was shortly before the Vuelta, and he left Cataluña in high spirits, despite finishing third overall, only three seconds behind old Poulidor, and 27 seconds down on the winner, the unbeatable Italo Zilioli, who had won in Igualada and Soldeu (Andorra). Zilioli rode for Merckx's Faemino-Faema; he was a good friend of the Belgian, apart from being a devout servant. Agustín Tamames, a 25-year-old cyclist from Salamanca, came fourth. After a poor year with Kas, Tamames had signed for Manzaneque's Werner and was beginning to show a lot of speed in uphill finishes, which would make him somebody to be feared when he was in top form.

'Slacken off a bit, Luis, and you'll see how much you'll win. Let yourself be guided. Listen to me.' said De Muer to Ocaña during their first important talk, in which he gave him some serious advice. It was Wednesday, 22 April. They were in a warm, luminous Cádiz, ideal days for the beach. The 1970 Vuelta (its silver wedding anniversary) would start the following day. Ocaña was the favourite: he'd come second the year before, and he'd been second in the Paris-Nice, and third in the Setmana Catalana. He was the favourite partly because the riders taking part in the Vuelta were not out of the top drawer. In the corridors of the hotel there was a lot of talk about Van Springel, and people were singing the praises of the young Lasa and Miguel Mari, José Manuel's little brother, who came from the same village as Perurena and rode for Miguel Moreno's La Casera team. Much was also being said about Andres Gandarias too, who had come fifth in the Tour the year before. The *parcours* was soft, with barely a mountain to climb, and without the Pyrenees. The only heights were in Montseny and Montserrat, and the usual Cantabrian cols and the Ordunya in the Basque Country at the end.

'We'll have to be patient and intelligent to win this Vuelta. And we'll also have to learn to play the game of bonuses, and round it off in Bilbao's time trial. Luis, I want to change you, but change you for good. I want you to be lucid, perceptive and organised. I don't want you to be the irresponsible sniper, playing into your rivals' hands, jumping away at every crossroads, because those attacks are counterproductive. I have noticed, and your team mates have mentioned it to me, that despite Janssen's efforts to integrate you in the team, you seem to be isolated at times, very much in your own world. Don't be mistrustful and you won't be mistrusted.'

'You are right, Maurice. I have to be more disciplined, at least in the race. I am very impulsive, I attack from too far out, and I get nervous in a slow peloton. Then I exhaust myself and I am dead before the finishing line. I promise I'll restrain myself in this Vuelta.'

'And Luis, go to bed early, please. However much a Spaniard you are, however much you like to listen to the radio, talk to Josiane on the phone, read the newspapers, however much you enjoy having conversations here, there and everywhere and want to discuss with Cescutti the progress of your new house under construction, you can't be up at 1 o'clock in the morning.'

Bic worked like clockwork and dominated the Vuelta from the prologue, which, like the year before, Ocaña won, and, like the year before when he had had to share tthe jersey with Gómez del Moral, there was an accompanying story to it. The Dutch specialist, René Pijnen, should have been the fastest over the six-kilometre ride, and so he was until the last 20 metres, already in the Carranza Stadium, when he fell. He quickly got up and ran as fast as he could, pushing his bicycle the last metres of the cinder track around the playing field. He lost by only four tenths of a second. However, the Dutchman stripped Ocaña of the leader's jersey the following day, when he finished better classified in the sprint at Jerez de la Frontera. The brave Perurena did not arrive there. The victim of a crash, he was taken to the Cádiz hospital suffering from concussion.

René Pijnen was a rider with more class than ambition. He was a real amateur. 'I am single and I don't need much to live,' he told his team mates at Willem II, the team in which Van Looy would eventually retire, the team mates with whom he shared the joy of wearing the yellow jersey until the ninth stage of a poor, devalued Vuelta, with no surprises or sprinters' stages. 'With winter Six-Days contracts I have enough to live on for the rest of the year. The rest of the money I save. I won't be bothered if I have to work on my parents' farm once I quit cycling. So don't talk to me about suffering in the Tour or other important races. I am happy enough with this, with the Vuelta and with less important races.'

The tenth day, the day of Montseny and of the first cols, was the day De Muer chose to bring those placid days of Pijnen's leadership to an end. It was the Catalan stage similar to the previous year when, on the way to Moià, Ocaña served the Vuelta up on a plate for Pingeon. But this time Ocaña was offering no presents. The race broke up on the Collfornic, the start of the Montseny and crossed through what was known at that time as the Catalan Swiss, with Pijnen already dropped. After the Coll de la Pujosa on the way to Monistrol, Ocaña attacked on the climb to Montserrat, as if drawn from the ever green oaks by those great, naked rocks that surrounded and protected the Monastery. He was well ahead when he passed through the peak, for which he got ten bonus seconds that ensured his overall leadership. On the descent to Igualada through the Bruc, he was caught by a small group of all the favourites, led by Tamames, who would end up winning the stage. From that moment on, Ocaña, in the leader's jersey, would only have to keep an eye on Van Springel, Tamames and the young Lasa. All of them separated by only a few seconds. The winner would be decided by the bonuses, and most especially by the final time trial, 29 kilometres between Llodio and Garellano in Bilbao.

During the following stages Bic organised its defence of Ocaña's yellow jersey. Ocaña would discover the sensational class and the value of his team mates. He won in Zaragoza after the great veteran, Novak, got into a group of escapees; Novak was an 85-kilo giant, known as the 'tractor' because of his capacity to pull the peloton along. Someone like him was very useful on windy days, because behind his extremely wide back two or even three climbers could find shelter. Johny Schleck won in the Retiro Park, in Madrid, sensationally catching everybody off balance. A hard man from Luxembourg, he was Bic's captain on the road, and never left any detail to chance. He rode very well on the flat and in the medium mountains. In Santander Roger Rosiers was the surprise winner (surprise because nobody believed he could cope with even the slightest slope) after a medium mountain stage which took in the Bocos and Alisas. It was a cold and miserable day, despite the joy brought about by young José Manuel Fuente, a boisterous, hyperactive debutant who had worn the Tiger jersey of best young rider from the very first day. Rosiers was a 23-year-old, typically Flemish rider, from Ambers, a fine *rouleur* but somewhat unusual: he spoke classical Latin and Greek, which he had studied at university, and he was as generous as he was big. He had no hesitation in working as a *domestique* despite his enormous class. He won the Paris-Roubaix the following year, riding none other than Roger de Vlaeminck off his wheel on the *pavé*. He signed for Molteni in 1974 to help his enemy, Merckx, but he came back to Ocaña one year later, and stayed with him until the end of his career in Super Ser and in Frisol.

A week away from the end of the Vuelta, Tamames picked up a 10-seconds bonus in a sprint at the top of Somosierra, which made him race leader by a single second. 'If I can get to the time trial with two minutes on Ocaña I'll win the Vuelta.' So said the rider from Monterrubio de la Armuna. 'Is it impossible?' he asked. 'I believe Ocaña is not at the top of his form. Haven't you seen Doctor Salinas, the Vuelta's doctor, giving him a painkilling injection on his knee in front of everyone?'

But he felt defeated and lost when it came to the last time trial, like Van Springel, Janssen's Buster Keaton, who felt depressed on the eve of the time trial as he recognised the route lacked the long straights and false flats that would play to his advantage; instead it was plagued with steep slopes, corners and mountains. It was over those 29 kilometres where Ocaña showed the class for which he was so admired in France. His average speed of 44 kph was a marvel. Second placed Jesús Manzaneque lost 1'–1" and Van Springel and Tamames were further back.

The following day, Spanish newspapers, won over at last, carried headlines such as: 'The dream champion' and their front pages insisted that the hopes of Spanish cycling were built upon this native of Cuenca. Ocaña smiled contentedly. It looked as if Spaniards were beginning to love him, to believe in him, but he didn't want to deceive himself. The Vuelta was nothing. There were no rivals. He had no wish to fool himself, not even when he remembered the lovely giant Anatole Novak, Anquetil's favourite musketeer, who, unable to restrain his elation, proudly proclaimed in the papers: 'Eddy Merckx will finally have a worthy rival in the Tour. Luis is now capable of brandishing the flag of our revolt to overthrow the despot.'

Josiane was waiting for him in Bilbao, already six months pregnant with Sylvie. She hugged him and kissed him. He returned to Mont-de-Marsan that same afternoon, almost without changing his clothing. He was eager to see the progress of the work on his new mansion in Bretagne, eager to help the workers. But, before leaving, Josiane had time to tell the press something that Ocaña would read the following day: 'I never had any doubts about his triumph. Luis is a great cyclist, an even better husband, and an excellent person.'

De Muer agreed with Josiane's words; he was delighted with the transformation of an untamed wild horse, or so he was told. De Muer was so elated he rang him only 48 hours after the end of the Vuelta.

'Luis, don't unpack your suitcases. Take the car and go to Saint Etienne in two days. You'll take part in the Circuit of the Six Provinces (which was how the Dauphiné Libéré was temporarily renamed after the merging of the newspapers *Dauphiné Libéré*, from Grenoble, and *Le Progrès*, from Lyon, in 1969 and 1970 when it was held in May). If you maintain that form and that spirit, there will be nobody to touch you.'

'But this was not the plan, Maurice. I was supposed to have some time to rest, then come back in June for the Midi Libre, which is more suited to our calendar, considering the Tour. Between the end of the Six Provinces and the beginning of the Tour there's only a month…'

'But Luis, think about it for a second. Merckx will ride the Giro, which starts one day before, so he will also have to stop in June. Both of you will be on top form. In your present condition, a victory in the Six Provinces with the same team mates you had in the Vuelta will make you the leader of the team forever. Didn't you notice how those rough Northern men you were afraid of at the beginning were becoming fond of you? The more you get to know them, the more you'll end up adoring them.'

Finally, Ocaña gave in. However, he would regret giving in so easily to De Muer's persuasion, despite winning the Six Provinces. In that race Ocaña would meet the best stage racers riding at that time, with the exception of Merckx, who was on his quest for a second Giro. Pingeon, Delisle, Bracke, Zoetemelk were all in the Six Provinces, and Poulidor as well, although he was suffering from a painful herpes, vertigo and sickness. He also became reacquainted with Van Springel, his rival in the Vuelta, and above all, he met Charly Grosskost.

Ocaña lost out to Raymond Delisle in the Terrenoire prologue by just three seconds, and so decided to go on the offensive as soon as the terrain was appropriate. That came on the third stage, between Lyon and Salanches. Under tempestuous showers, sometimes accompanied by hail, Ocaña sent Novak ahead to pave the way, then found an unexpected ally in the Belgian, Roger de Vlaeminck, when the key moment came – the ascent of the Col du Cordon. Accompanying them both was the slight Van Impe, who was starting to make a name for himself. Ocaña set the pace on the climb, easing somewhat to avoid De Vlaeminck being dropped, because he would be useful to him on the descent into Sallanches. The powerful Flandrian did not fail him. Like a locomotive he guided him down and on to the flat run-in, where they could get rid of the lightweight Van Impe. They arrived at the finishing line with a comfortable advantage, and it was there where Ocaña, who now became overall leader, let De Vlaeminck, known by everyone as 'the Gipsy', take the stage win. Ocaña admired his elegance, his class, his apparent casualness and ended up copying his long, thick sideburns, cut wide and square at the bottom, like the square De Vlaeminck's arms formed when he felt at his very best in the Paris-Roubaix. Once Ocaña was ahead in the classification, it was a matter of maintaining his lead and then deciding the race in the final time trial. And just as in the Vuelta, De Muer decided to defend by attacking. The following day, in the *etapa reina* that crossed la Chartreuse via the cols de Aravis, Cucheron, Granier and Porte, he ordered Jean Claude Genty to go alone on the first col. This he did so well that he arrived in Grenoble after a solo escape of 130 kilometres, with a sufficient advantage to become race leader.

'Don't worry Luis,' Genty told his team leader, 'I'll be happy to give you back the jersey in the time trial tomorrow.'

If Ocaña was becoming fond of Genty, the person he was really taken with was Charly Grosskot. Grosskot was a very useful pursuiter (he'd defeated Anquetil in one French championship), and a cheerful, dark skinned Alsatian, who had mastered the art of riding prologues and short time trials. He won the prologue in the '68 Tour and wore the yellow jersey for a few stages, and he could have built a career purely as a prologue specialist, but he was a rider from the old school, and quite happy to ride close to Ocaña all the time and help him whenever he was needed. Ocaña discovered that on el Cucheron. While Genty was relentlessly forging on ahead, Ocaña had three punctures on the climb up, and a fourth one on the fast descent towards Grenoble. But Grosskost, the good Samaritan, never left him, and gave him his wheel to prevent him from falling behind from the main group.

On the following day, in the 34-kilometres time trial from Privas to Vals-les-Bains, Ocaña delivered the *coup de grâce* in the style of the Vuelta. He finished 39 seconds ahead of Pingeon, and 1'–6" up on Van Springel, the two who were with him on the podium. The night before he had familiarised himself with the route, decided on which gears to use, and his strategy, all with help from Cescutti, who accompanied him to races as often as he could, and who continued giving him advice and being a comforting presence. They had De Muer's permission for this: he knew when to stand back. But they were as secret as possible as Cescutti preferred that nobody knew about his existence and his influence in Luis' life.

'I have been a carpenter like you, Luis, not in the South but in the fertile lands of the Vendôme, where the wheat grows tall and full; until I was 19 the only job I had was helping my widowed mother,' said Genty once he had taken off his yellow jersey.

'I was a carpenter like you but I didn't have either your ambition or your strength, but I do have your willpower. Last year I suffered a skull fracture, but three months later I was riding again and I even won a race in Belgium. I met my wife, Martine, at a criterium in Saint Tropez. We live at the other end of the country, in Dieppe, where her parents have a restaurant. It's next to the cold and grey English Channel, and it's got beaches full of pebbles that stick in your naked feet. I've already told her that the life of a cyclist lasts ten years. And after that – "I will never leave your side, Martine, and I will tell you stories about cycling every night." She is happy with that. I am not a super-cyclist, Luis, but I get by honourably enough. When you need it, Luis, my legs will be your legs.'

A few hours after Genty's confidence and his generous offer, during the next stage, De Vlaeminck lost control of his bicycle. He involuntarily pushed the rider closest to him, who happened to be Genty, against a banana tree to avoid falling off. The result was a sprained ankle for the Frenchman.

Cescutti was worried. It was only a week to the beginning of the Tour and he had misgivings about the performance of his friend Luis, for whom he was still designing his training plan. He had retired from the Tour of Luxembourg, the only race he'd taken part in for a month.

'Don't worry Pierrot; I pulled out because I don't like Luxembourg. It was enough to remember it was there that Antonin Magne told me he didn't want me for his Mercier team to make me feel sick. I fulfilled what my contract stipulated: to take part in a minimum of two races. I rode, I got the money and I went back home,' said Luis. They were sitting on the illuminated patio of Cescutti's house; he had invited Luis and Josiane for dinner. Luis had a long sip of a fresh rosé to help digest the *confit de canard*. They talked about the work on their house, and Josiane's pregnancy, only a month away from giving birth, and they talked about the Tour that was approaching.

'I am not only worried about that; I am worried about the excessive euphoria that surrounds you, Luis. All newspapers talk about how you are going to give Merckx a hard time, that you are the only one who can actually make him suffer and defeat him, that your ride in the Vuelta and in the Six Provinces was perfect...'

'I would also like to have a more discreet profile, Pierrot, but it is difficult to avoid what has happened; it can't be erased or hidden. I have enjoyed cycling these last few months, I can't deny it. In the Vuelta I was a cold boxer clinically focused on giving the final knockout blow. I was like the bullfighter who hides his sword behind his red cape waiting for the moment of truth. I was Joselito when he enters the bullring; that is how I felt. But I don't know if I am like that, nor if I want to be like that. Do you know Mendiburu is leaving us, Pierrot? After bringing him to Bic...He called the other day and told me that Luis Puig, the president of the Spanish Cycling Federation, had backed down and not signed Luis Otaño, his cousin, as coach of the national team because he was not sufficiently Spanish, and that he'd offered him the post? "I couldn't say no to Luis Puig," Mendiburu told me, so he's saying goodbye to cycling.

'You were there in the Six Provinces, Pierrot; you helped me and saw me in that time trial where I thought I was closer than ever to Anquetil. Anquetil is a pianist, a virtuoso, a sort of Mozart, and time trials are his particular solo concerts. I sometimes feel like a virtuoso in the mountain stages. There I feel I'm on a cloud, I feel capable of playing all the notes; I feel I can write music in every pedalling effort. But I still have a lot to learn as regards the time trials. But I am learning, Pierrot, and I feel I am getting closer to Jacques. I called De Muer the other day to thank him for persuading me to take part in the Six Provinces. This is my most important victory so far, even more important than the Vuelta, because I had to compete with real rivals there.'

'And that is why everybody is now talking about you and Merckx, as if there were no other riders. It's going to be just you and him. And what also worries me is that after the Dauphiné you had to rest for a number of days to recover from the continuous effort in both races.

These abrupt interruptions in the middle of the season are not good for you. I am afraid you will not be on top form going into the Tour, and Merckx will try to make things very difficult for you from day one, without waiting for the mountains, where he fears you most.'

'Don't worry Pierrot. The slightest mistake by Merckx and I'll be there, attacking him. Certainly I am thinking about beating Merckx, Pierrot. He is stronger than me, for sure, and stronger than everyone else, but he is also a man, and nobody's perfect. We all can have a bad day. I'll follow him closely every single day, and as soon as I see him weakening, I'll attack. It's that simple. Of course, it's most likely that I'll end up getting beaten – you don't need to tell me that, Pierrot. I really don't mind. I don't want to come second, Pierrot, you've always known that. I hate to not to be the winner. I hate to be mediocre, I hate to be part of those who never take risks to win. But I am also nervous Pierrot, I know I have no right to let down those who have put their faith in me. This duck thigh is very good. Could I have some more of that fresh wine please?'

The Tour of 1970 produced the first great performance by Thévenet, the robust Burgundian who won at La Mongie, and Merckx's first ever defeat in a short Tour time trial, at the hands of González Linares. It was also the Tour of Zoetemelk's first podium, and the Tour of the Cannibal's crushing domination as well as the drama of his collapse on Mont Ventoux – a victim of his own excess. Mont Ventoux was also a torment for Ocaña.

Nonetheless, Bic's arrival in Limoges, the Tour's starting point, was high-spirited and optimistic. Janssen, Berland, Genty, Grosskost, Leblanc, Novak, Schleck and the Vasseur brothers were the chosen ones to ride alongside Ocaña. De Muer had already filled his notebooks with ambitious and aggressive strategies to isolate Merckx from his Faemino armada as soon as possible, and so bring about a one-on-one with his Ocaña. Wrong strategy. Merckx's overwhelming performance in the prologue had already raised Ocaña's fears. Then, Merckx slipped Zilioli, his most loyal lieutenant, into an escape on the way to Angers that had been initiated by Bic's Berland – known as the little priest for wearing glasses without a frame. Taking advantage of Bic's work,

Zilioloi won the stage, so relieving Merckx of the weight of wearing the yellow jersey.

'We must continue to attack, we can't give in, but we can't do this on our own; we need the help of other teams,' exhorted Janssen to his team mates at the end of the team time trial in which an uncoordinated Bic ceded more time to Merckx. The following day, finishing on the steep slopes of Lisieux's, the Bic team shot itself in the foot again.

'They are going to attack us from the beginning,' Merckx warned his Faemino team mates. 'We are going to start out at 50kph, however strange that may sound, because that'll help us. With that pace, it will be impossible for anyone to escape and will make it difficult enough for the climbers to hang on and not get droped. And if I stay at the front all the time, not only will we avoid any risk, we will take charge of the race. I'm asking all of you, you Antheunis, and you Bruyère, and you Huysmans, and you Mintjens, Spruyt, Swerts, Vandenberghe and Van Schil, and you, too, Italo – looking so gorgeous in your yellow jersey – I am asking everyone: do you prefer to accept the law that Bic wants to impose on us, or do you prefer us to take the initiative and be in command of the race? Ocaña and his team leave us with no alternative: we have to foil their attacks. Nobody will take a step without our consent. It's a command. What will they think about us in Belgium if we allow 30-minute long escapes? We are ready to do all the work, and we know the only thing our rivals have in mind is to ambush us. That is the game, our game. I promise it will be allright.'

His nine Faemino friends, sitting around him in the small dining room of a hotel in Lisieux, stirred their coffee and agreed. 'Haven't you noticed how exhausted Ocaña was at the finish in Lisieux, short of breath, with his mouth open, just when he was setting up Janssen for the sprint? Everyone says he will be my rival in the mountains, but I want to see how he copes even before we reach the Alps.'

Merckx's predictions were right: and Ocaña attacked again next day from the beginning, on the road to Rouen, where Anquetil picked strawberries as a child in summer on the riverbanks of the Seine. Ocaña attacked once and Merckx responded, and later on, when Merckx punctured, Ocaña attacked again with Linares, Van Neste,

Wagtmans, Paolini, Hubrechts and Morgens Frey while Antheunis was giving his Faemino team leader a wheel. The chase was intense but short. Merckx himself was in charge of the operation, riding so ferociously that nobody else could relieve him and take a spell on the front. And next day, on the way to Valenciennes over the *pavés* of Roubaix, Merckx cut himself free again, inspired by the closeness of his territory and by Ocaña's weakness on the *pavés*. There, Zilioli did not resist either, and Merckx recovered the yellow jersey. He wouldn't relinquish it again. After another short time trial before the Alps, in which Merckx took his revenge on the upstart, Linares, Ocaña was already 3'–38" down. That was the closest he would get. By the end he would be much further behind.

'De Muer had his strategy wrong,' Cescutti analysed a few days later with Ocaña in Mont-de-Marsan. 'His aggressiveness on the flat stages played into the hands of Merckx, who was in top form in the mountain stages. Not only did you not isolate him, he left you exhausted.'

'Ah, Pierrot, you may be right. Maurice himself admitted we had done the job for others. "We gave everything in the first stages and in the Alps we could barely walk." That's what he said. But, as you know, there have been plenty of other factors, like my health.' Luis preferred to make this kind of confession to Cescutti rather than De Muer, who after all was his boss, and he did not want him to think he was making excuses for his defeat.

'There are people,' Luis thought, 'who, when they meet an artist, understand that they will never be able to understand him, his motivations or the reasons for his actions. They realise that the only thing they can do is follow him wherever he goes. But De Muer is not that kind of person. He is so pragmatic, and has been so tied to the land and to cycling all his life that, before trying to understand or follow the artist, he will try to destroy his artistic soul, to make him ordinary. That's why it makes no sense to open up to him or discuss your most intimate thoughts with him: he won't follow the artist, nor admire him. Geminiani isn't like that. He is an artist who believes in artists. And Cescutti, who was not an artist himself, believed in him, in Luis.'

'You were right as well, Pierrot. I shouldn't have stopped after the Six Provinces, because instead of progressively reaching my best form, I had to start abruptly, and my body reacted. When I arrived in Limoges, my treacherous and obstinate liver, my weak point, was already affected. From the very first day, Pierrot, I was suffering from various pains and weaknesses. I haven't told you anything until now. If I pretended otherwise in our telephone conversations it was only because I didn't want to worry you, neither you nor Josiane. As you know very well, you've told me this a thousand times, states of grace quickly fade away. We are always on the razor's edge between top form and collapse.

'When the Tour began I was close to collapse, out of shape. Once there, the bronchitis, my other weak point, started to give me trouble before the liver did. And, as if that wasn't enough, I suffered from haemorrhoids, like in the Giro, so I did not feel comfortable sitting on the saddle. That's the condition I was in when we arrived at the Alps, where I suffered like a blessed martyr. The Divonne-les-Bains stage, which only had one third category climb in the Jura, the Rousses, where Merckx launched a strange attack, I suffered another *pájara*, one of the worst in my life, and, if that wasn't enough, it was so hot that Janssen had a sunstroke and we couldn't get any life out of him. That day Bic disappeared from the Tour, and it was thanks to the good Samaritan Grosskost that I lost only 12 minutes. I was so downhearted that my nose was hitting the handlebar; I was afraid the snot would gunge up the headset. I did not even dare look ahead.

'By the tenth stage I was already finished. I did not think I was in such a bad condition, but I had had three punctures, Pierrot. After the first two I came back to the peloton, but the third coincided with an attack by Merckx and Poulidor and Aimar went after him. Grosskost waited for me, which affected his position in the overall, which could have been very good – remember he was third the next day in the Divonne hippodrome time trial. He was in excellent shape but he stayed with me again in the afternoon after the second time trial, when I was suffering like a mad dog on the way to Thonon. It was even worse than the day before. I was exhausted, but Charly wouldn't let me pull out. He threatened me: "If you pull out I'll kick you all the way to the Galibier." So I had to continue coping with my torment. Two days later, on the Gap stage, the Col de Noyer was decisive. Do you know the Col de Noyer? It is no more than a goat's path meandering up the hillside, where the tarmac has either melted because it is hotter than hell, or it simply does not exist and the only thing left is gravel. Agostinho attacked there and Merckx, very aware that he couldn't let someone like him escape, went after him. I was left behind, suffering. And in that place, the worst possible place, Charly, my brave friend through thick and thin, collapses. He got off the bicycle. He said he couldn't ride anymore and that I should go on alone. He said we had to consider the whole team and that I couldn't pull out after all I had done to be there. We hugged each other. We cried. He couldn't cope with more suffering and jumped into the broom waggon. I was about to pull out as I passed by a little spring that in my almost catatonic condition looked to me like an oasis. But I thought about Grosskost and I felt embarrassed. I thought I was not worth his sacrifice. From the car, De Muer and Morin insulted me and encouraged me at the same time to bloody well finish the stage and not even think about pulling out. I looked like Christ, and I felt like Christ must have felt on the cross. But I finally managed to increase the pace a bit and finish, thanks to them blowing the horn and their cries of encouragement.

'After several horrendous days and an atrocious pain that prevented me even from signing autographs, the curse on me seemed to have vanished. I recovered my pedalling power and I waited and waited like a dying man holding on to the sunset, so that it shines forever in the horizon. I also made a resolution that I would win a stage and dedicate it openly to Grosskost. Just a symbolic victory, a proof of my homage. In Saint-Gaudens, after a 60-kilometre escape, always me on my own, I won with a two-minute advantage, which is even more remarkable considering that Merckx, the bastard, sent his great hulks after me! He didn't even want me to win that, and he forced me to ride the last 30 kilometres on the tip of the saddle. That was too much. That day he earned my resentment and that of the whole Bic team. We can say that the war broke out that day. This has been my Tour, Pierrot, and these have been my misgivings. Can my willpower ever get rid of the evil eye that haunts me? Do I have the right not to sink into depression? Does it make sense to be optimistic?'

'Luis, there is no one like you, and there will never be. I promise you will achieve something no other cyclist has achieved before, because you are destined to do it. You are great, a giant, Luis.'

Jean-Louis would finally have a little sister. Sylvie was born ten days after the end of the Tour, a Tour which, nonetheless, left Ocaña with a hint of optimism thanks to his win on the Saint Gaudens stage. This victory was welcomed with joy by the French press: *L'Équipe*'s Antoine Blondin, for instance, referred to it as the sign of a genius who never surrenders, the proclamation of future battles, or the sign of an established giant. All that was published on 28 July, the day Sylvie was born. After he'd recovered and taken part in the World Championship in Mallory Park, Leicestershire, which was won by the young and unfortunate Jean Pierre Monseré, ahead of Mortensen and Gimondi, and from which he retired, came the round of criteriums promised by his manager, Daniel Dousset. And after that, the Volta a Catalunya, where Ocaña showed he had changed little, he was still the Ocaña of old, making yet another furious but useless, all or nothing escape which took him to the point of total exhaustion on the Puigcerda stage. (Bitossi, the Italian with the 'crazy heart' won). Then came the Montjuïc hill climb, followed by the Grand Prix des Nations where he was third, and which granted him second position, behind Merckx, in the Pernod Points Championship, thanks to his Vuelta and his Dauphiné results. The only thing that troubled him was the news from the Paris-Tours, in which his friend Janssen suffered sunstroke: he fainted while riding and fell into the kerb. Doctors spoke of cardiac fatigue. Janssen spoke of taking it easy.

'My glory days are over, Maurice,' he told De Muer, who was sitting next to his bed in hospital. 'From now on I will only take part in little races that don't require much commitment, and I will go on holiday during the Tour.'

1971

That winter, Ocaña visited a liver specialist in Bilbao who subjected him to a hard, three-month long treatment. After that, he felt recovered, like new. In February, the Ocaña family started living in their new home in Bretagne-de-Marsan. The block of council flats, the symbol of their emancipation, their beginnings, was left behind forever. Their new country house was made of white walls and a white patio. It had six big bedrooms designed by Luis himself, with the Castilian-style furniture that he liked so much, and a small park with a pond where he would see the reflection of his face, that of a man who had achieved everything with the sweat of his brow. Ocaña could not ask more from life. He felt extremely happy. He put an easel and an empty canvas on the patio and started to paint, following wherever his imagination took him. Strong colours, thick strokes, the half-finished portrait of his father, Cuenca's hanging houses, a landscape, an Andalusian girl.

'At the beginning, Jean, when I heard, "eh Frenchman, eh Frenchman," I didn't even turn around. I thought they were not talking to me. I thought whoever it was only wanted to attract the attention of Pérez Francés for some reason. But then I thought, wait a minute, Pérez Francés belongs to the past…and then someone turned to me and said "eh, Frenchman". Jean, I swear I don't mind being called French because I live in France and I ride for a French team, although I was born in Spain and actually I am Spanish. And I don't mind if I am called "Frenchman" affectionately, as if a friend is calling me by a nickname. But that's not their tone of voice and the tone used by Spanish newspapers is not exactly friendly: it is aggressive, excluding, as if they were telling me: "however much you want it, you'll never be one of us". Honestly, I don't mind where I belong, but it annoys me: it's me, not them, who chooses who I want to be with, or if I prefer to be alone. And I don't really care if they call me sullen, arrogant, or conceited…But there's one thing I don't understand. Am I not accepted because I am not, according to them, 100% Spanish? Is that the reason? Or is it because of the way I am? And if they consider me French, why did the organisers of the Vuelta not pay me what I asked for, which was what I am worth, whereas the rest of the foreign cyclists were paid accordingly?'

June, a strange month in Paris, was coming to an end. Some days were so heavy, like those of an unbearable summer, that they only invited you to move slowly and at night; but June also has light days as in spring or autumn; those days seemed to call for you not to stop, as if you were wasting your life if you were not forever on the move. Jean, the person Ocaña was talking with, was sitting opposite him on the other side of a table with a white and red checked tablecloth, in Casa Alcalde, a Basque restaurant in rue Grenelle, next to Les Invalides. They were having a Spanish omelette with hake. After that they would stroll around Saint-Germain for a while and would visit Auberge Basque, in rue Verneuil, where they would sit down in a corner and watch Paris go by. Later, they would reach the Courrier de Lyon in the corner of rue du Bac, where Jean used to meet Antoine Blondin, a place where Serge Gainsbourg and Juliette Gréco used to spend some time as well. With Blondin, Jean drank and talked and talked....and with him, Luis also wanted to talk. And if the conversation just carried on, all of them (Jean and Antoine, Luis and Bastide, with a few more acolytes of the alcoholic night) would end up going down the rue de Seine. Here they bumped into the market fruit stall-holders who were opening before the milky, grey dawn, singing 'los borrchos en el cementerio juegan al mus' [drunkards play cards in the cemetery] on the way to the Alcazar, a couple of streets down. There they would meet de Gribaldy and also Geminiani and there they would enjoy the night and meet beautiful women. It was in moments such as these when Ocaña felt the king of Paris, like all Parisian night birds, but also he felt far from Spain, from what he called Spanish nastiness, a subject that he regretted having broached with Jean.

He'd met Jean, Cormier, a journalist for *Le Parisien*, in his first Tour. Luis used to treat journalists with a certain disdain, even aggressively, but with Jean or Juanito (which was what Jean asked Luis to call him) it was a different story: he gave him two kisses every time they meet and hugged him like a bear. In a certain way, Jean saw in Luis the reflection of his own life, as if he lived inside the mirror that Luis saw every day when he shaved, and between them, the Pyrenees. Born in Saint Engrâce, a small Pyrenean village between Larrau and Burdinkurutxeta, very close to the border with Spain and to the smugglers' paths through the Irati beech forest. Jean did not feel Spanish or French although he spoke both languages very well. But he did feel Basque. He was a French Basque who felt free in Paris, because nobody asked where anybody was from in Paris: in Paris everyone is a Parisian. And apart from being Basque and eating Espelette pepper, Jean loved rugby and was a very good friend of Benoît Dauga, the giant from Mont-de-Marsan, then perhaps the best player in all France. When he had time Luis used to go and cheer him when he played at the Stade de Montois, because Luis enjoyed rugby. After a match they used to drink armañac and Benoît hugged him calling him 'l'enfant de Mont-de-Marsan'. When Luis crashed on the Col de Menté, he was waiting for him at the door of Luis's house in Bretagne-de-Marsan: the giant from Montgaillard was an honest friend, and the best back row forward ever. Jean did not talk to him about Benoît, he talked about Che, with whom he was truly fascinated. He had even written books about him and also had a collection of books about him and his life. Although Luis's ideas were not exactly revolutionary and he found it difficult to identify with Che, he was certainly fascinated by him, by the story of the doctor who organised the communist revolution in Cuba, and gave his life for a crazy guerrilla in Bolivia.

'Just like Che, I am a rebel, Jean,' Luis sometimes told him, 'But my rebelliousness does not spring from the mind, like that of Che's; it comes from my guts, from hunger. I am not fighting to transform society, but to be accepted by society and to be considered a full legal member. And I am also a rebel because I don't take orders from anyone; I don't let anyone tell me what I have to do. Look what happened to me in the Vuelta, Jean, look at the year I have had. I came third in the Paris-Nice; I am always defeated by Merckx in this race, but I don't mind because he is always better prepared than me and he loves to leave his mark right from the beginning of the season. But I did not like being beaten by Gösta Petterson, who is a real bloodsucker who only seems to ride for second place. Every time I attacked he sat on my wheel and he'd never take a turn on the front. On top of that, one day, when we were going downhill towards the finish at Draguignan, Merckx attacked with Petterson and a black cat crossed in front of Janssen, and he came down hard. I was left behind, isolated. When we arrived at the hotel we heard that poor Monseré, such a happy World Champion, had died in an accident in a critérium in Amberes, when he crashed into a car that was coming the other way. What a day, poor chap....He wanted to conquer the world too quickly.' He took a plane to Belgium the very next day after the Vuelta a Andalucía ended, because he was racing in a velodrome that night.

'In the Turbie time trial, I had the wrong gear and Merckx beat me again. But in that Paris-Nice, Jean, Merckx made a mistake he would end up paying for. Twice when I attacked on the Alpilles stage on the way to Bollène, along with Mortensen, he came after me and when he caught me, he started to whistle and look at me defiantly, as if saying, "Where do you think you are going?" He was showing off how easily he could catch me. The third time he attempted to do that, I put my hand on his back and told him in Spanish: "He who laughs last, laughs best." But I don't know if he really understood me. Later I came third in the Setmana Catalana, but it didn't feel so good because I was beaten by Poulidor, who is a real pain. Yet, Poulidor's victory made me feel happy, however strange that may sound. In fact, I gave him a hand to defeat the Italian Zolioli, whom I don't like at all. As I couldn't make it, I preferred a Frenchman like Poulidor, who has never attacked me, rather than an Italian. I won the prologue (as you know, I win all the time trials if Merckx isn't there), but on the third day I got distracted and a few cyclists broke away; it was little Lasa who put me in trouble, and Poulidor gate-crashed it and that pest Gösta Petterson also managed to sneak into the group, yet again...'

'That Swede is not as bad as you think, Luis,' Jean interrupted. 'I think he has just won the Giro.'

'Whatever he's won I don't like him. The thing is victory slipped out of my hands, and what do I find that night in the hotel? A telegram from Darras and De Muer, who had stayed in France. They said: "We can accept you being beaten by Merckx, but by Poulidor..." as if I liked losing a race in Spain. I was lucky to be able to take revenge on Poulidor in the Tour of the Basque Country. I think I did the time trial of my life, Jean. I took almost two minutes out of the old boy. It looks easy, doesn't it? And there, in Eibar, where the Basque tour finished, I got in the car and drove down to Almería, where five days later the Vuelta was set to begin. And what I found there was that it was full of famous people like Yul Brynner, Ursula Andress, Yves Montand, Alain Delon. It looked like Paris, Jean, our Paris, but it was not Paris, it was the desert, and they don't stop filming westerns there. To my surprise, the first thing I read when I got there was Spanish journalists criticising me for having said, during the Paris-Nice, that I would bet on me against Merckx. And as I didn't win they reminded me of my defeat. But what have I done to them to be treated like that, Jean?'

'What you really like, Luis, is being a one-off, contradicting everyone, and you want to be accepted like that. But you'll never integrate that way; you'll never be Spanish or French. You don't really want to be just an ordinary person. Do you know Buñuel, Luis? He is a Spanish filmmaker, born in Aragón, who went into exile after the war and now wants to return to Spain because he has always felt Spanish. He shot the film *Tristana* in Spain and he almost got killed for it. What a scandal, Luis. He is not accepted in sad, small-minded and mediocre Spain, not because they don't consider him a Spaniard; he is not accepted because he is a genius who breaks the rules. You are like that, Luis, you are the Buñuel of cycling – which deserves another drink.'

Jean finished in one gulp the cup of armagnac they had ordered after the coffee. Before, he warmed it up with his big hands, he covered it and then he shook it. Then he put it to his nose very gently and lifted it with a finger, inhaling the pleasing aroma of alcohol and wood.

'You said, Jean, that they are mean, those Spaniards. I am going to tell you a story that will make you laugh. Last year, after the end of the Vuelta, the organisers, Bergareche and Albéniz, prepared a gala dinner which they'd told me I couldn't miss, of course, because I was the winner. But I got in the car and drove back to Mont-de-Marsan. I apologised to them with the excuse that Josiane was pregnant and tired. I said that her mother was waiting for us there and that my mother was busy because she had to go Bilbao. They did not take very kindly to my absence, my "disdain" as some of them called it, and they made me pay for it this year by organising the Vuelta without a time trial. Well, there are time trials, but if you count the prologue and two miniatures, it doesn't amount to ten kilometres. Just imagine! A Vuelta without mountains or time trials and with millions of bonuses; I think there are bonuses just for getting to the hotel. What a disaster. I told them that under those conditions I would not take the race seriously, that I would regard those three weeks simply as training for the Tour. For that I was almost crucified. What people, Jean.'

'Despite that, despite there being no time trial, you were about to win Luis. You were in top form.'

'And what's even more ironic is that one of the best time-trialist, the Belgian Bracke, won the race. He gave up track riding, took the hour record and now rides for Peugeot. It was thanks to his team mate Godefroot that he won it, and also thanks to me, or so they thought in Madrid, where I was booed on the last day. I don't know if they did it because I was French, or for being a Spaniard in France, or because, after all, the winner was not a Spaniard. I would have won if I hadn't lagged behind in Pamplona, like our leader Pijnen, when little Lasa and Tamames attacked at the Lesa reservoir. I lost five minutes and the will to continue, but that night De Muer came back to the Vuelta; he'd been in France up to then, directing those who were taking part in the Four Days of Dunkirk, where Grosskost lost everything on the last day. De Muer arrived in Bilbao, and after a reprimand, he told me: "There's a solution Luis, but if you want to find it you'll have to be yourself again."

'He took out a map of the Vuelta, spread it on the table, and he showed me the route of the next stage, the one that finished at Vitoria through Orduña and the Puerto de La Herrera. "This will be your day, Luis," he said to me as if he had discovered the moon. He didn't need to say anything else; I was ready to shut everybody up. In Orduña, a group was formed up ahead, and I launched a strong attack from behind, reached the breakaways, and then carried on. Lasa and Tamames began to suffer. On the Herrera, the last obstacle before Vitoria, only Martos, Scheper and Bracke could stand the pace. When I was three kilometres away from the peak I was alone, and I arrived in Vitoria alone, two minutes up on the three who had been able to keep up the pace, and almost eight minutes up on Lasa, Tamames and also Poulidor and Zoetemelk, who had been really crawling throughout the entire Vuelta…'

'Yes, I read the article; what really caught my attention was something some journalists said: when you were by yourself on the plain very near Vitoria, you took off a safety pin from your number and started to poke your thighs and legs, and they said you did that in order to decongest them.'

'That is a myth, Jean, it's not important. What is really important is what I felt when I attacked, Juanito. My aim and the reason why I am a cyclist, is to attack, to see the fear in the eyes of my competitors, and after fear, defeat. And I feel joy when I see them screwed and defeated. The rest is secondary: riding alone, winning a stage, victories, honours…these are just consequences of my rivals' defeat.

'For me, the moment that marks me is when I look into their eyes and see the reflection of defeat in them. That day, in Vitoria, Tamames, Lasa, Poulidor and Zoetemelk were defeated, but I wasn't able to do so with Bracke. I broke away from the hour recordman but I didn't take enough time out of him. He became leader, and two days later on the Puerto of Mazorra, going towards Burgos, Bracke was done for, Jean, he was dead. The ones that had been beaten in Vitoria had got away and I was left behind with Bracke. But I didn't give up and I attacked again. With Zoetemelk on my wheel, always on my wheel, I began to get back to Lasa, Galera and Wilfried David, the Belgian from Peugeot who'd stuck to us like a leech. Instead of destroying Bracke's hopes, it kick-started him and he managed to hang on to the lead, thanks to Godefroot. And do you know what everyone said? They said that if I hadn't made a move, if I had stayed on Bracke's wheel, Lasa would have won the Vuelta. They said I was anti-Spanish for helping the Belgian. I was booed; they called me "the Frenchman", Jean. That's how my Vuelta went.'

'Nobody understands you Luis, simply because nobody is able to understand you. For you, Luis, cycling is you on the one hand, and the peloton on the other. However great a cyclist Merckx is, the best on all terrains, he belongs to the peloton. Luis, you are unique, different from everyone else, atypical. Merckx is the son of a shopkeeper, who became a cyclist; he could just as easily have become a pharmacist, like his brother, or some expert in commerce. But he was good in many sports, he was a multi-talented, well-fed, gifted child. One day he told his parents he wanted to be a cyclist, and so he became a cyclist. He married the daughter of the Belgian national coach, which is usual in that section of the bourgeoisie: doctors marry doctor's daughters (except Anquetil, of course, who stole his wife Jeanine from his doctor); lawyers with lawyers and so on. Merckx's passion for cycling did not spring from his guts, as in your case. This is why he's not a rebel but prefers authority and domination. You are you, Luis; you are the blood of all the Ocañas and the Sorias and Pernias that always fought and never surrendered. They did it in war, in resistance, in the river with the tree trunks, and you do it with the bicycle. The bicycle is your weapon just as it was for Anquetil, who was also different and unlike everybody else. The bicycle is an instrument like the piano or the violin, it was his means of artistic expression. The rest are the peloton, Luis, and Merckx is one of them.

'Look, I haven't been long in this world of cycling, but I have seen quite a few things. I am like food critics: they see the cooks in their kitchens, they see what and how they do it, but they never talk about the messiness of the process. They only talk about the final product, the tasty and well-presented dish. It's not that they want to hide something; it's just that there are certain things that cannot be said because once said, the mystery and the beauty are lost forever. In my first Tour in '67, I was there on Ventoux, next to Simpson in his agony. And when he died I saw how his pockets were emptied of pills and tubes that fell from it. He had drunk a lot, Luis: water, cognac, rat poison…he drank everything he was given. And I saw everything. Goddet, the director of the Tour, was with me, and he told me: "Jean, you will inform Simpson's widow, but you haven't seen anything. She mustn't know anything about what we have seen here." And so I did. Then the widow married Hoban, Simpson's cyclist friend. I am not sure whether he told her the truth about her husband's death, the truth about cycling. I have seen a lot, Luis, but I have not seen anyone like you. And no one with such a beautiful name for a cyclist.'

Jean pronounced his name the French way, 'Ocaná' and also with a Cuban accent: although he lived on Boulevard Saint-Michel, in a house that seems to have been decorated following the description of one of Georges Perec's extravagant flats, Jean Cormier, as a reporter, had travelled throughout Latin America, where he had loved and been loved.

'It is my look that impresses, Jean,' said Ocaña. 'Do you know what I did last summer? I had to travel from Lille to Bordeaux to take part in a critérium and I was overtaken by a guy on the motorway. I couldn't believe it, Jean. Someone was faster than me. Of course, he spurred me on and I crossed France following him until I finally overtook him: I could see the image of surrender in his eyes. The problem is we were now in Marseille. Trying to chase the guy, I took a 600-kilometres detour with the Jaguar. But I didn't mind because I had finally managed to overtake him. In the Dauphiné I saw that Merckx was not as he had been in previous years. I had never seen him so strong, Jean. Yes, he beat me as usual, but he didn't control me as much as he would have wanted. He beat me in the time trial, but only by 24 seconds and I saw his weakness on the Granier. When we were only two kilometres from the peak, we went after Delisle – a group formed by Agostinho, Van Impe, Thévenet, Poulidor and someone else – but Merckx did not come with us. I saw this as a symptom of weakness: as you know his motto is nobody moves without his permission. Then he caught us on the descent and I heard someone saying that it wasn't that he couldn't, but that he was just testing new material he was thinking about for the Tour: his bicycle was not working properly. Later on I attacked again, on the Forclaz de Montmin, and he did strike back quickly, but he didn't seem to me to be all that strong. Then we had a terrible hailstorm and I didn't feel like trying anymore. Moreover, my friend Labourdette, that friend of yours from the Pyrenees we signed this

141

year for Bic, such a nice guy and such a good climber, took advantage of the situation to win the stage. I promise you Jean, Juanito, that in the next Tour I am going to see the look of defeat in Merckx's eyes. The rest doesn't matter at all, except honour.'

In the Tour you always encounter the same people, the same places, the same cols and summits, the same cities and landscapes. At the same time, each Tour is different from the previous one: the light has changed; the look of cyclists has changed, one year inspired, the next sunk in despair. That's why cyclists would prefer not to have any memory at all, not to have to remember the names of the places they go through, nor fix in their minds the details that might help them discern, next year or two or three years later, if they had been in that place, that bend, that oak tree. Cyclists would love every moment to be unique, the experience of a lifetime so that they feel free rather than overloaded by memories.

The Tour of '71 started in Mulhouse, in the north-eastern tip of the French pentagon. It began with a long march towards the north-west, through the plains bordering Belgium, with its winds and *pavé*, reaching the English Channel at Le Touquet, where the route traced an audacious diagonal back to the east, the Alps, after going via the Puy de Dôme. The last week was for the Pyrenees.

'I don't know why, Josiane, but I have very positive feelings about this Tour. I can see things more clearly, as if the cloud that was blurring my thoughts had suddenly disappeared.' After dinner, from his room in Le Salvator Hotel in Mulhouse, Luis was speaking to his wife about his hopes. Josiane would have loved to have been there in Alsace with her husband, but she was tied to home with the children.

'I have called Cescutti but he doesn't pick up the phone. He must be having dinner out. When you see him, tell him that this time my optimism is well grounded, that it is not just wishful thinking. Tell him I have come across Merckx, that he averted his gaze when I looked into his eyes, tell him that I think Merckx has not forgotten what happened on the Granier during the Dauphiné, tell him I think this time he will suffer. And also tell Cescutti that I will follow his advice, that I will not do anything provocative until we are in the mountain stages, that

I am aware that what I have to do is to follow Merckx, or at most play the card of counter attack. Josiane, how are the children? How are Jean-Luis and Sylvie? Do they leave you any free time?'

In the Alsatian stages at the beginning of the Tour, one couldn't really tell if Merckx was worried or afraid. On the second stage, on the road to Strasbourg, the Cannibal was the animator of a fifteen-man break which had been initiated by José Manuel Fuente on the small Col de Firstplan. However, the fast-climbing Asturian could not keep up the pace on the descent, nor on the flat, and ended up anonymously among the 115 riders who had lost the Tour almost before it had started. The group of 15, containing all the favourites, including Ocaña and his special team mate for the flat roads, the Dane, Leif Mortensen, arrived at the cinder track in Strasbourg with a lead of more than nine minutes. There, Merckx suffered an anxiety attack after risking a fall while attempting to beat De Vlaeminck on the line. Van Springel (known as 'Buster Keaton' for their similarity of appearance) was Merckx's new *domestique*, the man who launched him into the sprint. Van Springel was a rider who had enjoyed some great achievements in the Tour and in the Vuelta, but he seemed to have decided not to fight anymore. 'I signed for Molteni because it's easier to win stages with Merckx rather than fighting against him,' said Van Springel.

'Merckx is anxious, uncontrollable, he doesn't let anybody move, he sprints towards all the finishing lines, he even attacks his own Molyeni team mates. If we are intelligent, we can make this work in our favour,' Luis told De Muer on the eve of the Puy de Dôme stage. 'Let's annoy him, let's throw out a bait for him, let's see if he takes it, Maurice. On the way from Mont-de-Marsan to Mulhouse, I took a bit of a detour to see the Puy de Dôme, which I've never climbed. I have seen it now from the car and I guess it will be a hard nut to crack. I will need a small gear and also the lightest bike, and 200 grams tubulars. You'll see if we don't make Merckx suffer a bit.'

'I think we're both thinking the same thing, Luis. We are both of the same mind. I think tomorrow will be Bernard's day.'

Bernard Labourdette was a shy fellow who had travelled away from

Bearn, from the cows, from the farm, from the Pyrenees, southwards of Pau. He rode the Tour of '69 with Mercier, and De Muer saw that he was an interesting cyclist with plenty of unexplored virtues, who needed to free himself, to thrive.

'He is the complete rider for a stage race: he eats, he sleeps and drinks with splendid serenity,' De Muer told Luis when they signed him up in 1971. Luis did not hesitate in 'adopting' him, because he had finally found a southern team mate in Bic, a man from the mountains. They got along very well and even shared the same room.

On the day of the Puy de Dôme, Merckx himself made it very easy for Bic: he attacked at kilometre 40. A group of 20 cyclists formed around him with a very alert Ocaña among them, but without Zoetemelk or Gösta Petterson. They all came back together, however, after a high-speed chase: the race being ridden flat out. On the first slopes of the Auvergne volcano, on the steep sides of the crater, Labourdette launched a strong attack as they had planned. And, as everyone wanted and suspected, Merckx himself, greedy Merckx was the first to react to the attack with an exaggerated change of rhythm, which if it did not defeat his rivals, definitely exhausted his team mates.

Merckx was now exactly where they wanted him to be, alone, without his team around him. Labourdette dropped back but Thévenet attacked in La Baraque, where Geminiani had his hotel. Merckx responded again, but with difficulty, his reaction somewhat laboured. On his right, a vigilant Ocaña observed him, and four kilometres before the peak launched his first victorious attack against the Cannibal. Without getting out of the saddle, Ocaña accelerated brutally. In two pedal strokes he reached Thévenet; 'Stay on my wheel,' he told him. But the Frenchman couldn't. On his left, Merckx saw Luis moving away and did not make the slightest gesture – no standing on the pedals, no taking his hand to the lever looking for a gear that would allow him to react. 'It wasn't my day,' he said at the finishing line. 'When Luis broke away I didn't feel my legs responding as usual. So I decided to go at my own pace.'

Although in the mist surrounding the cold crater of the volcano the advantage Ocaña pulled out over Merckx, who was also overtaken by Agostinho and Zoetemelk, was minimal – just 15 seconds – the moment itself was powerfully symbolic: it was the first time that Merckx had not responded to an attack in the Tour. At the summit Ocaña took refuge in one of the Saint-Bernard ambulances. Did he pass out? Was he ill? 'No, not all,' replied Luis later. 'I got in the ambulance to protect myself from the people. I didn't feel bad at all. I could have ridden even faster.' That was the first act in the task of bringing down the the dictator's rule. The second act took place a couple of days later, Letort's day.

Désiré Letort, a proud Breton from the village of Plancoët, was one of the new Bic signings. Despite the reputation he had at Peugeot for being undisciplined and selfish, De Muer was confident he could tame his unruly character. 'I am aware that the Italian-style discipline imposed by Merckx on his men is not for you. But here it is different. In Bic we don't use the word *domestique*, we say *équipier* [team member].' Just in case, early on in the Tour Luis reminded him of his duties and obligations to the team. 'Don't worry,' replied Letort. 'In the Alps you'll find out just what I'm made of.' In the Alps, in La Chartreuse mountain range, Luis could confirm that. In the climb up to Le Cucheron, under a hellish sun that burned the back of their necks and forced the riders to turn back the visors of their caps, like snipers. This was the sun that Merckx hated; he preferred it cold, a cold and dry sun. This sun was as implacable as the midday sun in July on the reapers and day labourers in Castille, a sun that caressed and toned up Luis' thighs.

It was then that Letort attacked and, inevitably, Merckx led the chase. Equally inevitably, he was again left with no *domestiques*, and when he punctured on the descent of Le Cucheron once he had caught the Breton, his director, Guillaume Driessens, was further back giving water to Van Spiegel. Merckx got his replacement wheel, but by then it was too late. Ocaña had initiated an attack on the descent accompanied by Thévenet, Zoetemelk y Petterson, the ones who always followed him, the ones who were beginning to know him well, the ones who could confirm that Ocaña would, as he had promised, be the first to force Merckx to his knees. 'I wasn't sure about following Luis,' said Thévenet, who won the stage into Grenoble. 'I was surprised he took advantage of Merckx's puncture to attack, because I had always considered him a gentleman and a Spanish nobleman. But well, I was up ahead and I couldn't let him go off alone. After that, he was so strong and untameable on the climb up the Col de Porte that it was as much as we could do to follow him without getting dropped. He was a supernatural force.' Zoetemelk was the new leader, one second ahead of Ocaña. Merckx arrived into Grenoble at 1'–36" and now stood at one minute in the general classification.

'Tomorrow will be your day, Luis. I can read it in your legs, in your muscles, compressed like a spring awaiting to be liberated, to jump; I can read it in your slow, strong, full heartbeat. I can read it in your eyes. It's going to be very hot, Luis, so hot stones will melt on those grey and dry roads. And you are the sun, Luis.' Some days he did not exchange a single word with Emilio Cruz, his masseur. In some massage sessions, he simply lay down with his gaze lost on the ceiling while his friend crushed his legs, and spread oils and ointments to help him breathe better. The massage table that he set up every day in his room resembled a confessional in which the first to speak would be the spirit of the cyclist, and the masseur would only listen in silence and nod. That afternoon Luis felt expansive and Emilio did not wait for another sign to animate him. They could both end up devising the strategy. Or rather, Luis might end up telling Emilio about De Muer's ideas as well as his own, as if trying to convince him De Muer was a donkey – not that Emilio, who kissed the ground Luis walked on, needed to be convinced. Emilio, who was aware that Luis was impossibly stubborn, nodded and replied 'of course'. How could he contradict a champion like Luis? And Emilio also knew that, despite appearances, it was Luis who gave the orders in that team. Always Luis, and nobody could get near Luis without confronting Emilio, who permanently stood guard at his door.

Emilio Cruz was a Cantabrian, the son of immigrants who lived in Saint-Étienne, and Ocaña met him in Mont-de-Marsan. Some friends encouraged him to become a cyclist and he ended up as one because he was not at all bad. That's how they met, bumping into each other on the roads of that region, and that's also how he met Manuel Manzano. They ended up becoming friends as they were all Spaniards. In his second year in Bic, in 1971, Ocaña found a place for Emileo as a massaeur in the team, his masseur from then on.

'Yes, Emilio, tomorrow those bastards will know who I am. Merckx won't forget that day.'

'Today is the day. Today's the day you've been waiting for, Luis, a short stage but non stop, 134 kilometres on your own and without big cols, unbridled medium mountains, but without any respite either, and at the end – Orcières-Merlette, where there isn't a tree to give some shade to those who are afraid of the sun. And you are the sun, Luis.'

That was what Anquetil promised Ocaña. They had met in the main square in Grenoble, where the 11th stage began. Anquetil was happy; he was covering the Tour as a commentator for television and various newspapers, and he enjoyed seeing his friend Ocaña performing a work of art as a soloist, a concert without orchestral accompaniment.

'I have been talking to Gem and I think there's something I must tell you,' and he lowered his voice so as not to be heard by the circle of people surrounding them. 'He has told me that Merckx is about to crack, and that he's going to launch Agostinho on the first col, that nightmare Côte de Laffrey, just to test him. He is going to unleash the rhinoceros, which is going to do enormous damage. Do you remember when Agostinho attacked on Divonne last year and Merckx rounded it off to win the Tour on your worst day? Well, this time it's going to be the same, but it's going to be different because you are going to follow Agostinho. I am telling you Luis, Agostinho and Gem will be your allies.'

In fact, Geminiani hadn't been away from the peloton for very long. At the beginning of the year, in the Alcazar bar, his friend De Gribaldy had told him that he needed someone to get into Agostinho's impenetrable mind. He was a full-bodied, tenacious force of nature, impervious to tactical subtleties. He thought that if Geminaini had been able to do that with Anquetil, why couldn't he do it with Agostinho? It

147

was not that Geminiani was very successful with him, but he had learnt one thing: if he said 'Attack!' the Portuguese would lower his head, pedal forcefully, and away he'd go. That was exactly Geminiani's shout on the Côte de Laffrey, which was extremely hard, and discouraging for the weak. Laffrey was a strange mountain formation in the Alps, with hard and continuous gradients, which gave no opportunity for a change in pace because it is one long straight where everyone can see each other, and those who are dropped don't have the consolation of bends that prevent them from seeing the increasing distance between them and those up ahead, which is depressing.

'Joaquim, attack!' and without looking back the Portuguese bull pushed his bicycle with his arms and legs, his head lowered over the handlebar, his expression black and empty, and the veins in his forehead tense as the strings of a violin. However much Merckx wanted to follow him – someone like Agostinho must never be allowed to escape – he couldn't. The one who could was Ocaña, and behind him only three of the few who were strong to follow him stood on their pedals: Van Impe, the yellow jersey Zoetemelk and Gösta Petterson. In the race director's car, Jacques Goddet, who loved Ocaña for his politeness and extremely good manners, and also for his roaring pronunciation of 'rr', would be the only and privileged witness of a historical epic moment.

Goddet would write in his memoirs years later:

Yes, I am aware that the word 'epic' and the adjective 'historical' may be worn out by overuse, but on that occasion they were the most appropriate; no others would do. This kind of unexpected, violent attack at the beginning of a difficult stage always has consequences. And the consequence was a fabulous battle with moving images, like the determination of Ocaña on the attack, or the desperate defence of Merckx, majestic like an offended prince. This fight had everything: top sporting performance, aggressive violence, and the refusal to accept a defeat which contained the germ of utter annihilation.

De Muer and Darras were following Ocaña in Bic's car. Like a premonition, Darras was wearing a yellow T-shirt.

'What an easy ride, Luis,' Darras shouted. 'While the rest of them look like slaves chained to the tarmac, you fly Luis. You don't even need to touch the handlebar of your lightweight bicycle nor lean on it; it's like you pedal in the air, as if you were on a cloud.'

In fact, under a scorching sun which for once had become Luis's best ally, Zoetemelk, Van Impe, Petterson and Agostinho (who'd hitched his waggon to the express once he'd been caught) all suffered behind the winged Ocaña. Little by little they fell behind. Ocaña did not have to turn back a single time, didn't ask for a relief, and didn't need to change his pace, his dark gaze only looked straight ahead.

The start of the Col de Noyer was reached via a narrow road, scarcely more than a path with very little tarmac that climbed through the crest of the Baumes. It was the same sticky col on which, accompanied by Grosskost, Ocaña had suffered a thousand torments the year before. This time, he climbed it alone and proud, without looking desperately at the ground to find some consolation. This time he only had to look towards the horizon for inspiration. Ocaña was making Merckx pay for three years of dictatorial rule, moving steadily away by himself, while Merckz, exhausted by the heat, with half the peloton dropping behind him, would not allow anyone to relieve him. Thévenet, who was riding on the wheel of this proud man who refused to accept his inevitable defeat, had to rub his eyes everytime he looked at the motorcyclist's slate board that showed the lead number 98 had on them.

'I saw two, three, four, five minutes and I couldn't believe it. We were literally stuck to the tarmac. And, as Ocaña's lead increased to six, seven, even nine minutes, I came to believe he was being propelled by an engine, that he was flying in a plane,' Thévenet said later.

Just at the very moment when Ocaña went after Agostinho he had seen the fear of defeat in Merckx's eyes. At that moment Ocaña was transposed into his father chopping down giant trees with a tiny axe, and his uncle Soria, staring at the eyes of the German soldier who was laughing at him in the concentration camp before he plunged the pick into his face. He saw himself as that child who rebelled against his carpenter boss, who treated him with contempt. That was the force of his destiny. All his force. His blood. It was almost a quasi-mystical feeling that lifted him up. He had lived all his life at the foot of a mountain that seemed impossible to climb, and he was finally scaling it.

'Luis,' shouted De Muer from the car, sweating so much he had to take off his shirt, showing his naked torso. 'We are 70 kilometres away, do you think you'll make it?' How could he even ask? Ocaña simply bowed his head and nodded several times.

Second on the stage, Van Impe, arrived 5'–52" after Ocaña; Merckx came third, 8'–42" down, with Zoetemelk, Petterson, Thévenet and Labourdette on his wheel. Agostinho came in at 8'–50". Only 38 riders arrived within the control time, which had to be extended from 12% to 15% to prevent the disqualification of 70 riders, among them, José Manuel Fuente, who finished 35 minutes down.

On the podium Ocaña was calm; only his bursting clear eyes showed a glimpse of a smile. At last, he could wear the yellow jersey. To the multitude of journalists pursuing him, Merckx also had a few calm words. 'There's little one can say today,' said the dethroned Cannibal. 'I think Ocaña has killed all of us today, just like bulls are killed by el Cordobés. Today he was the strongest. I was hugely impressed.'

At the Bic team dinner, champagne flowed and the yellow pages of the classification list passed from hand to hand among exclamations. It was as if only the physical verification of the stopwatch, officially sealed with the Tour's letterhead, could convince everybody that what had happened that day had really happened, and they had not imagined it. In front of the eyes of Ocaña, sitting between Grosskost and Labourdette, the numbers that spelled out his performance danced a joyful and dizzying ballet.

'This is the evidence that I was not dreaming,' he told all his team mates, standing up and with one finger of champagne kindly served by De Muer. 'Listen to me: this is the truth, however unbelievable it may sound to you: First: Ocaña, 58 hours, 53 minutes. Second: Zoetemelk, at 8'–43". Third: Van Impe, at 9'–20". Fourth: Petterson, at 9'–26". Fifth: Merckx, at 9'–46"...' Here Ocaña was interrupted by the merriment and the 'bravos'.

'Ten minutes. The monster is at ten minutes! This Tour is ours!'
'Attention, attention,' Ocaña warned them. 'With Eddy Merckx, neither ten minutes nor an hour are enough. I have just spoken to Anquetil; he hasn't told me anything I didn't know, but let me tell you what he said. "If Eddy had given up, he would probably have abandoned on the climb up to Noyer. But if he hasn't quit, there's something you must know Luis." That's what Jacques told me. "If he hasn't quit it's because he believes he can still beat you. And you and I know that this means it's going to be a fight to the death and this fight will not end until one of the two of you disappears." That's what Jacques told me, and I believe him. Merckx and I have decided to attack each other every metre of the race and we know one of us won't end the Tour. There will be war even if Eddy is ten minutes back. But don't worry, I feel strong. The moment of truth will be in the Pyrenees. In the Pyrenees I will see defeat in Merckx's eyes.'

Both teams, Bic and Molteni were lodged in the same hotel at Orcières-Merlette's ski station, Le Club du Soleil, but the hotel was so big there was little chance of them meeting in the corridors and halls. But they would meet on their bicycles the following day, a rest day, during their training session on the roads around the station which criss-crossed with the tracks that went up to Lake Estaris. Merckx and Ocaña greeted each other with a nod, nothing else. Ocaña could see in the Belgian's look that he had no intention of wasting his time lamenting his defeat; rather, he was plotting his revenge.

The next stage was supposed to be a transition, a long, tedious 250-kilometre descent from the Alps to the Mediterranean shoreline, the Old Port de Marseille.

Nemesio Jiménez was tall and robust, the tallest in his team. Together with González Linares, from Kas, he was the tallest at that time. He was unusual in that he loved riding on the flat, the París-Roubaix, and he enjoyed organising echelons with his friend Gómez Lucas. He was Fuentes' bodyguard on the road. He smoked, although he did not smoke as much as Tarangu[1], who would take out his Marlboro and

---

1. 'El Tarangu': Fuente's nickname: 'unconcerned for himself' in the Asturian language.

get through the entire packet on the eve of a time trial or any other important day.

'But why are you so nervous Tarangu? Stop tossing and turning in bed. Aren't you ever going to get to sleep?'

Tarangu, José Manuel Fuente, made his debut in the Tour, to which he contributed with his knee-jerk reactions, his stroke of genius, his passionate cycling monologues, and the smoke from his Marlboro cigarettes that he used to calm his nerves. Nemesio was an observant man, and on the afternoon of the rest day, while he was enjoying his inactivity lying in a deck chair at the hotel's swimming pool, he saw the whole Molteni team in formation, training behind the car. 'They're not content simply stretching their legs like everyone else. They're having a double session. They're plotting something,' Jimenez thought to himself. He also thought he would warn Ocaña if he saw him, and would tell him: 'Merckx is preparing an ambush, stay alert Luis,' but he didn't see him. He also thought that Ocaña might already have his own spies. 'Someone will tell him,' he decided and stopped worrying about it. The following morning, at the start, Nemesio would have liked to have said something to him. He let his eye wander over the bicycles of the riders waiting for Lévitan's starting signal. Without knowing why, he spotted something strange on one of them, to be precise on one of the tan coloured Moltenis, that of the Dutch acrobatic giant, Rius Wagtmans, who could descend like nobody and who had that distinctive white lock of hair. On the seat tube of his bicycle there was a mark, a sure sign that the front derailleur had been moved. Nemesio realised that the mechanic had raised the derailleur, and the only reason for doing that would have been to put on a chainring bigger than the normal 52-tooth – a 54 or 55. Nemesio concluded their intention was to attack from the start. He warned his team mates in Kas, but it was too late. He was trapped in the first row on the start line, surrounded by Moltenis who were grouped around Merckx, like a band of scheming swordsmen. He couldn't even think of reaching Ocaña; he was the leader, and was wearing the yellow jersey for the first time, so he was at the far back of the peloton happily signing autographs and talking to the press.

With Nemesio there was only Uribezubía, Katarra's cousin, and Zubero. They were all wearing several jerseys because it was cold in the mountains at that time of the day. Even before Lévitan had fully dropped the flag, the Moltenis had shot off like bullets out of a gun, spitting fire, screaming for vengeance, like true warriors. What a temperament they had. There were only three Moltenis with Merckx, the strongest descenders and *rouleurs*, Wagtmans, Spruyt and Huysmans. The rest had the task of sowing discord in the peloton and disrupting any attempt to chase Merckx. Everything was carefully planned. They started running on foot, like the motorcyclists in the Le Man 24-hours, to get moving quickly and get into the biggest gear straight away. Nemesio's Kas were alert enough to sneak into the front group. Zubero fell off his bike, which blocked Ocaña's path. He'd received the warning honks from De Muer's 404 Peugeot, but too late. De Muer was desperately trying to get him up to the front, but those who were already at the front didn't notice as they were now flying downhill. Nemesio and Katarra continued down to the bottom where, regrouping on the flat, they noticed that Zubero, their man for the overall classification, wasn't with them. Soon after Langarica appeared. 'Wait for Zubero,' he told them. While they were waiting, Ocaña's group came flying past, driving for all they were worth. 'Give us a hand. Work with us!' they shouted. So Nemesio's Kas joined the group, offering to take turns on the front as they had promised to help them, but then Langarica was shouting again from the car: 'I told you to wait for Zubero!'

Zubero was not the only casualty. Merckx had lost Spruyt from the leading group and behind, Bruyère, his road captain, had punctured. Robert Lelangue, Molteni's director who had taken over from old Driessens, ordered two of his riders to stay with Bruyère, which enraged Merckx: he was dying to have an all or nothing fight for the Tour.

It was a five-hour, 250-kilometres wild chase through the Durance valley under a merciless sun. In the car of the Tour's director, Goddet was going through an ecstatic experience. 'This is the most impressive and extravagant strategy I have ever witnessed in my long career,' he wrote, a few years later. 'And a monument to audacity, because this attack was meant to last for 250 kilometres.' After the first shock Ocaña reunited his troops around him and made some calculations. 'There are nine ahead,' he thought, 'and behind we are sixty. If we want to catch up quickly we must increase our numbers and make an enormous effort. But instead, if we put pressure on them by getting it down to one minute or one and a half minutes, they will have to make more effort because they are fewer than us. We must take into account that I still have ten minutes advantage over him, so losing a couple of minutes shouldn't be so bad.' Merckx's group arrived in Marseille 1'–56" ahead, which might have been disappointing given the effort involved if it weren't for the fact that the tactics employed affected Ocaña's morale and his sense of justice.

The Tour flew into Marseille after averaging 45 km/h, arriving two hours ahead of schedule, with the streets empty and the barriers not erected, and the authorities not yet arrived. This was the reason why the Tour (which had not visited Marseille since 1967 because the Mayor, Gaston Deferre, didn't consider the TV revenues were substantial enough) would not return to the Vieux Port until 14 July 1989, with the excuse of the bicentenary of the Marseillaise and the revolution, and when Deferre was no longer the Mayor. Nemesio and his Kas team mates, who waited for Zubero, arrived outside the time limit. 'We didn't eat anything,' he remembered, years later.

'We did 100 kilometres flat out, bit and bit, non-stop, and we managed to get really close to them. Almost all of us in Kas were there, including Fuente, who on one steep slope pulled like a Cossack. He used up so much energy that he collapsed and wanted to get off the bike. I tried to cheer him up: "Hold on, Tarangu, two of the stages in the Pyrenees are tailor-made for you and you're going to win them." Fuente was hanging on to me; if he hadn't he would have fallen. "Leave me, Neme, leave me, I can't carry on anymore. Let me get off." Langarica ordered me to leave him and Fuente got off the bicycle. Then I got really angry and I forced him to get back on the bike again. I slapped him on the neck. "Get on the bike or I'll kick you up the arse." I finally managed to get him on the bicycle. He gripped my shorts and started riding again, with Uribezubía pushing him from behind. We rode more than 70 kilometres like that. Although in Italy it was fashionable to push the leader, it is certainly scandalous and in France it was not permitted, but the *commissaires* didn't say a word. We looked after him, we gave him food. We arrived in Marseille more than half an hour ahead of schedule, but surprisingly the control was closed. Perhaps that's why they gave us a second chance.'

The Tour's first ever transfer by air took the riders from Marseille to Albi. The organisers made Ocaña and Merckx sit down next to each other in the first row, the former in the window, the latter in the aisle seat. They didn't speak to each other during the flight and even refused to make eye contact. It would take years for Ocaña to forgive Merckx for his 'treachery' in Orcières, his attack on the starting line.

All the racket stayed behind closed doors, preserving the silence inside the clinic. Journalists were not allowed in, although Chico Pérez, the correspondent for *El Pueblo* newspaper, cunningly managed to impersonate a distant relation of the Spaniard to enter room 15, getting round the control of the nurse on guard in reception. There, Josiane was holding Ocaña's hand, who was feeling dozy. 'I thought I was going to die, Chico,' said Ocaña to the journalist, who immediately turned to find a telephone to have Ocaña's words sent to his newspaper, along with Doctor Bergès' first impressions. 'It's nothing serious; only a few blows and the shock.' In the afternoon, a bit before three o'clock, Chico found a pharmacy at the foot of Portillon from where he had permission to make an international conference call to send his first report to his newspaper. It would make the blood of Spaniards run cold before the rotary presses closed in the evening newspaper *El Pueblo*. 'Luis Ocaña has fallen, he has fallen and he has withdrawn from the race. It's a tragedy.'

Jacques Anquetil arrived in Doctor Bergès' clinic in Saint-Gaudens soon after Chico Pérez had gone running out. He went to room 15 and looked at Josiane questioningly. Josiane hadn't moved from the chair next to the bedhead where Ocaña seemed to be having some sleep.

'He's ok, don't worry Jacques; he's only shocked and in despair.

It's me who has been in shock. I was at home listening to the news in the kitchen (the TV didn't have the images yet), when I heard that radio speaker with a hoarse voice saying: "Sur la route des Pyrenées…", and then changing his voice while he said, "Ocaná est tombé, Ocaña est tombé!" Then he said the leader didn't stand up and remained apparently unconscious. It wasn't even three o'clock and I'd managed to put Sylvie down for a nap, but Jean-Luis was with me, as he liked to listen to the Tour broadcast about his dad. I immediately phoned Cescutti, who was also listening to the radio and he immediately picked me up. We left the children with my mother and we rushed to Saint-Gaudens. Well, in the end we decided to go to Saint-Gaudens because the news was not clear. First they said he had been taken to Saint-Béat by car and then to Saint-Gaudens by helicopter. And there we found him, in the same village where he won a stage last year. The nurses said they had to cut off his jersey with scissors. He was complaining of pains in the chest and in the back. I was scared his spine might have been broken, leaving him paralysed. But, as they said, he has nothing broken. I hardly know how he fell, Jacques.'

'I've also been trying to find out myself; there are not many pictures either. Riders have told me that it was really sunny when they started the climb up to the Col de Menté; but just when they were reaching the top it got really dark, Josiane, just like Luis's sad omens. Very dark clouds gathered and immediately it started to rain violently and hail. The dust on the sides of the road turned to mud and began to slide down on to the tarmac. Nobody could brake because the wheel rims and brake pads were soaking wet. Merckx was going down behind Fuentes, who was ahead by a few minutes. Luis was on Merckx's wheel. On the first hairpin bend to the left Merckx fell and so did Luis after him. Guimard, who was third, managed to avoid them. Merckx fell on the grass and he got up straight away. Luis took a bit longer because he had hit a rock, and when he was finally standing up Zoetemelk ran into him. Then Agostinho crashed into both of them and went flying over them. Most of the riders were coming down scraping their shoes on the road to try and slow down. Many of them had them completely torn apart by the finishing line. "When Merckx and Ocaña fell I had been left behind and I was riding as hard as I could to try and close the gap, Jacques," Zoetemelk explained to me. He was completely devastated. "Suddenly I saw Ocaña's yellow jersey appear in front of me. The brakes didn't work. I tried to skirt around them putting all my weight on the other side, but I lost balance and, what's more, my front wheel had gone flat. I hit Ocaña. It was inevitable. Nobody could have avoided it. I got back on the road and I even considered stopping when I saw Ocaña was not getting up, but what good would that have done, Jaques?"

'Yes, we heard Zoetemelk on the radio saying something similar.'

'But Luis's bicycle wouldn't have helped either, Josiane. The frame was shorter and lighter than usual, which made it difficult to control on the descents. But what I find really difficult to understand is why Luis decided to ride so close to Eddie, following him everywhere... He could have let him gain as much advantage as he wanted as he would never have taken Ocaña's yellow jersey. He was more than seven minutes ahead....'

'I did it for honour, Jacques.' Josiane and Anquetil looked at Luis in unison while he half sat up to take part in a conversation that he had probably been following in silence.

'Nothing is more important than honor. I followed Merckx downhill on the Menté. I was very aware he wanted to take chances downhill because he wasn't able to do anything uphill. I followed him although I knew it wasn't my terrain and I was in a dangerous zone. I knew I couldn't back down there. A true champion never refuses a challenge. This is what pride is about, to take part in a battle where you know you can lose everything. This morning I woke up with a premonition. Sometimes I wonder if I am not a toy in a beautiful dream that's beyond my control. That is exactly what I told Labourdette, however corny it might sound. It was he who opened the window in the room this morning. He was dazzled by the splendid sunlight reflected on the yellow jersey that I had laid out on the back of the chair. "You have to settle the Tour today," Bernard told me with a laugh. I was afraid of taking for granted something I wasn't sure was going to happen. I know the Portillon by heart, of course, because it is the col that separated me from France when I lived in Arán, and I had made up my mind to attack there, in front of all the Spanish supporters who had probably painted my name on the tarmac. I would have attacked Merckx there and I would have nailed him. It would have been my most complete victory, for sure. I couldn't say this to Bernard because of my superstition. But I did phone Cescutti because I tell him all my plans every night before I go to sleep. I couldn't tell anybody else, though. What's more, I was annoyed with Merckx because of what happened on the evening of the Albi time trial, on the Séquestre circuit, where a scorching sun burned the back of our necks. Merckx beat me by 11 seconds, which wasn't very serious considering the lead I had on him overall. But what I didn't like was the inelegant way he claimed he would have taken back more time if the TV car hadn't protected me against the sidewind, whereas the motorbikes hampered him when he was overtaking Zoetemelk.

'For all this, for my honour, I felt I had to teach Merckx a lesson on the Portillon. And I had to do it for myself, of course. And for De Muer, who had come up with a very funny pun that he repeated over and over between drags on his cigarette. He used to tell me all the time: "You're going to slaughter Merckx on Portillon, automatically." ['Portillon' means 'gate' in French, and De Muer was surely referring to electric garage gates, which are automatically activated by a photoelectric cell]. I was the leader of the tour and I had to demonstrate it. I was certainly very strong. After having breakfast, before heading for the start line, I went to Bebel's church with Labourdette. There, I prayed and thought about my father. I could picture myself entering Spain and reaching Paris wearing the yellow jersey. "At last I am lucky," I thought, unaware of what was awaiting me. Behind dark clouds, an evil eye seemed to be lurking.

'We climbed the Portet d'Aspet in line, keeping an eye on Merckx, who was pedalling in an inscrutable manner. We climbed Menté under a scorching sun. Merckx attacked me seven times, and seven times I easily slipped in behind him, all the while thinking: "Wait till the Portillon. You'll see there….". Then the sky turned black and I barely remember myself waking up, on the ground, with a killing pain and terribly distressed as I couldn't breathe; the image of Rivière's similar accident, where he was paralysed, came to my mind, and then I think I fainted. That was my destiny. When I crashed, I had already lost because I would never have caught Merckx, even if I had stood up quickly. This is the story of my life, where golden pages alternate with black ones.'

'Merckx did hve a very hard time on the Portillon, if you wish to know,' Anquetil told him. 'All the Spanish supporters blamed him for your crash; they threw stones, spat and insulted him,. But you know him; he proudly coped with it and at the end of the stage refused to put on the yellow jersey. He said he wouldn't wear it tomorrow either.'

'It's a nice gesture; I am very grateful,' said Ocaña. 'But he shouldn't overdo it. The Tour must go on and he's the leader so he must wear the yellow jersey.'

'And when a journalist asked him if he had won the Tour today Merckx, looked very sad, or so he seemed on the television. He said, "No, just the opposite: I lost it today." I understand him. He knows it will always be remembered that he was going to be defeated and only your crash gave him the victory. But he says that now; later on he will justify it saying that, after all, crashing is part and parcel of cycling; that, in the end, if you crash it's because you've made a mistake, and that champions are successful because they ride more carefully and they know how to avoid risks.'

'Or provoke them,' said Ocaña, who didn't like the tone in his friend, Jacques. 'By the way, who won the stage?'

'Unfortunately, it was Fuente, although he also crashed descending the Menté. Suddenly, he disappeared off the road and everyone thought he had fallen down the ravine, but he reappeared as if nothing had happened. He was very angry at the finishing line because nobody paid any attention to him; everyone was talking about you.'

That night the Tour issued a press realease: 'The Tour organisers have been informed by Eddy Merckx that as homage to the bravery of the unfortunate Luis Ocaña, who had to withdraw from the Tour while he was still the leader, he wishes to refrain from wearing the yellow jersey in the Luchon-Superbagnères stage. The jury of *commissaires*, in agreement with the directors of the race, understanding the chivalrous nature of this gesture, agreed to revoke the regulations of the article 14 paragraph 2, and to authorise the rider Merckx not to wear the yellow jersey at the start of stage 15.'

The following day, Merckx was crying in the start line. It was a very short stage from Luchon to Superbagnères, hardly 20 kilometres, but Fuente was determined to win and finally have the attention of the Tour. Merckx was in control. He ordered his *domestiques* to form a strong train. Tarangu couldn't resist attacking but he was quickly caught by Van Impe. He attacked again, and again Van Impe was on his wheel. But at the third attempt, the chain slipped while he was shifting on to the big ring. Next to him, Nemesio pushed him enough force to enable him to put it on the 53 and he started to ride like a rocket. In two kilometres, he doubled, or more than doubled the gap he had over everyone else. Everyone looked at him as he rode with tremendous power. His speed was incredible. His ascent left everyone astounded. At the finishing line he reminded journalists that no one had talked about him the day before even though he had won the stage. He dedicated his victory to Uribezubía and Nemesio.

At home in Bretagne-de-Marsan, Ocaña only switched on the TV two days later, just in time to see his friend Labourdette win on the Aubisque after a terrible storm, like the one on Menté, which had made the man from Bearn consider getting off the bicycle and quitting. He dedicated his victory to his friend Luis, and then he shook with fear when he heard on the radio that a 28-year-old young man who was watching the race had been killed by a lightning strike during the storm.

The next morning, Merckx visited Ocaña in his home as the stage started precisely in Mont-de-Marsan. It was just a formal visit, aimed only at pleasing TV reporters and photographers. The two champions shook hands coldly. He was also visited by the whole Tour organisation, Goddet, Lévitan, hundreds of journalists, team managers, Luis Puig, the president of the Spanish Federation, Mendiburu, the national coach. They invited themselves for lunch at his home and they set him a date for the Mendrisio World Championship, to be held two months later. 'You can take revenge there, Luis,' they promised him. 'It's an extremely hard course.'

In his house Ocaña could literally swim among the thousands of letters and telegrams he received. He weighed them, with Josiane's help: 80 kilos.

'I have lost the Tour, Josiane, and yet I am more popular now than if I had won it, and I doubt if I will ever be more popular. It's clear that fallen heroes attract more sympathy than routine winners. I've lost the Tour but I've won the love of the people. Let me tell you one thing, Josiane, I feel as happy as if I had won the Tour.'

However, Ocaña did not accept the Tour's invitation to attend Merckx's third Tour coronation in the Cipale, the small velodrome in the Vincennes forest. 'I still can't breathe well yet,' he told Lévitan, who had even told him he would also be awarded a yellow jersey while he took a lap of honour in a car with Merckx. Zoetemelk and Van Impe, second and third, ten minutes behind Merckx, were heavily criticised by the press and the public, for their lack of adventure.

In Mendrisio's World Championship, Ocaña did not take revenge on Merckx. Never again in his career would he ever have a chance to feel the happiness of staring Merckx in the face and seeing the fear in his eyes. Ocaña had been perfectly placed during the whole race, attentive and at the front, but at the most important moment, he disappeared mysteriously from the top places. This was only two laps from the end, just when Merckx launched the most decisive attack, which only Giamondi responded to. He apologised, saying he had gone back to the car to get a bottle of water. 'It was an unforgivable oversight.' Mendiburu, the Spanish team selector, was less charitable: 'He couldn't keep going anymore and he used the excuse of the water to pull out.' He also withdrew from the Tour of Lombardy, but this time he did so with rage rather than apathy. 'I am fed up with you, Italian losers,' he shouted to Bittosi, Zilioli and Gimondi. 'Merckx has been allowed to ride 50 kilometres alone and I am the only one who dares to chase him... and what do you do? You just sit on my wheel. What do you do it for? Just to come second? Is that the reason you ride? You don't ride to be second.'

Ocaña won the end-of-season time trials in the autumn, a great achievement in the pure style of Anquetil. In the Volta a Catalunya, with his last time trial victory in Sabadell, he brought misfortune on one of his friends, Labourdette, who had been the leader ever since his great attack in Puigcerdà. He had to pass the yellow jersey over to Ocaña by just 20 seconds. In the Grand Prix des Nations, he reached an average speed beyond 45 km/h, overtaking Zoetemelk, who started three minutes in front of him. On the hard ciruit of Diessenhofen, in Switzerland, over 50 kilometres, he defeated the Dane, Ole Ritter, the recordman for the hour, beating the race record at 44 km/h. In Lugano the victim was Gösta Petterson, this time for just two minutes. And in the Baracchi, pairing up with Mortensen, in a 109-kilometre race, where his Danish friend ended up practically dragging himself along (he admitted he couldn't maintain Luis's pace), he was also capable of taking more than two minutes out of the two Swedish brothers, Tomas and Gösta Petterson. They were two of the four brothers, together with Sture and Erik, who had won the silver medal in the 100-kilometres team time trial at the Mexico Olympics.

During the training sessions with Ocaña over the pan flat lands of Les Lande, the affable Dane lost his temper with Ocaña. 'Go on, but go on alone and don't make me suffer anymore,' he shouted. Ocaña turned round, surprised to see that, without intending to, he had left his friend behind. Such was the power of Ocaña's pedalling, his partner couldn't take his turn on the front. He won out of admiration for Anquetil, because he wanted to feel like a virtuoso soloist in time trials too, just like Anquetil. 'They don't mean the same as the Tour, but these victories are important because, thanks to them, I can feel the love of my supporters, their warmth and encouragement,' he said.

1976

'You wouldn't have your syringe here, would you, Luis? I've forgotten mine and I need to get some vitamins in me. It's only three days to go to the Tour but I need to perform well.'

'Yes, here you are, Viejo, but be careful when you use it because I've got hepatitis and I could infect you with it.'

'Don't worry, Luis, I'll be alright.'

José Luis Viejo was 26 years old and strong, invulnerable, immortal. That was how he felt in the prime of his life – afraid of nothing. He had no fear that anything would happen to him.

'When I was around about four years old, Luis, my parents took me to the well of Valdearenas, some 50 kilometres from their house in Azuqueca de Henares, to cure the hernia I had. I was all the time in my mother's arms up on a donkey with my father on foot beside us, and it took us a day to do it. And I still remember it. I still have that feeling of suffocating, of being smothered whenever I remember that day – and I was only four, you know? How some moments stay etched in your mind. They tied a harness around my waist and chest and lowered me into the well, down and down and they left me in the water for what seemed like an age, and that way they said I'd be cured. That was medicine in those days, Luis. Don't you think that somebody who has gone through that experience, survived it and remembered it, isn't entitled to believe that nothing bad is ever going to happen to him?'

Since the two of them joined Super Ser in 1975 they normally shared a room together. Luis was pretty silent and Viejo not much of a talker, either. Luis had seen it all before, but was now past his best, something which he himself frequently acknowledged. His repeated 'I'm no longer what I was' rang in the ears of his young team mates like a grandfather's apology. Viejo, on the other hand, was very much on the way up. As an amateur he was one of the best in the history of Spanish cycling, one of the best amateurs in the world at the time. He was a medalist at the World Championships, a celebrated specialist in the 100-kilometre team time trial, and he won the Tour of Poland, beating all the so-called amateurs of the Soviet Union and its satellites. In his third year as a professional, after two seasons with Bahamontes and Moreno at La Casera, he joined Super Ser, the great team, built around Luis Ocaña, who even in his decline, still remained an appealing figure.

Super Ser (called Super Ser because Ser by itself was already the registered name of a chain of radio stations) was the firm set up in Pamplona in the 1960s by Ignacio Orbaiceta to make butane gas stoves. He'd been a cyclist in the 1940s, and began in business as a smuggler and then a manufacturer of mopeds, before turning to gas stoves. These were the first years of Spain's economic development, the first moves towards modernity. Seat 600s owned the roads, and in the homes gas stoves replaced coal fires and wood-burning heaters. Such was the success of his mythical heaters that Orbaiceta then diversified into refrigerators, ovens, washing machines and all kinds of household appliances. In the '70s his business was at its zenith and he was able to satisfy his cycling urge with an amateur team and by supporting various races and criteriums in Pamplona. So, when his old cycling partner, Gabriel Saura, the Spanish youth team selector and track racing organiser, put to him his dream of creating his own professional team he didn't hesitate. They would make a great partnership. The best. In July 1974, together with Boliche, the popular announcer and presenter at cycling races in Pamplona, they went up to la Seu d'Urgell to see the stage of the Tour which ended there that year. Merckx had won the stage and, despite the opposition from Aja, his fifth Tour was practically in his pocket. And with Merckx in the yellow jersey they went to speak to him to propose the contract of the century.

It wasn't exactly the best day to visit the Tour. Anxiety about the political situation, and the fear of what the foreign press might make of the mobilisation in Spain against Francoism produced practically a state of emergency in the Tour village. None other than Jacques Goddet had been hit mercilessly by the Guardia Civil because he wasn't wearing his accreditation badge. The Kas riders had convened a meeting among themselves. Perurena was talking about it to riders from other teams.

'We've been considering whether, out of solidarity with the fight in Spain, we ought to carry on or retire from the Tour. The directors have told us that anyone who doesn't want to carry on can retire; the team will respect his decision, but the thought of abandoning hasn't occurred to anybody. We are in a world of our own, here in the Tour, and we haven't learned much, only that the regime is making use of our victories, but we accept that; it is part of our wages,' Txomin told them.

'In any case, the person who almost messed things up is Eddy Merckx himself. Can you believe that when we crossed the Spanish frontier he began to shout, "Gora Euskadi Askatuta?" Santi Lazcano taught him that one day and Eddy liked it; thank goodness we had time to get to him and make him shut up. "Don't you know that Franco can put you in prison for shouting that?" we said, to frighten him.'

The Cannibal made it quite clear to Orbaiceta, Saura and Boliche that he would not be moving from Molteni, and rejected their offer. Then they went for their second objective. Through a mutual friend, Henri Labadie, who would be the team's general manager and would also provide their Zeus bicycles, they got in contact with Ocaña, who with the disappearance of Bic had been left out in the cold. Although he was now in decline, it was on the basis of his reputation that the foundation of the team was laid. It would, of course, have open access to the Tour de France. So, five years after leaving Fagor, Ocaña returned to a Spanish team, to carry on selling domestic electrical goods. He had gone off like an untrained starlet, misunderstood; he returned like a figure from the past, misunderstood and tired.

In 1976, his second year at Super Ser, things didn't go well for Ocaña. That was the year when Eddy Merckx also started to feel his age and Fuente had to retire with his diseased kidneys. He felt shrouded by a sense of an early twilight. They were all now in their thirties and it seemed their golden age was over. He rode the coldest and wettest Paris–Nice for a decade. He shone on the Mont Ventoux stage and initiated a beautiful attack on Les Arcs, in a torrential downpour which sunk the tenacious Zoetemelk. It was a stroke of genius – like something from the past – but an isolated one, which he couldn't continue into the *cronoescalada* on the Col d'Eze. There he was fifth behind the triumphant young Michel Laurent. From the cold and rain of the French race he emerged with flu and a high temperature which put him to bed for two weeks, a fortnight in which he had been thinking he would hone his form for the Vuelta, which obsessed him. There he feared the young Thurau, the Dutchman Kuiper and the Portuguese Agostinho.

With an attack on the Fito of the kind that only he knew how to make, he disposed of Thurau. Although captured on the descent towards Cangas de Onís by a very strong Kas group and by an incredibly strong, vigorous Agostinho, who took over the race leadership, Ocaña had already given a sign of his brilliance. He would repeat that several times over on the following day between Cangas de Onís and Reinosa, where he would finish with his habitual 'I'm not the man I used to be'. Super Ser's Director, Saura, had sent the Swiss rider Fuchs, Ocaña's best team mate, up ahead. After the first climb, on La Collada, Ocaña jumped after him in a fantastic pursuit. He caught him on the *puerto* of Carmona which he went over alone after a memorable climb which destroyed the peloton, and gained 55 seconds on race leader Agostinho. On the Palombera, the last *puerto* of the day, in mist and freezing temperatures, Ocaña was caught by the diminutive Loos. There were still 50 kilometres to the finish which meant the two of them were doomed. Agostinho had cracked, but the pair were caught by a six-man pack – Thurau, Pesarrodona, Nazábal, López Carril, Pedro Torres and Kuiper, who became the new overall leader. In spite of everything, Ocaña was an even stronger favourite than before.

His second Vuelta was within reach: what remained was the final time trial and, before that, the last summit finish at the Shrine of Our Lady of Gold in Murgia. There, alone, without any team support, attacked by the Ti Raleigh pair of Kuiper and Thurau, and by Pesarrodona and his Kas team mates, Ocaña's body cried out – enough. He lost only 23 seconds to the Kas riders and he kept himself in second place overall, two seconds behind Kuiper, but he had Pesarrodona breathing down his neck and knew he could not rely on his strength to hold out over the 31.7 kilometres of time trial in San

Sebastian. The great Ocaña of '71 and '73, and the one who won the Vuelta in '70 would have been happy to arrive at the last day of the Vuelta in that position. But that Ocaña was in the past. Today's Ocaña ceded 1'–02" to the up-and-coming Thurau and 1'–01" to the ultra regular Pesarrodona, the most regular, at least among the Kas team. It was Pesarrodona who prevailed and won the Vuelta, without having taken a stage and without having worn the leader's jersey except on the last day.

'That day, in San Sebastian, I think I suffered the biggest disappointment of my life,' Ocaña said to Viejo while the rider from La Alcarria was on the bed, preparing to stick the syringe into his thigh. 'I never had a bigger upset. Remember, everything was in my favour, Viejo. I had the race completely under control. I was so sure of my chances that I never for one moment doubted that I'd win. But I failed, and on my favourite territory – the time trial – and I cannot explain it to myself. I set off tight, perhaps because of nerves and never found my rhythm, Viejo, and you know what that means – you're a good time triallist – it means you go in fits and starts; you don't dominate the bike; it dominates you. When they told me halfway through the ride that Pesarrodona had taken 20 seconds out of me I just collapsed in misery, Viejo. The following day I think I felt worse than after falling on the Col de Menté. There it was a question of bad luck, an accident; here, when I was thinking I had overcome the illness and the bad luck, I get this completely unexpected blow which I don't believe I'll ever recover from.'

'In the Tour it was quite clear that you hadn't recovered,' Viejo said to him, more realistic than compassionate. But then he was not used to these confidences from Luis, who was normally so reserved, nor to this tone which was more like addressing the gallery, or the press, than a chat between colleagues where you don't know in which direction the conversation is going to go. 'You lost the respect of your team mates. Not mine, because you'll always have that, but the others couldn't figure you out. They reckoned you were just a petty dictator, that you were domineering just like when you talked to Josiane. And that's the way they answered you back. Well, didn't Jesús Manzaneque tell you the other day, before he abandoned, that he wasn't going back to the car to get water for you? He comes up with that joke – at least that's how I heard it – "the problem is the well is too deep, Luis. I can't reach the bottom." He didn't give a damn about going back to the car. And if that isn't enough, it's you, the leader, who says nothing and goes back to the car.

'What do you want me to say, Luis? You weren't up to much in the mountains, nor in the time trial. It makes me feel odd to see you every morning making a detailed little sketch of the stage, which you stick on the handlebar, and yes, it is good to see you with that look of pride, like you used to have, that air of a champion you had in those days, but then in the race you are something else. Merckx is not here and times have changed, Luis. You saw that on Alpe d'Huez, where you lost more than six minutes to Zoetemelk and came in thirty something. And it's the rest of us who have to pull the chestnuts out of the fire for the team's sake.'

'Yes, I know that without having to extend yourself, Viejo, you have been much better than me. Sure, you won a stage – and how you won it – and you've frequently finished in the first ten.'

'Yes, I won a stage, and what a stage it was – Montgenèvre to Manosque, 224 kilometres through the most beautiful Provence. I shall never forget it, that's for sure, and I think very few will ever forget it. I took off alone and nobody could follow me, and I went so well, Luis, and I'm sure in the peloton they were talking about how well I was going, so I got to the finish almost 23 minutes up, Luis. You already know that – 22 minutes and 50 seconds exactly. And Goddet, in person, Goddet told me that it was the biggest lead which a solo break had ever got on the whole peloton. And usually when this happens Goddet likes to castigate the peloton, to call us all idle layabouts, and use that expression he likes so much – "dwarfs of the road". But this time he was so impressed by my ride that he congratulated me sincerely.

'That night, talking with my wife on the telephone, she told me that in Spain things had gone crazy, that all the radios called her at the same time so that she could comment live on my escape, and talk about my life and that we had a daughter. But the next day I went to look at *L'Équipe* to see what they were saying and there was just one line about my solo escape. The whole report was about some Jean Giono. Labadie translated it for me over breakfast. Evidently he was not a cyclist but a novelist who died a short while ago, and who lived there, in Manosque, at the foot of Mont d'Or, the last hill we had to climb, and the journalist thought it funny that this Giono described Mont d'Or as something like: "That beautiful rounded breast is a hill." So that's how I found out that I was climbing a tit!'

'I remember that tit, I definitely do. Edouard Fachleitner loved it; he was a rider who was as daft as a brush and he lived at the side of it, and in one Paris–Nice they made us climb it and Merckx made me shift … Good, you did well, Viejo, definitely, but you're not going to deny that my little show yesterday, on the Peyresourde, also deserves some applause. It came from pride, Viejo, from the only thing I still have left. I might have lost my strength, my punch, but I will never lose my pride, the desire to be the best. And yesterday I showed it. It was a stage which had my name on it, starting from Saint-Gaudens and passing over my puertos, the ones that have ruled my life, those of my tr http://ebay. com/ agedy and those of my life, over the Portillon and over the Menté, and passing through Luchon. The whole of the Pyrenees have my name carved on them, you know, Viejo? I broke away on the Peyresourde and only Van Impe was able to get back to me, on the descent. But although he caught me and all that, I didn't let him take a turn on the front, Viejo, because it was me, me the same as ever, who wanted to be ahead of him, with nothing in front of me except the horizon and far off in the distance, the prior warning of that final climb.'

'Well neither Saura nor Orbaiceta, who was there with him in the car, thought that way, Luis. You've seen how annoyed they were at dinner. Labadie told me that when Van Impe caught up with you, coming down off the Peyresourde and on the flat leading to the last climb up to Saint-Lary-Soulan, you were pulling for Van Impe like a man possessed, and from the car they were saying you should stop. "Stop, Luis," they were shouting to you. "Let Van Impe do the work, there's no way you're going to win the stage like that." But they said, according to what Labadie told me, that you didn't pay any attention to them.'

'I am Luis Ocaña, Viejo, remember that. I never pay attention to anyone. I never have done. I always do what my spirit tells me to do, and my spirit is my past – the misery, the hunger, the desire. And you've seen already that I put four minutes into Pesarrodona...I tell you, it's always the same. Those who rip you apart in the Vuelta don't do a thing in the Tour... Like Tamames...'

'Well, they really didn't see it that way, Luis. They reckoned that what you were doing was not very intelligent, and since, as they well know, you're not short on intelligence, they immediately drew the conclusion that you'd sold yourself to Van Impe and were helping him to get rid of Zoetemelk. And bearing in mind what then happened they were right: you were finished on the last climb and lost almost four minutes while Van Impe won the stage, gained more than three minutes on Zoetemelk, and more or less won the Tour there and then. So they were convinced that you did it all for money, Luis, like in the Vuelta of '69 when you helped Pingeon. And they also knew Van Impe's Director, Guimard, and that he knew his way around the peloton well enough, and that he got on well with you...'

'Well, let them think what they like, Viejo, but for me it was all a matter of pride, because I am Luis Ocaña.'

'And the worst is yet to come, Luis. According to Labadie, Orbaiceta is so disappointed, so sad that he told him the team was finished. It wouldn't carry on next year. That would really be tough, Luis. I'm young; I've got my whole career in front of me.'

'As for me, there's not much left in cycling, Viejo. I'll try to continue for one more year to pull in a bit more money, and then go back to the land. It can't be said that things have gone well for me in Super Ser, it really can't. Last year I needed to have won the Vuelta, Viejo. You know that.'

1975

The Vuelta of 1975 should have been another great duel between Fuente and Ocaña. Fuente, sick and injured, retired from the race in an ambulance after deliberately crashing to avoid facing a doping control, and Ocaña had the ground taken from under him by the man who should have been his closest *gregario*, Agustín Tamames. Tamames was now near the end of a career which had been rescued by Orbaiceta of the Portuguese Benfica team, where he'd had to make do on minimal wages. And his main rival was not Ocaña, but his friend Txomin Perurena. In that Vuelta of 1975, Tamames, who'd been Ocaña's principal adversary in the '70 Vuelta, was an irrepressible force of nature. He won five stages and ended up by beating Perurena on his home territory in the final time trial, when the Basque was the only one to be hampered by the rain. But Tamames won thanks to Ocaña, to his work and to his weakness. On those two decisive days, first at Formigal, where Ocaña's attack from far out struck down Fuente, and the second on the Urkiola, where Ocaña said to Tamames, 'Go on, go, because Lasa is coming back,'. Tamames, who didn't start out as a favourite by any means, finished off the early work that had been put in by Ocaña, who was looking to rediscover one of his better days. But on the podium it was Perurena and Miguel Lasa who accompanied Tamames; Ocaña was fourth.

'Tamames betrayed you, Luis, that's for sure, but you wouldn't have been able to win that Vuelta. It was too much for you. But it was a real triumph for Super Ser.'

'Yes, but I was the one who ought to have won. I was the Super Ser leader; I wasn't in bad form, at all, Viejo, and I was motivated. I wanted to believe – and that's how they they sold it to me – that I was coming back to Spain as the prodigal son. And I wanted to be at the top. But I wasn't the prodigal son, nor did I manage to get to the top. Tamames was tremendous that year. Just remember – in Andalucía I had beaten Maertens in a time trial and finished second overall, and in Paris–Nice, where Zoetemelk was in total command, I finished ninth.

I didn't do so well on the Col d'Eze, but as you know it wasn't a good distance for me. In the Setmana Catalana Merckx only took 19 seconds out of me in a 25-kilometre time trial. I was in good form, truly, Viejo, but yes – Tamames was flying.'

'And there he finished you, Luis, there Ocaña was broken. All that was left of you was skin and bones, and your heart and blood turned into pride and fury, but not into strength and into cycling. You were finished in 1973 after you won the Tour.'

'In the Dauphiné of '75 I really proved that, Viejo – what you put so bluntly. In that Dauphiné Thévenet showed that when it came to the Tour, he would be the favourite. Merckx was no longer the real Merckx and I was even less likely to be the real Ocaña ever again. Everything was crystal clear on that climb of the Granier in the Chartreuse. It's not a giant of a col, but it always reveals so much. Thévenet's performance was extraordinary there, and neither Merckx nor I could follow – not just him but the peloton. We were dropped by the leaders, Viejo. Merckx lost ten minutes and I lost a quarter of an hour. And the next day it was worse on the Croix de Fer, then the Télégraphe and the Galibier. These were my cols, Viejo, the ones I loved from the '73 Tour. That was just misery.'

Ocaña's morale was so low in that Dauphiné, a race that was very close to his heart, a race he'd won three times. It was his springboard for the Tour and it was there that, for the first time, he confessed he was over the top in an interview for the journal *Cyclisme-Magazine.*

'I've no longer got any juice left, Michel,' he told the journalist Michel Claré. 'I'm like a flat battery. My health's perfect: I'm not suffering from bronchitis; my heart beat is strong; I sleep well. But I haven't got that essential thing that made me unique, that 'punch'. I'm annoyed about it, too, because this winter I prepared like never before. I trained better than ever. I did everything to perfection. And in spite of all that – look at me. On the Chartreuse stage, first I escaped with Merckx and we were doing 48 an hour. Then I had to go alone to chase down the group that had got away on the Col de l'Epine, and carrying the usual wheel-suckers. And then, on the Granier – nothing. My body couldn't give any more. I had nothing left inside.'

In spite of everything, in *L'Équipe*, on the eve of the Tour, they still wanted to believe in Ocaña; they compared him to the Phoenix rising from the ashes, without knowing that the comparison Ocaña himself was making was with an angel who'd had his wings clipped. He went to the Tour with scarcely any rest, because Super Ser forced him to ride the Tour of Asturias (where he finished third behind Lasa and Linares) rather than letting him follow his training routine in the Pyrenees. It was an absolute disaster. Ocaña got to the Pyrenees, the first mountain range they would confront, more than five minutes down on Merckx, who seemed to be making his imperial progress towards his sixth Tour, picking up time in the time trial and on the *pavé* of Roubaix. In spite of that, on a couple of days he'd been conspicuous with attacks on the flat. He continued his tactic of starting the day with his pockets full in case he couldn't get his *musette* later on, and these were surprise attacks at the feeding station which had strung out a cursing peloton into single file. Then, on the first day in the Pyrenees he was with all the leading riders on the Soulor, and on the second day he was part of the group of principals which rode away on the Tourmalet. He held on over the Aspin and only on the final climb to Pla d'Adet did the elastic break. He fought back and finished fifth, scarcely a minute and a half behind Merckx and Van Impe and a little more than two behind Zoetemelk and Thévenet. And that afternoon he was as optimistic when talking to the press – fifth overall with all the rest of the Tour in front of him – as his masseur, Emilio Cruz, was pessimistic back in the hotel room.

'Have you see what your backside is like, Luis? With that boil you're not going far.'

'You don't have to swear to that, Emilio. Climbing the Pla d'Adet I suffered like a dog. I didn't know how to sit on the saddle.'

Despite all the creams, all the washing and care and attention, the following day between Tarbes and Albi it was torture for Ocaña, who had to pedal sitting on one side. Straining his left knee so much in that position, he ended the day with his knee joint hurting more than his backside. In the night he called Cescutti again: 'Pierrot, come and pick me up. I can't put up with any more of this.' And he returned to Caupenn d'Armagnac.

It was stage thirteen, and his fourth abandon in six Tours. He would miss by three days the great moment he had been waiting for all his life: the first conclusive defeat of Merckx in the Tour. On Orcières-Merlette it had been a partial defeat; this time, not far from that finish on Pra Loup, Merckx's defeat was total, and he never would win that sixth Tour. It was inflicted not by Ocaña, but by Thévenet.

'Now they were all going, Fuente, Merckx... You know, Viejo, I was never again going to be able to look Merckx in the eyes and see that look of defeat? I never would again feel that happiness. I only managed it once, in '71, and I never repeated the moment, Viejo. My fall on the Menté was his great victory, his definitive victory.'

'But you won a Tour, Luis, and you were great. You were very great, Luis.'

'Yes, I won a Tour, Viejo, but I didn't beat Merckx. I never beat Merckx. And, you know what, Viejo?

'Go on, tell me, Luis'

'Do me a favour. Have a shave, man, and take care of your liver.'

1972

After working on the accounts at the end of 1971, Christian Darras, the marketing man, reached the cool, detached conclusion that the best thing that could have happened to Bic, from the point of view of publicity, was precisely what had happened – Ocaña's fall, his transformation into a tragic hero, a character more admirable and more admired by the people than the dominating ogre. 'Isn't it the case that Poulidor is much more popular in France than Anquetil?' he thought to himself, to ease his bad conscience. And as proof that his intuition and his calculus were not wrong Baron Bich himself supported him, something he showed when he said to him, 'Call Ocaña; tell him to come and have dinner at my house.'

'That's a gesture,' thought Darras, 'that he never made to Anquetil,' whom he respected as a sportsman, but didn't admire. At dinner the Baron presented Ocaña with the latest product to come out of his laboratory of ideas, a throwaway lighter which had still not yet been put on the market.

'I'm going to give you a piece of advice, Luis, if you'll allow me,' he said, after they'd both spent some time enjoying themselves igniting and putting out the lighter. 'Every day, I am the first to get into the office and almost the last to leave. Whether you're at the top or the bottom of the hierarchy; the only thing that counts is work.'

'You don't have to tell me that, Baron. My whole life has been built around work. You only need to look at my hands to see that.'

In winter, in the year's first glimpse of the Provençal sun in Seillans, the boys from Bic, the spoilt millionaires, tried on a new uniform. The fashion designer, Guy Laroche, had produced some stylish and futuristic suits which delighted Ocaña and made everybody look like the cabin staff on Concorde or walk-on extras in Jacques Tati's *Playtime*. It gave them an air of invincible modernity.

'How Merckx will tremble' was the war cry, the optimistic shout of the happy group. And the press echoed it and lamented how slowly time passed. Waiting until 1 July, for the start of the Tour in Angers, for the continuation of the unfinished duel of 1971, would seem like a century.

At Bic, there had been some changes. Gérard Morin, the man from Bayonne had retired, to be replaced by De Muer, along with a friend of his from the North, Edouard Delberghe from Stablinski's Sonolor team. The team had also signed Serge Lapébie, son of Guy and nephew of Roger, and persuaded the 35-year-old Novak to carry on, in spite of him insisting that his liver was worn out. And also they signed Eric Leman, a very fast Belgian, who wanted to be a butcher before he became a sprinter; every year he rode well only up to the Tour of Flanders (which he won on a number of occasions). The mechanics were the same: Robert Rychenbusch from Dunkirk and Jean-Claude Vincent from Villeneuve d'Asq, another two boys from the North, friends of Janssen and Rosiers, lovers of Paris-Roubaix. Emilio Cruz and the jovial Italian, Mario Ferri, remained the two masseurs. Ferri lived in Paris and won all the games of boules those in his trade played at la Cipale while the cyclists lapped the nearby vélodrome in the Vincennes forest.

If it was an interminable wait until 1 July for the fans, for Luis Ocaña the route leading to the Tour became an obstacle race, full of controversy, polemic, misunderstandings, doubts and a final disaster. All the elements which had tormented him throughout his life, all the circumstances which had made him a fatalist and, to his own regret, given to excessive behaviour all came together in those few months of 1972. And this despite the optimism he mustered to combat it. On top of all that it was as cold and rainy a spring as anyone could remember, and Ocaña didn't see the sun nor feel the warmth which, as Emilio Cruz used to tell him, dried out his lungs and revitalised him.

At the beginning of March he had his first race of the year – the Tour of Levante. Perurena won and Ocaña finished up with flu. Despite that, he went on to Paris–Nice where he finished with tendonitis in both knees, but thoroughly satisfied with himself because Merckx had had to work so hard to get the better of him at the finish in Manosque, on Viejo's beloved Mont d'Or. And he'd taken a quiet pleasure in seeing the 36-year-old Poulidor beat the Cannibal in the mountain time trial up the Turbie, and take the overall by six seconds. Ocaña was third.

A promise is a promise, and even with his knees mashed up he went to Hyères, where his friend Lucien Aimar had invited him, along with Anquetil, to a criterium. The same day, 19 March, with a high temperature, he flew to Barcelona, aiming to be in Castelldefels on the start line of the Setmana Catalana. That same day, 19 March, Merckx won the Milan–San Remo for the fifth time. And the Belgian also went on to win the Liège and the two Flèches – the Wallonne and the Brabançonne. And, of course, he would also win the Giro – his third Giro – where he encountered Fuente.

Ocaña finally gave up the idea of riding the Setmana, and the 150,000 pesetas the organiser was going to give him. He went to Paris where he underwent sessions of kinesiotherapy to cure his knee ligaments. In April he also withdrew from the Tour of the Basque Country, where he was due to start as joint favourite with Lasa, although that didn't preclude him from appearing on the eve of the race in Abadiño, where Zeus presented him with the 'Cyclist of the Year' award and 50,000 pesetas. On that same occasion, and it came as a surprise to everybody, Ocaña announced that he'd received a telegram from Maurice de Muer, the boss of Bic, expressly forbidding him from starting in the Basque Country the following day. 'It's a shame,' said a sad-looking Ocaña, 'but he who gives the orders gives the orders'. The Spanish press, however, weren't going to buy that story. Unsympathetic as ever, in spite of what had happened in 1971, they were convinced that the only criterion which guided Ocaña's racing programme was the financial one. And neither the cyclist, who had never denied that he raced only to earn money, nor the facts themselves, would convince them otherwise.

A few days before the Basque Country troubles, Ocaña had already announced that he would not be riding the Vuelta a España because he hadn't reached an agreement over money with the organisers, who, he felt, were treating him badly. As he knew the offer they had made to Merckx to get him to participate, which the Belgian had turned down, it was not surprising that he rejected the offer they were making him as second choice: 30,000 pesetas for each stage he rode and 100,000 more if he won. He was asking for a straight one million pesetas before the start and a 40-kilometre time trial included in the race, and they told him he was mad.

A Vuelta without Ocaña was saved, unexpectedly, by the sudden emergence of José Manuel Fuente, a mercurial character who came from Asturias, and from the mist, the rain and the cold which seeped into his house in Limanes, where, as a child, scarlet fever nearly left him blind, and who described his life as a 'cycle of pain'.

'El Tangaru' never worked in the fields as his father did. He used to sleep with his bicycle in his room; it had cost him 3,500 pesetas, which he'd paid for in instalments from the overtime he did in the foundry where he worked. He wanted a bicycle to have races against a friend and when that stopped being much of a challenge – when the exploits of Bahamontes were filling his mind – he decided he'd become a real cyclist. Every day he went training on the Naranco. He climbed it seated, without getting out of the saddle, because he'd been told that you used up less effort that way. He became a unique climber with extraordinary abilities. As an amateur he was legendary. Stories of exploits which seemed fictitious were passed on by word of mouth, but they were as real as Tarangu was real. Once he was riding in an amateurs' race, a Mountain Circuit or a Tour of Cantabria, and there in front of him, in the middle of the race, he saw a friend with a serious expression on his face. Tarangu immediately realised that something serious had happened, and so it had. It turned out that his brother had died in a motorbike accident. That night Tarangu went to his brother's wake to say his farewells, and in the morning returned to the race. He arrived in time for the start of the stage, which finished at the top of the Escudo, with a sign hanging from the back of his bike: 'The person who wants to be second, put yourself on my wheel.' And he won.

When he was doing his military service he was once put on a charge, and as it happened, it was just at the time of the Tour of Valladolid. Tarangu goes off and says to the captain, who was a cycling enthusiast, 'My captain, I will make you a bet. What would you bet on me winning the Portillo stage of the Tour of Valladolid?'

'But how are you going to win it if you're in prison?'

'Well, that's the bet: you let me out to ride and if I win you lift the punishment, and if I don't, you double it. What do you say?'

And after throwing out the challenge he takes a deep drag on his cigarette and looks the captain in the eyes.

'Done,' replies the officer.

The following day, without knowing how he did it, Tarangu, the imprisoned recruit, beat the cream of Spain's amateur cyclists in the Tour of Valladolid. After riding for the Werner amateur team he turned professional with Julio San Emeterio's Karpy squad, and in 1971 Dalmacio Langarica signed him up for Kas.

Fuente always used to share a room with his fellow Asturian, López Carril, and as he smoked so much, people used to say to Carril, 'It will take years off your career having to breathe in so much smoke.' Despite that prediction, López Carril had a long and very steady career until he was 37, but he died young. He participated in nine Tours in which he won three stages. Five times he finished in the top ten. A year after retiring he suffered a heart attack playing football on the beach at Gijón.

'Tarangu, attack! Attack, Tarangu, you can do it.!' It was Perurena who encouraged him on the eve of the Formigal stage during that Vuelta of 1972. 'Lasa and Tamames are stronger than me, but you, Tarangu, you are stronger than anyone. You are a climber out of this world, Tarangu.'

'But, Txomin, how can you tell me to attack if you are the leader and what they've taught me is that you always have to respect the team leader...'

'I'm saying it to you because I'm so fond of you, and because you are my friend, Tarangu, and because I know you'll pay attention to me, and only to me. I won't be able to cope on the Formigal; it's too hard a mountain for me, I'm sure of it, and it wouldn't seem right to have the whole team around me defending the impossible and depriving some of them – you for instance – of a victory. Especially depriving you, since you deserve everything because you are such a good man, because of your quality on the bike, because of your wonderful spirit.

Because you ride with the moon just as easily as you smoke. Ocaña only loves the sun, but you, I've seen you on sleepless nights looking through the window, searching for the moon, and its calm.

And Tarangu understood a little of the reasoning, but found it difficult to assimilate. He was very difficult to control and he made his team mates nervous with his fussiness. He only had to splash a little water on his clothing for him to stop the team car, where there's always a spare pair of shorts and a jersey, and start changing without any sense of urgency. His Director would be pulling his hair out and his team mates would be urging him: 'Come on, Tarangu, the peloton is getting away. You won't catch them.' And he would reply with a 'Oh, fuck off. Stop making me nervous.' And that would happen in the Giro or the Tour, not just in any little race. 'So what do you do?' the Director ended up saying to the others. 'If you make him hurry, he's worse.'

Nemesio was also fond of Fuente, and he understood him.

'Tarangu is a loonie,' he tried to explain to the many team mates who, unlike Perurena, didn't know what to make of this capricious Asturian. 'His mood changes with the moon. Remember: when he began the Tour in 1971 he had problems with the team, and Dalmacio wanted to chuck him out, but because of the two stages he won he went through a radical change – he became a champion. He's had a bad kidney since childhood, since the scarlet fever almost left him blind. And he forgets to eat; take that into account when you laugh about his *pájaras*, you smart alecks. He makes a huge effort and the kidney doesn't cleanse his system. Fuente is combative by nature, but he has no tactical sense; he thinks his strength will last for ever. When he is focused, as well you know, his head is perfectly clear, but his heart deceives him. So sometimes I have to stop him from attacking. But that has ended, because Peru has spoken to him, and he is the leader. Tomorrow he will attack.'

As it turned out, on the Formigal stage they didn't need to stop him, nor could they have done. He jumped away with Werner's Pepe Grande (who would become the National Selector during the Indurain period) and Fuente sat on his wheel, at first not daring to take his turn on the front. Antón Barrutia, the Kas director, hesitated, but Perurena, the captain, made him give Tarangu a free rein. When he began to cooperate with Grande the gap back to the peloton increased, and when at Monrepós he dropped the brave Valencian (who happened to be such a good guitarist) it continued to stretch.

At Sabiñánigo, at the foot of the Formigal, the gap had gone out to seven minutes. It was a long-distance flight in the purest Ocaña style, a gap that hardly diminished all the way up to Formigal, that ghostly ski station covered in snow, on an afternoon in May which seemed as cold and dark as in January. At the end of the day Fuente was the leader of the Vuelta, six minutes up on the second man. Four days later, another performance in Orduña convinced the fans that they'd discovered a unique rider, whose flashes of brilliance in the previous year's Giro and Tour had more solidity to them than they'd thought. He was something more than just a wild man. Suddenly Ocaña didn't exist.

Spain had a new idol, and Eddy Merckx a new Ocaña to confront, as the Belgian found out a few days later in the Giro. Fuente went there without a pause, arriving with no trace of fear, convinced he could deal with anything. 'To beat Merckx it's necessary to attack all the time and make the race hard,' he pronounced. 'To beat that son of a bitch you've got to make him suffer every day.' And Merckx heard him and trembled. The fear that Ocaña couldn't inspire in him this Asturian goblin could. Already on the fourth day, on the Blockhaus della Majella in the Abruzos mountains, he'd taken the stage and the *maglia rosa*. But Merckx was not just Merckx. Merckx was also a fabulous team of riders who could finish in the top ten of the Tour, cyclists who set an impossible pace on the flat, men like Vandenbossche, who rode with his body twisted because he was so tall, and only the strongest riders could hang on to him. At the end of the Giro, which he won, Merckx breathed a sigh and said: 'It's as well we took Fuente seriously from the word go, because if we hadn't killed him off on the flat stages I couldn't have won this Giro.'

Fuente finished second, at five and a half minutes, but he never stopped making the Cannibal tremble. On the Stelvio he crushed him, and on his finest day, when he should have finished him off, an unsurfaced goat track called the Bardonecchio via the Jafferau unfortunately proved too much for him; he collapsed in the last kilometre and Merckx miraculously caught and passed him.

On 4 June 1972, the very day when Fuente failed in his assault on the Jafferau, Ocaña won the Dauphiné Libéré. All the tribulations of a lopsided year seemed to have ended. Ocaña had begun to recover his morale and the form he'd had some weeks earlier in the Four Days of Dunkirk, where he finished second, and only a puncture in the time trial had prevented him from overtaking Yves Hézard. But in the Dauphiné, where for the second time he beat a continually improving Thévenet, he really felt himself. 'I'm fed up to the back teeth,' he thundered one day and everybody knew that Ocaña was back to his very best. 'People here know only one way to ride – and that's on your wheel. They're all waiting for somebody to make a move so they can stop him.'

The following day, in the Chartreuse, a stage of only 68 kilometres between Chambéry and Grenoble, over the cols of Granier, Cucheron and Porte, Ocaña attacked on the first climb and went off alone. He reached the vélodrome in Grenoble more than a minute up on Van Impe. This was the great Ocaña riding as only he knew how, the Ocaña of Orcières-Merlette on a smaller scale. In the following day's time trial, 31 kilometres from Valence to Crest, he again rode with complete authority. His victory was absolute. That 4 June, which saw Merckx frustrating Fuente on the Bardonecchio and a revitalised Ocaña in the Dauphiné, the world was more than ever divided between the *Merckxistas* and the *Ocañistas*. The Tour of '72 was going to be like none other and the fans were promised a fiesta. And Ocaña, they pointed out a few days later, would turn up more handsome than ever in the Spanish national champion's jersey, which he had just won in Segovia in a solo exhibition which had left second-placed Txomin Perurena gaping in astonishment.

So it was strange that in the Hotel la Boule d'Or, in Angers, where the Bic team were staying on the eve of the Tour, that the guests should find the atmosphere so tense. Poisonous rumours were flying through the corridors of the old hotel, whose dusty carpets were constantly trodden by the urgent footsteps of the journalists. The annoyance evident on Emilio Cruz's face and the bad temper of the bodyguards looking after Ocaña, who, as everybody knew, despised journalists, were unmistakable symptoms. So, too, was the vacillation of Darras and De Muer whenever they were questioned. Ocaña, himself, was playing dumb, although he had an irritating cough from time to time, a dry cough – the sort that doesn't clear the lungs. *L'Équipe* had reported the day before that he was 'ready to beat Merckx again: he didn't fear him; he had arrived perfectly prepared and was sure that he wouldn't suffer from the jinx, the bad luck or the setbacks that had been his downfall in his three previous attempts.' His view was that the Tour would be decided in the three Pyrenean stages, the Ventoux and the Alps. His only regret was that the bronchitis which he'd suffered in the Tour of the Levante meant that he'd come to the Tour with what he regarded as the meagre total of 10,000 kilometres in his legs. But he said nothing about what was preoccupying the journalists that 30 June. Was it true that after the Spanish championships he'd shut himself away to train in a small Spanish village? Was it true that instead of going directly to Angers from Bretagne-de-Marsan, he had made a detour to Paris on the Thursday, where some specialists had examined his chest X-rays which showed up two suspicious stains on his lungs? Was it true that he'd had a further outbreak of his haemorrhoids problem? Nobody was admitting anything; nobody was denying anything.

The Tour began with Merckx dominant, untouchable in the Prologue and Ocaña putting up a valiant fight. On the fourth stage it was Ocaña who was the principal animator of the leading echelon of 19 riders which formed as they ran down past Merlin Plage on the Vendée's Atlantic coast. 'What punch, Luis' said Thévenet, who'd always admired him and called him 'Hidalgo' (Nobleman). Zoetemelk, Van Impe, Agostinho, Pingeon, Poulidor, among others, had lost more than three minutes, but as usual the orthodox critics denounced Ocaña's verve in organising the echelon. 'He just helped Merckx to make a general clear out, so now the Belgian will only have him and Thévenet to worry about,' some said. And Poulidor threatened: 'Putting time into us has meant he's lost some very important allies.'

'What allies?' wondered Ocaña, ironically. 'All those critics – including Poulidor – they never do anything except sit on my wheel; they never attack Merckx, they just wait for me to do the work.'

It rained. Once more it rained. The rain and the mist which seemed to have been born on the Aubisque, in that narrow valley where the cows absent-mindedly stand in the road, and get lost in the tunnels and never come out of them. The day when Ocaña attacked in the Pyrenees it rained, but he was strong and fit – fitter than anybody thought – and the rain held no fear for him, not that day, when he was again going to put Merckx to the test, look him in the eyes once more to see what was there. 'Rain is not an omen,' he thought, 'it's just an accompaniment; you can't climb the Aubisque without rain.' And on the Aubisque he attacked three times, and three times Merckx stuck to his wheel, and together they went over the summit, behind Alain Santy, who'd been sent on ahead by Bic for whenever he might be needed.

On the descent the pair were joined by a group containing Thévenet, Poulidor and Zoetemelk when Ocaña punctured. In all the confusion and lost in the mist, De Muer's Peugeot 404 was slow getting to their rider. It then took them almost a minute to change his wheel – an absolute age on a descent. Guimard, the race leader, had passed him, hurtling down like a meteor, and had joined up with Merckx, who, remembering his contretemps the year before on the Cucheron, didn't hesitate to attack as soon as he saw Ocaña puncture. Risking life and limb, the tyres squealing round those dangerous corners, De Muer hurled the 404 after the fleeing Santy to get him to stop and wait for Ocaña, who was himself now descending fearlessly. He quickly caught Thévenet, who was always very timid descending in the rain, and now, with Santy alongside him, was flying in pursuit of Merckx, passing Ward Janssens en route.

Before he became a cyclist Alain Santy was a cross-country runner and he pedalled like a page boy. He was a rangy elf-like character, blond as wheat and his pedalling was velvety. That was how Roger Bastide, one of the best biographers of the young Ocaña, described him. He was called the Paul Newman of the peloton; he had the shy but appealing smile of the film star and his blue eyes. He seemed a posh boy, but he wasn't. He had worked on building sites and in the winter, to complement his earnings he carried on doing that with his brother, Guy. 'That way we built up our muscles,' he said. He got married at 18 and already had two children.

Coming into the little village of Arthez d'Asson Ocaña went flat out into a tight turn, and half way through, realising there were a number of cars parked on the right-hand side, turned sharply to the left. The wheels skidded, he slipped and came down against a steep slope to the right. Thévenet and Santy went flying over the top of him. Only Janssens, miraculously, avoided the fall. Ocaña and Thévenet were quickly up, Ocaña with a bloody cheekbone and his jersey and shorts in shreds; Thévenet with a wound on his scalp from where the blood flowed gently on to his face. It didn't look serious.

Alain Santy didn't get up. He remained stretched out on the ground, unconscious. The anxiety which enveloped the peloton only diminished during the evening, when from the hospital in Pau came the news that the much loved and admired 'Paul Newman' had suffered a broken vertebra, a fracture to his jaw, and a wound to his forehead which needed 20 stitches. Serious injuries, but not ones that would put either his life or his career in danger.

Ocaña wasted no time shedding his companions. Thévenet, who was pedalling groggily, quickly lost his wheel. So too Janssens, whom he caught and overtook in his furious, frenetic pursuit, under the rain which drenched him and made locks of hair stick to his face and bounce against the raw wounds revealed by his tattered clothing. A little later he reached Van Impe, who also couldn't hold on to that unleashed back wheel. He chased magnificently and by himself, but when he reached the finish at Pau, one minute and 49 seconds had already passed since Merckx and his group had gone over the line. On the day when he was going to make an assault on the overall classification he ended up fifth, 2'–40" down on Merckx, and a further eleven seconds behind Guimard, who still led the race.

Ocaña was cursing at the finish, but not against the bad luck which seemed to follow him, nor was he surrendering to fate. He was shouting about Merckx.

'It's incredible. Now you can attack on the descent. That's the new fashion,' Ocaña clamoured. 'And what's more, you can now attack a man when he's fallen. Alright then, I'll accept that things have changed, but I won't forget those who've taken advantage of my puncture and my fall. You might need my help one day.'

'What you you talking about, Luis?' Merckx answered, in a peculiarly ingenuous tone. 'You say you punctured? I didn't know anything about that. I never turned round to look on the descent; there's no time for that, and I thought you were with me all the time. And in fact, didn't Guimard catch us? If you had descended well you, too, could have caught us, Luis.'

'Oh yes, of course I could, if the *commissaires* hadn't obstructed me disgracefully and if I hadn't fallen, Eddy. Or are you saying you didn't realise I'd fallen, either? And you pulled harder at that very moment, or that's what those in your group told me... Alright then, we'll see who finishes second tomorrow in Luchon, behind me!'

In Luchon, however, it was Merckx who won. He attacked at the very top of the Peyresourde and came in with an eight-second lead over Ocaña. 'It was essential to hit Ocaña again,' he said at the finish. 'Even if it was just to hurt his morale the day after his fall. I couldn't let him recover. Today I believe I won the Tour.'

And he didn't let him recover. From that moment on, with cruel indifference, Merckx subjected Ocaña and the whole Bic team to the Molteni steamroller. And when the two were by themselves, with no team members around them, as they were on the Ventoux climb, he resisted to perfection each and every one of the Spaniard's attacks. On the Ventoux Thévenet took advantage of the two marking each other, and Ocaña again found himself taking on everybody, a posse of opportunists. It was now the Tour of him alone against Merckx; him alone against the rest, who admired him and pitied him – in silence.

'Merckx would not have done what Ocaña did coming down the Vars with no air in his back tyre. And he'd never have got away from him if he hadn't punctured. On the contrary; Luis would have dropped him.' So said Van Impe. The descent of the Vars was on the Orcières-Merlette to Briançon stage, the day after the Tour returned to the ski station where the year before Ocaña had reduced Merckx to his knees. But this time it was Merckx who had the pleasure of sprinting past Ocaña in the final metres to finish in front of him. Just a second in front, but in front, and in that symbolic town.

Merckx won in Briançon, and Ocaña, in between irrepressible coughing fits, confessed he was beaten. 'Eddy has won.' And in their reports the journalists underlined that this was the first time since their confrontation in Pau that Ocaña had called his rival by his first name rather than by his surname. They also reported that it was now known that two nights before, in Orcières-Merlette, in the same hotel, Club de Soleil, in which he had slept so contentedly the year before, Ocaña had spent a dreadful night, with a temperature of 40 degrees and acute pains in his shoulder. He also had a leg so painful that Emilio Cruz didn't dare massage him. The cold picked up in the rain on the Aubisque had brought him down with something, and infected his lungs already ill at the start, already weakened from when he was a child and had to overcome tuberculosis. Cruz stayed awake all night at his bedside, treating him with suppositories, with eucalyptus vapour, with the whole arsenal he had at his disposal. The objective was that the following day nobody would realise his poor state of health, but as everyone could see this was not Luis Ocaña, but a chronic invalid, scarcely capable of keeping himself upright on a bike, who was aiming to ride over the Galibier. Sustained by some unknown strength, and an incontrovertible obstinacy, he managed it, to everybody's surprise and admiration.

Cescutti had gone to the Alps to help at the feeding station, and was on the Grand Cucheron when he saw his friend Luis, a ghostly figure, his approach heralded by violent coughing. At the finish in Aix-les-Bains it didn't take much to convince him that there was no sense in continuing, and to abandon. The two drove back to Bretagne-de-Marsan.

'This Tour was so hard only the devil could cope with it,' Ocaña said to him, and fell asleep in the passenger seat.

On the car radio which Cescutti kept low so as not to wake him up he suddenly heard the voice of Merckx, analysing the race and his rivalry. 'It's true that last year Ocaña inflicted on me the hardest defeat of my career at Orcières-Merlette,' said the Belgian calmly. 'But cycling didn't come to an end that day, and today everybody will acknowledge that I've got my revenge. I've ridden four Tours and I've won all four. Ocaña has started in four and only finished in one, and then he was an hour behind me. People speak of good luck and of bad luck, but in four Tours there's time for good and bad luck to even themselves out.'

1973

Before the end of 1972, in the middle of a melancholic autumn, Luis Ocaña called on Cescutti at his house in Mont-de-Marsan.'Speed up the paperwork, Pierrot, I want to be French. My wife is French, my brothers are French, my family speaks French, I live in France...I am the only one who carries on being Spanish, and having to put up with Spain's ingratitude. I am the Champion of Spain, and I ride in the national jersey with the Spanish flag on my vest and yet they call me French, don't they? Right, now I really will be French.'

'Are you sure, Luis? Twenty times you've made me start the process and twenty times you've withdrawn it at the last minute. You know how many papers are already prepared, and I've got them all ready, just waiting for you to tell me to set it in motion. I've already got the Deputy for Les Landes, André Mirtin, to write to the Sports Minister, Joseph Comiti, telling him that you want to become naturalised as quickly as possible, but that you were hesitating because you wanted to be certain that you wouldn't have to do military service in the French army. Immediately – and I've kept all the correspondence in my office – Comiti spoke to the Ministers of Defence and Social Affairs to see what could be done. Their reply was ambiguous, but, I believe, positive. They said, and this is what Diputado Mirtin passed on to me, that the law was limiting and established that all foreign-born naturalised French citizens are obliged to serve the country until they reach the age of 29.'

'But I'm still 27, Pierrot. That's hopeless.'

'Calm down, Luis. I've already told you that their reply opened a window of hope. Look at the text of his letter: "In respect to M. Luis Ocagna it is practically certain that, given the time it will take in handling the request for naturalisation by one party, and given the time between him appearing on the census roll and his name being entered on the list of those due to be called up, will be more than two years. So, even if the request for naturalisation were placed with the

Prefecture of Mont-de-Marsan right now, there would not be sufficient time for him to be called up before he reaches 29".'

'Well, get going then, Pierrot. Don't waste time. You don't know how awful it was in Cataluña this autumn. The things I've had to put up with and to read. The only good thing has been that Doctor Francesc Coll Colomé has come up with a magnificent treatment to cure the pneumonia I had when I finished the Tour. What with the three months of complete rest he ordered, his vaccines and the infusions from the herbs of my friend Maurice Mességué, which Josiane prepares for me every night. I can see I'm recovering my stamina and my strength really quickly. This rest is doing me a lot of good, but what I've suffered in Cataluña...On 11 of September I'm going to ride the Masferrer Trophy, which formed the prologue to the Volta and I have a fall. I give myself a really good bashing and I feel empty, wounded, with no strength at all. So I announce that I am not going to ride the Volta, and that the only thing my body is telling me to do is to go back to Bretagne-de-Marsan to rest and recuperate, with my family. Why on earth did it occur to me to read the newspapers the following day? The most gentle I read was this, so just imagine the least pleasant. I read things like: "he's frightened of a tiny little scratch", that "the man from Cuenca has decided to reserve all his troubles for us, Spaniards, so he can devote all his affections to the French", that "his disdain towards Spaniards is glaringly obvious", that "his preference for France is eloquent, let him clear off and become French once and for all..." Things like that, Pierrot. And things that make me feel worse, even things saying I am a failure, that if I fall it's because I'm useless, that it's Merckx who is definitely a super-champion, that in the Tour I fell because I don't know how to descend and I ride a bike that is very light, that I am very fragile, that I'll never cope with three weeks... One actually said that even if I hadn't fallen we would have had to have waited to the end to see if I would have won the Tour of '71 because Merckx was stronger. Can you believe that? And they even blamed me for the pneumonia. They told me that if I hadn't been so cocky all year, ignoring some of the racing, I would have arrived at the Tour in top form. They told me that in any case Merckx already had me beaten, and I got the pneumonia because I was too idle to get out of bed. If on the rest day in Orcières I'd gone training in the morning with everybody else on the Gap World Championship circuit, instead of staying in bed, I wouldn't have had to train in the afternoon and so I wouldn't have got caught in that downpour which drenched me. That's what I had to read, Pierrot. And you, you were there, you know how everything happened; you know that ever since the fall on the Aubisque my whole body felt paralysed. Like in Luchon, after I'd worked my bollocks off descending the Peyresourde with only one leg, they had to give me infrared treatment on the leg that was locked up with cramp, and you saw how stiff my neck was so I couldn't turn my head, nor sleep comfortably. You know what balls it took for me to put up with that, and even though I was stiff and everything, Merckx couldn't stay with me. On the Izoard, before I punctured on the Vars, sick as I was, I took 30 seconds out of him. You know I wanted to carry on, in spite of the Tour doctor, Doctor Miserez, showing me the x-ray plates with my lungs looking like one black stain.

'And what about the article that poet Antoine Blondin wrote – do you agree with that? He said I was more consumptive than the Lady of the Camellias. Spitting out blood from the corners of my mouth, I was nothing more than an invalid...And you know, Pierrot my friend, how difficult it was for you to convince me to abandon. But the worst was still to come. I went back to Cataluña for the Subida a Monjuïc, a couple of weeks later, and I wasn't in a good state when I got there, because the day before I'd had a row in a criterium with that half-blind Mariano Martínez. They call him the Frenchman of Burgos and that's right, because he really did become French, and the race was a disaster, Pierrot. I just wasn't in the right state of mind. I ended up twenty-something, fourth from the end and the public whistled at me and booed me as if I were a bad bullfighter, Pierrot. I've never been insulted like that. Now, with my morale gone and my strength, too, I decided not to ride the time trial, nor watch (which would have made me feel even worse) as everybody cheered Merckx, who won, of course, because everybody just surrendered to him, and to Tarangu, who fought well. While with me they didn't show a shred of pity, Pierrot.'

'You have to understand their disappointment, Luis. After 1971 the whole of Spain was expecting you to win the Tour in 1972; they only had eyes for you, and the blow was terrible; they are still in a state of shock...and it really annoys them in Spain that you didn't ride the Vuelta. And what's more, as you know, there is always this question nowadays about destiny and character – is it a matter of you making yourself what you are, or is it the work of destiny? You are fatalistic because your life has made you that way, in spite of your essential optimism; you believe in destiny, but in this time of economic development and modernism, when it seems the Yanks want to teach us everything, it is the theory of character that has the upper hand. You know what they say – bad luck is just a symptom of weakness. It is so Cavinistic, yet curiously, Spaniards, and you're one of them, seem to believe it, too – "It's simply a matter of will power; just a question of having the balls for it; the hard man doesn't collapse." I'm not surprised you are mixed up, Luis.'

'State of shock – call it what you like, but I am a champion. I am the only one who has dared to challenge Merckx and the only one who has beaten him. And that deserves everlasting respect. They ought never to have lost that respect for me. Bunch of mediocrities. Go on! Get the naturalisation papers ready, Pierrot.'

'Have you read that Merckx has flown to Mexico with Colnago and the Doctor Cavalli, and has beaten Ritter's hour record? This man never stops. Your friend Anquetil wrote about it in a newspaper, because he was sent as a special correspondent. A bit more in the Olympic velodrome, at such a height, and he would have reached 50 for the hour; he made 49.431 kilometres.'

'Yes, sure. I had seen it and it delighted me. I want Merckx to stay strong, to be stronger in 1973 than he's ever been, because that way my victory will be all the greater. It will be worth more when I beat him in the Tour, Pierrot. I told Doctor Coll and I'll tell you, in 1973 I will not be the fragile rider they say I am.'

In November, Ocaña was operated on for haemorrhoids, and after returning to training in December, and despite a minor car accident on

Christmas Eve on the Narbonne road, he began the 1973 season like a new man. Full of optimism and strength, he declared in *L'Équipe*, 'I have recovered my morale. 1972 is dead and buried. Long live 1973!'

As ever, he said it as a Spanish cyclist; he never would get to become French. The papers, rushed through by Cescutti, had met with an unforeseen obstacle in December, when the zealous French bureaucrats discovered a small discrepancy. Acording to his birth certificate, Luis had been born on 9 June 1945, but on his marriage certificate, due no doubt to the recording clerk's error, this was put down as 11 June. So Ocaña had to request a new marriage certificate with the date corrected.

'Are you mad, Luis? Cescutti has told me that he's already well advanced with the paperwork for you to become naturalised. How come you haven't said anything about this to me? This is a disaster.'

'Calm down, Daniel. I thought of telling you once we met to take stock of the season, and right now the papers are stopped because of this little bureaucratic mistake.'

'Well thank goodness for that,' said Daniel Dousset, Ocaña's manager, who'd rushed down from Paris to Bretagne-de-Marsan the moment Cescutti told him that, as from the following year, Luis would be French.

'It's out of the question, Luis. You must realise that it's far better for you to remain Spanish. It would be a disaster for your earnings. Forget about the moral reason; forget about your feelings; think practically.'

'I don't want to carry on being Spanish, and that's all there is to it.'

'Think about it again. Think more carefully. What do you imagine will happen if you become French? Well, the first thing would be that the Spanish races will turn their back on you, the regime would ban you and you'd be in for some hard times. Think about it rationally, work out the costs. Do you know that you earn three times as much from Spanish races as you do from French ones? You'd lose all that. And do you also know that the French organisers pay you more because you're Spanish than they would if you were French, because that gives their race a more international flavour? They want an Italian, a Belgian, a Spaniard…they don't want an all-French race. And finally, do you know that Bic would pay you less if you were French? For them, for Darras and for the Baron your great value is being Spanish, because thanks to you the doors to the Spanish market have been pushed wide open. Biros are selling there like there's no tomorrow.'

In spite of his proverbial pig-headedness, Ocaña had no hesitation in accepting his manager's arguments, and he told Cescutti to stop, once and for all, the naturalisation procedure.'I am condemned to being Spanish, Pierrot.'

In the Paris–Nice he came up against Merckx but there was no battle. Both were surprisingly beaten again by the aging Poulidor, who had the measure of the final mountain time trial and broke Zoetemelk's heart once more. During the race Ocaña's followers were full of admiration for him again, not for what he did on the bike, but for the discussions he had with the race directors. Outside, in the open, and with no protection from the elements, he argued to persuade them to annul one of the stages due to a terrible snow storm and an icy wind. If anyone doubted Ocaña had overcome his pneumonia, he was out to prove them wrong. But even then his irritation with Maurice de Muer persisted.

'You consult a leader and you keep him informed, Maurice. I've had to learn from the newspapers that you've signed Agostinho. He seems to me an excellent signing, and I'm sure I'll not find anybody as good as him to help me beat Merckx. I can still remember how on the Laffrey he initiated the big attack during the Orcières-Merlette stage. But you should have told me, Maurice. I have the right to know,' Ocaña told his Director during their regular team gathering in the Hotel de France in Seillans, where the Portuguese appeared a bit too smug at the prospect of riding in the orange of Bic alongside Ocaña.

'And a director should also be consulted about the decisions that are taken, Luis. Not only the race tactics which you organise by telephone with Cescutti and which Emilio Cruz always applauds you for, but the calendar of races, because I often have to ask Dousset, your manager, what your plans are.'

Two weeks later both de Muer and Ocaña happily embraced each other in Cataluña; the past was forgotten; bygones were bygones. Merckx had been beaten and that was a cause for celebration. The 30 March 1973, an historic date. For the first time in his career Ocaña defeated Merckx in a time trial. It was the mountain time trial to Vallvidrera from Mollins de Rei, the decisive stage of the Setmana Catalana, and in a mere 13 kilometres Ocaña had taken 28 seconds out of the Cannibal.

'And this, Eddy, is just a foretaste of what's waiting for you in the Tour,' Ocaña goaded the Belgian – somewhat too provocatively since it was known that Merckx had fallen ill during the snow-bound Paris–Nice, and then had to withdraw from Milan–San Remo. He was still convalescing when he arrived for what was to be a very hard Setmana Catalana in which his pride tried to carry him where his legs couldn't. In the very first stage, with its extremely tough final stretch up to the Sanctuary of Queralt, overlooking Berga, Merckx had been forced to let the group of favourites go and concede seven seconds to Ocaña. The following day saw another spectacular hilltop finish in Engolasters (Andorra), where the stage winner, the Dutchman Vianen, had to get off his bike and walk the final 500 metres – his gear too high and his strength gone, after a long escape. Here Merckx lost a further ten seconds without Ocaña or anybody else needing to attack him. Thanks to a magnificent echelon in which Merckx took full part on the road to Castelldefels on the penultimate day, Ocaña was able to displace Delisle from the leadership and confirm his victory in the final day's time trial – his first over Merckx.

'Well, no, Luis my friend,' Merckx replied coldly. 'I'm afraid we're not going to meet in the Tour. I've had such an exceptionally good offer from the Vuelta that I can't turn them down. So I'm riding your country's race this year, Luis, and I want to write that in my palmares; Anquetil and Gimondi will not be the only ones to have won Tour, Giro and Vuelta. And of course, I can't not ride the Giro; Molteni is Italian and they'd never let me not sell their sausages in their own country. And also Torriani pays me very well. I shall be the first man ever to win the Vuelta and the Giro in the same year, and obviously

I'm not going to ride all three grand tours in one year. So, there you are, Luis. We'll have to wait till '74 for our return match, unless you think you can do me some damage in the Vuelta. But the person I fear most is Fuente; I think he is more likely to make me suffer in the Giro than anything you can do to me in the Vuelta.'

'You know only too well that I won't, Eddy. You know there's nothing I'll be able to do in the Vuelta. Knowing what I know of the organisers, and how they suck up to foreigners, there's no doubt they will have made a route to suit you, full of bonuses – here, there and everywhere – so you won't have to exert yourself too much to win. It'll be a farce this Vuelta. But you'll see me there, come what may.'

Before going to the Vuelta Ocaña strengthened his morale by beating Linares, in the time trial at Tolosa, and winning a Tour of the Basque Country in the cold and the snow. And two days later, he flew north and immediately back again because, overcome by curiosity, he wanted to find out what Paris–Roubaix was like. He rode it for the first time in his life, and saw Merckx triumph yet again, and his friend Rosiers fight hard with Godefroot for second place. He himself finished a respectable 29th. 'And if it hadn't rained I'd have done better,' he said. He felt there were no limits to his ambitions nor did he have ears for the whistles from the Belgian fans directed towards him in the Roubaix velodrome.

There were only 80 participants in the Vuelta of '73 and scarcely any mountains, and Merckx, as was pointed out at the time, sprinted for everything, even the intermediate sprints under the publicity banners. It was the Belgian and his massive henchmen from Molteni, ruthlessly imposing their law, who were most conspicuous. Merckx won six stages, including the two short time trials, gorged himself on time bonuses and won overall almost without breaking sweat. Yet the man most admired was Ocaña who, on the climb to Orduña, the great moment of the Vuelta, attacked furiously from low down and for a while managed to get clear of Merckx, who fought to the point of exhaustion so as not to be dropped by Ocaña and Thévenet. On the long descent towards Miranda de Ebro, into a headwind, Ocaña was caught and Merckx won the stage, but in Spain all the talk was about

Ocaña, the protagonist of the one moment of genuine cycling in the entire race.

'I knew I couldn't beat Merckx in this Vuelta,' remarked Ocaña ironically. 'It was the Kas I was riding against – they're so complacent – and against Pesarrodona who was second without deserving to be. In the final general classification, Ocaña, at 3'–46" accompanied Merckx on the podium, with Thévenet at 4'–16".

While Merckx went off to conquer the Giro, subjugating the rebel Fuente, who only hurt him on the Tres Cimas de Lavaredo, Ocaña made ready for the Tour in his usual way, riding the Dauphiné, followed by the Midi Libre.

'Luis, in all my life I haven't seen you so strong,' Thévenet said to him after the Dauphiné, in old Saint Etienne, where the race finished. 'It's a pity that Merckx is not going to the Tour. It would be a magnificent duel and I'm convinced that even if he were taking part, you'd win. You remember how he beat us in the Vuelta; he did it thanks to the bonuses, but it cost him, and on the Orduña stage, with your great attack, Luis, you stripped him bare. And seeing how you are now, Luis, in the Dauphiné, where I haven't been able to stay with you in the mountains, and you beat me in the time trial, I reckon the only place where I could put time into you in the Tour is on the flat. And for me, with my capabilities, that's also out of the question. I'm going to the Tour knowing I can't beat you, Luis, but please, don't take a quarter of an hour out of me, Luis, like Merckx would, please.'

'But have you heard what Merckx has been saying, Bernard? All he talks about is Fuente – just to provoke me. Everywhere he keeps on saying that only Fuente could beat him in the Tour. He doesn't utter a word about me. His winning bet – I've heard him say it – is Fuente, Zoetemelk, Poulidor. He doesn't talk about you either, Bernard.'

Ocaña won the Dauphiné for the third time, but it was Thévenet who was really spectacular. In the *etapa reina*, between Grenoble and Briançon, via the Croix de Fer, the Télégraphe and the Galibier the Frenchman attacked several times, and only Ocaña was able to hold on to his wheel. They arrived together at the finish, more than nine minutes up on the third man, the Asturian López Carril, who was followed by a string of disheartened, solitary individuals. Thévenet won the stage, but in the final time trial, from Montceau-les-Mines to Le Creusot, Ocaña settled the overall with victory on a new titanium bike. In 31 kilometres he took more than a minute out of Thévenet.

In the middle of June, just as Ocaña, without any particular ambitions, was polishing his form in the Midi Libre, Fuente was dominating the Tour of Switzerland in spectacular fashion. He had ridden virtually without rest since the Giro, and this was his final preparation for the Tour. On one stage, the Grächen–Meiringen, he launched a solo attack and finished five minutes up on the peloton, in the city where meringue was said to have been invented, at the foot of the Reichenbach Falls where Conan Doyle killed off Sherlock Holmes. So it was that el Tarangu, a lover of the literary resonance of a victory which made him favourite for the Tour, bacame the anti-Ocaña of 1973.

Everything was ready in Scheveningen, The Hague's beach, from where the Tour would start. No detail had been left to chance. Nothing had been overlooked. Ocaña was relying on his team, Bic, and also on the two Spanish teams – Kas and La Casera, Bahamontes' team which Miguel Moreno was directing. It was the team of Gómez Lucas, Abilleira, Dámaso and Pedro Torres, Tamames, Jesús Manzaneque, Jesús Esperanza, Félix González, José Luis Viejo and Luis Balagué, an Asturian who was already a friend of Ocaña. The army which knew it would win had already divided the spoils even before the battle had begun. For Ocaña, the overall classification; for Fuente, the mountain prize, for La Casera, some stage or other. That was Spain. This was the Tour, however. And Ocaña and Fuente were not two ordinary men.

At midday on the 1st July, Josiane was ironing at home in Bretagne-de-Marsan. Jean-Louis, who was five years old, was playing with the radio, from which it had just been announced that they were about to go over to Jean-Paul Brouchon, the Tour de France special correspondent, and Sylvia was rummaging about in the clean washing basket. *Sur la Route du Tour* came over the radio and Josiane called for silence, and for nobody to move. And from *la route du Tour*, the guttural baritone of Brouchon, a man as serious in appearance as in his voice, announced what Josiane didn't want to hear. 'The peloton is all together as it reaches kilometre 17 of the first stage, from Scheveningen to Rotterdam, but it's already worth mentioning that at kilometre 10, while the Tour was going through the quiet hamlet of Wassenaar on this pleasant summer's day, a dog invaded the peloton. Only one cyclist had the bad luck to run into it; that was Luis Ocaña, the big favourite for overall victory, who was unable to avoid the animal and was brought down...'

Josiane didn't carry on listening to the radio; her nerves had got the better of her. She ran to the telephone, having taken the intuitive precaution of not leaving the iron on the bed on which the clothes lay but putting it in its support, beyond the reach of the children's hands, and called Cescutti.

'Have you heard the radio? Oh, no! It's beginning all over again. I can't put up with three weeks of this.'

'Yes I have, Josiane. Now take it easy. Brouchon has said that he's spoken with Doctor Miserez, who has examined Luis, and he's said that there's nothing broken; he's just had a heavy blow to his ribs. He stopped for a minute at the side of the road, with Labourdette beside him, then the whole of the Bic team. The peloton waited and now everything is back to normal. Be calm, Josiane.'

'No. I'm not calm, Pierre. I'm not going to be calm in the whole of this Tour if I'm not at Luis's side. Right now I'm going to leave the children with my mother, and I'm going to get in the Honda and I'm not going to stop till I get to Holland and join up with Luis.'

'But, think about it a little, Josiane, they don't allow women into the Tour, except to give out the flowers and the kisses, and certainly not the cyclists' wives. Goddet won't give you accreditation and as soon as De Muer sees you he'll chuck you out of the hotel...'

Neither Cescutti nor practically anybody knows the strength of a determined woman in love, a woman convinced that her man needs her.

Josiane had understood that from 1971, from his fall on the Col de Menté, everything had changed for Luis and, as a consequence, for her, too. Before that date few Spanish journalists used to speak about him, she thought, as she drove her Honda northwards up the Routes Nationals; for Spain he was 'the Frenchman', nothing more than that. And he didn't realise that now he was a legend; he carried on as he always had done, as if all this amounted to nothing.

'I had no idea how you were becoming so famous, Luis,' she confessed to him late that night in the Rotterdam hotel where the Bic team was lodging. Thanks to the silent collusion of Emilio Cruz, she'd been able to get into Luis's room, where he was lying serenely on the bed with a bandage wrapped around part of his chest. Exceptionally, in that Tour each team comprised eleven riders; ten shared rooms; the leader had the priviledge of an individual room. 'You know, Luis, I married the man not the bicycle rider, but I have climbed the same staircase with you. I'm going to be with you through every stage. De Muer can say whatever he likes, I am going to follow you for the whole of the race, Luis. And at night I will prepare Maurice's wild herbal infusions to take care of your lungs. And we will make love whenever you want, too. And afterwards we will spread the map out on the bed and look at what is waiting for you next day: you will see the roads and the cols, the bends and the winds, and you will know what you need to do. And then you will see how nothing bad is going to happen to you, Luis, my Luis. And there will not be a day when it rains, and your lungs will stay strong because there will be a sun which will melt the stones and you will glitter because you are the sun.'

It was their will and determination that made the plan possible, although it was no easy matter. De Muer didn't want to see a woman within a hundred kilometres radius, except for his own wife who had the responsibility for all the logistics of the team, and the Tour organisation refused point blank to give Josiane accreditation. She solved that problem by getting two of the arrows which mark the route and fixing one to the front of her Honda and one to the back. That way she managed to get through all the controls. At night she crept secretly upstairs to Luis's room, from where she emerged almost before daybreak, before the team's doctor arrived to check his weight and blood pressure. Later she would worm her way into the starting area of each stage, between the cars and the hundreds of fans and there she'd slip him his favourite ham and garlic sandwiches. It all went well until a couple of days before the finish when her ruse was discovered. A zealous official at one of the controls didn't swallow the business with the arrows on Josiane's car, and after a brief discussion detained her and called the police. They were all set to imprison her, but when they discovered she was the wife of the man who was about to win the Tour they released her. Years later, Josiane felt possibly she'd never enjoyed herself so much in the whole of her life as during that Tour, and that the pair of them had never been so happy. She also saw herself as something of a pioneer. She was certain that neither before nor since had a woman spent the whole of the those three weeks, sleeping each night with her husband, who, on top of all that, won the Tour.

During that Tour, that Tour of '73 which Luis won, Josiane also became aware of a transformation in him, which she experienced at his side.

'Have you realised that you're wearing the same number as Merckx did in '69 when he won his first Tour, when he demolished everybody?' she said to him as she lay in his arms one night, while her gaze was fixed on the yellow jersey hanging over the chair. The meticulous Ocaña had already pinned the number on the back ready for the following day – number 51. 'I don't know if that's why, but every day I see a bit more of Merckx in you, more unmoved in victory, more the dictator of the Tour...'

'Yes,' he replied. 'I've certainly realised that. And, sure, I have to confess there are days when I feel like Merckx, or at least I believe that's how Merckx would feel, ruling everybody, deciding on the life and death of anybody, and on all their hopes. The other day, on the Les Orres stage, I felt a bit like that. It's curious and difficult to explain. I wanted Fuente, who's gone out of his way to make life impossible for me, to be my Merckx, because you know my frustration when I learned that Merckx wouldn't be coming to the Tour. I don't need to win the Tour; I need to beat Merckx, to crush him. And that's why I wanted to turn Fuente into Merckx. But throughout the Tour I've realised that deep down Fuente is more like me: he's an adventurer like Ocaña, a rebel who'll never submit to anybody's authority. And that's where it gets complicated, because deep down I can see me as I am, as Ocaña, fighting on the cols against me as Tarangu. That's just what it was like the other day on the Galibier. And so, without wanting to, I end up turning into Merckx, just to get out of this tangle. And that day in the Alps, when I destroyed the peloton, I felt just like Merckx must have felt during his stage to Mourenx in the '69 Tour. He was also in yellow; he also had number 51 on his back. It was a quite unnecessary adventure, from a rational, calculated point of view, but absolutely indispensible from the moment when I realised that what I really wanted was to leave my mark on the Tour, on cycling, when I realised that there was no point in winning at any price, that I didn't just want to win. Finally, I was Merckx, Josiane, and if that means that Mercks has ended up beating me, so be it, but I want to win this Tour like Merckx won four years ago, taking six stages, leaving the second man quarter of an hour behind, the fifth at half an hour. And wearing number 51.'

In spite of his fall on the road to Rotterdam, Ocaña didn't change his plans. He had an ambush prepared for the following day between Roubaix and Reims and his team carried it out to perfection. His team mates from the North, Sylvain Vasseur and José Catieau, who trained over those roads, had told him about the narrow lane at Querenaing, a steep *pavé* climb where you had to arrive well placed because the wind changed at the summit, and Ocaña had discovered that during his Paris–Roubaix ride. Bic went to the front and the peloton shattered on the narrow climb. A small escape group arrived at the top: Ocaña, Guimard and four more from Bic, their devoted Catieau, Vasseur, Schleck and Mortensen. The climbers suffered their first bloodletting. Poulidor, Zoetemelk, Van Impe and Thévenet lost two minutes; Tarangu, six.

The Tarangu's lieutenant was José Antonio González Linares, not his regular Nemesio, who'd fallen on the Fito during the Tour of Asturias and was suffering from tendonitis. Dalmacio Langarica was no longer in charge of Kas. Antón Barrutia had taken over from him, and he was having a bad time. All he could do was repeat: 'With

Fuente it's impossible to live a normal life. You just have to let him do whatever he wants.' Linares, a Cantabrian, was very tall and strong, one of those who when they sprint are cabable of breaking the bike's chain. A very fine time trialist over short distances, he even beat Merckx in the time trial at Forest during the 1970 Tour. It was his most precious result: now his principal work was in leading out his Kas team mate, Perurena, in the sprints and protecting the climbers on the flat stages.

'I'm going to break the pact we've made, Linares. I want to win the Tour,' Fuente said to him one night, and Linares couldn't believe it. He thought about the spoils they'd stored up to be shared out at the finish – Fuente's King of the Mountains prize, Carril's stage win, whatever Ocaña had paid them.

'Are you mad, Tarangu? He's already got eight minutes on you, Tarangu. They're going to destroy us. They won't let us win another stage. They're going to bury you.'

'I want to beat Ocaña. Ocaña is Merckx; I am Ocaña. That's the way things are. The Tour always has to be a fight. I was born to fight, to gouge out the bastards' eyes, not to make pacts with them. And anyway, I've told Pedro Torres that I've got no interest in the mountains jersey and he can have it if he wants it.'

'You mean you've offered the jersey to Torres, Bahamontes' bloodsucker? Tarangu, I can't believe it. I see you now fighting to the end to get it back, and you won't be able to because on the fourth category climbs Torres will sit on your wheel. He'll mess things up for you!'

Linares couldn't convince Fuentes; nobody could have done. For the French press, looking on from afar, curious at what was happening, the duel was a purely Spanish affair, as Spanish as honour, as jealousy and as the Civil War. Tarangu, utterly resolute, faced up to Ocaña and the two of them embarked on an Homeric battle on the Télégraphe, and then on the Galibier and the Izoard, up to Orres, 237.5 kilometres and all the Alpine greats for just the two of them. On the Télégraphe, 170 kilometres from the finish, when Ocaña, Fuente, Thévenet, Mariano Mártinez and Michel Perrin were the sole remnants of the front group, the Tarangu attacked fiercely. Ocaña got back up to him; the rest were dropped and organised themselves as best they could, like shipwreck survivors tossed into the sea on a plank of wood.

'Where are you going, Tarangu? Don't attack, come with me, let's work together, take turns on the front, follow me and I'll make sure you're second in Paris.'

Fuente didn't respond. He attacked again. On the big ring, the veins standing out in his calf muscles. Twenty times Fuente attacked; twenty times Ocaña answered. He answered calmly till Fuente had nothing left. Then Ocaña felt like Merckx.

'Follow me, if you can.'

Fuente grabbed his wheel like someone holding on to the tail of a bull and let himself be carried, and in that way they climbed the Galibier from Plan Lachat, 135 kilometres from the finish. And after that they climbed the Izoard and crossed the Casse Déserte, where they felt not on the moon – that is the Ventoux – but on Mars, and always with Ocaña leading, his sight fixed only on the horizon. He never looked back; for him Fuente didn't exist. He only saw him at the summit of the Izoard when he sprinted to take the mountain points. The Tarangu held on until he punctured. Just 30 kilometres from the finish at Les Orres he stopped, while Ocaña, who was Merckx in search of immortality, carried on. But a Merckx in whose past there was his father sawing logs and destroying his hands, his uncles fighting in the war, and Cescutti entering Berlin, and the reversals on the Menté, the Aubisque, the Ballon d'Alsace, and the going hungry and the misery, a Merckx made of flesh and blood, of victories and defeats, of pain – and not just of glory. He carried on as before, as if he had always been climbing alone.

At Les Orres Fuente arrived 57 seconds down. Mártinez, whom Thévenet accused of wheel-sucking, was third, at 6'–57". Sixth on the stage was Zoetemelk at 20'–24". The last man, Tabak, came in at 59'–22", outside the time control, but was reinstated because the penultimate finisher, Pustjens, had arrived at 58'–36". Twelves riders were expelled for holding on to their team cars. A report from the front line that Merckx would have been proud of.

'It's incredible. It's incredible,' said Ocaña at the finish. 'I've never suffered so much. Fuente climbs better than anybody, but on the Télégraphe I outfought him. I've done 150 kilometres solo, with a parasite on my wheel, into the wind, through all those mountains – that is hard! Let me go; I'm tired.'

'You have reminded us of Coppi, Koblet, Merckx.' The journalists were ecstatic.

'I am Luis Ocaña.'

'It was a massacre, a collective annihilation,' Pierre Chany, L'Équipe's reporter told him.

And through the loudspeakers at the finish could be heard Radio Europe 1 and the voice of its great commentator, Anquetil, his friend Jacques. 'It has been one of the great exploits in the history of cycling,' an irrepressible Anquetil was saying. 'It has been even greater than that on Orcières-Merlette. And yes, today, as well, Luis Ocaña would have beaten Merckx.'

Ocaña went straight to the hotel, got into bed, still in his sweat stained jersey and shorts, without changing, without showering, without removing his race number, without eating. At one in the morning he woke up and asked for some cherries.

Fuente and Ocaña didn't face each other again in the Tour.

Ocaña recovered quickly from that huge stage. His ability to do so impressed the doctors. On the Puy de Dôme a few days later they were able to test that. Crossing the finishing line, victorious, after having jumped away at exactly the same place where he had dropped Merckx two years before, Ocaña's head sank down over the handlebars of his titanium bike. He seemed about to faint, and was quickly taken into an ambulance where the Tour doctor, Dr. Miserez, examined him. At that moment his heart rate was 160 beats per minute; three minutes later it was down to 70.

In the Pyrenees Poulidor fell on the Portet d'Aspet and his friend, Tour director Jacques Goddet, stopped his car, and went over to the cliff edge from where the old warrior from Limousin emerged. He shook his hand: 'Ah, it is you, Monsieur Goddet,' and rejoined the race. In the Pyrenees, too, an exhausted Fuente tried to hang on to his second place overall by sticking to the wheel of his main threat, Thévenet, just as he would on the Puy de Dôme, but eventually he lost it in the final time trial.

Neither Jean-Luis nor Sylvie were there in La Cipale velodrome when their father went up to receive the trophy he'd won in the way that Merckx had won. He had taken six stages: Gaillard (stage 7, where he took the yellow jersey), Les Orres (stage 8), Thuir (stage 12, time trial), Luchon (stage 13, over the Menté and the Portillon, his cols), Puy de Dôme (stage 18) and Versailles (stage 20, time trial). This final stage win he owed to his old friend Stablinski who, sympathising with him for the saddle boil he was suffering from, lent him a pair of soft, well padded shorts. Second overall was Thévenet, at 15'–51", just as he had feared after the Dauphiné. Fifth overall was Van Impe, at 30'–20".

'Don't bring the children to Paris, Josiane. I hate that spectacle of them going up on the podium.'

'Don't worry, Luis. I don't like it either. They'll be happy at home, watching it on the tele.'

The following day his friend, Jean Cormier, interviewed him for *Le Parisien Libéré*. He showed him the monday newspapers. Dominating the front page of *L'Équipe*, in capital letters was the exclamation: 'and now Ocaña-Merckx!' Somewhat disingenuously he asked him:

'Were you happy with Merckx's absence from the Tour?'

'You are insulting me, Jean!' replied a very irritated Ocaña. 'I don't like being asked about Merckx. I am fed up being asked about Merckx. If he didn't come to the Tour, he has his own reasons. Go and ask him about it. Even when he's not here all you do is ask me about him. Alright then, since you ask about it I will answer you, sincerely: I regretted and I regret that Merckx didn't come to this Tour. I prayed that he would come, I swear to you. We would have picked up again the conversation that was interrupted on the Menté, but don't ask me to tell you that I would have beaten him. You can't beat somebody who isn't there!'

Merckx was present one month later at the World Championship which took place over the Monjuïc circuit in Barcelona. After the Tour, Ocaña had to have an operation on the cyst that was troubling him, and that kept him off the bike for two weeks. The rest of August he was riding criteriums, so he wasn't in the most animated of spirits when he arrived in Barcelona three days before the Worlds. Nonetheless the entire Spanish strategy hinged on him, just as he had demanded. He had even vetoed Fuente's inclusion in the team so that it would be absolutely clear who the leader was. In the race he showed off both the magnificent form he was in, in spite of everything, and his lack of tactical experience in one-day races, which he had never liked, and together with Gimondi, Maertens and Merckx he made up the quartet that vied for victory to the strains of Manolo Escobar and his *Viva España!* Ocaña knew nothing of the tactical subtleties of a classic nor the internal strife in the Belgian squad – the emergence of the young Maertens, the pride of the established Merckx. At one particular moment of the race Merckx attacked and Ocaña had no trouble going with him, but didn't take a turn on the front. 'If I go with him, the only thing I can get is second, what I hate most,' he thought. 'With four of us in the mix, Gimondi and I might be able to isolate Merckx and that will give me a better chance.' At the end he was taken by surprise. He saw Maertens launch into the sprint from far out – 350 metres on a steep slope. It was treachery, but Ocaña, ingenuously, thought he was preparing the sprint for Merckx and stuck to the Cannibal's wheel. Gimondi, however, jumped on to the impatient younger man's wheel. Only when it was too late, only when he saw that Merckx was not going to make a move, did Ocaña understand the true essence of the finish. His late effort gave him the bronze, while Gimondi overtook Maertens in a classy move and went away from Montjuïc with the rainbow jersey.

Some days later Ocaña had his last win of the year, in a time trial on that same Montjuïc circuit in the Volta a Catalunya, which he had lost to Perurena on the Andorra stage. And he ended the season, by then exhausted and without any competitive drive, losing to Merckx in the Grand Prix des Nations.

He'd begun the year feeling he was Spanish only because he was forced to be; he ended it proud to be Spanish. The Tour victory, Spanish cycling's second, after that of Federico Bahamontes in 1959, had made him an indisputable hero. No longer would they call him 'the Frenchman', he thought; now he would always be 'the Spaniard of Mont-de-Marsan'. He had now achieved everything he'd dreamed of.

1974

Maurice de Muer was an optimist who didn't really know Luis Ocaña, and never would get to know him.

'Look, Luis,' his director said to him at the first team get-together of the year in the usual Hotel de France in Seillans, where even in January the Côte d'Azur is beginning to smell of Spring. 'You are 28 years old. Do you know how old Louison Bobet was when he won his first Tour, after five failed attempts including two abandons? He was 28, Luis. And then, as you know, he won another two Tours and a World Championship and many other races. The first Tour unblocked him. Why isn't the same thing going to happen with you? That victory in '73 is going to get rid of all your doubts; I am certain of it.'

'I've got four years left in my sporting career, Maurice. That's what I've calculated I need to pay off the investment I made in the estate I bought for producing armagnac. I want to earn as much as possible. This year I want to ride the three Grand Tours, Maurice. I want to overcome the biggest challenge of my career – what nobody has done before. I want to ride the Vuelta, the Giro and the Tour, Maurice. I want to concentrate my whole season into three months: May, June and July.'

'Nobody has managed that before, at the top level, Luis. I think it is a challenge too far.'

'I think the opposite. Haven't you realised that I do better if I don't have any rests between the races? I believe the best thing would be for me to begin carefully: I don't do Paris–Nice nor any of the Classics and I start in the Setmana Catalana.'

What Ocaña hadn't told De Muer was that he had spent the winter working on his lands and the renovation of the C18th mansion, practically a château, which he had bought and that in his head he could only picture vineyards and distilleries, not cycle races. Nor did he tell him that he had barely touched a bicycle, that the post-Tour depression had left him with an emptiness that he only felt able to fill with fine-sounding words and declarations of grandiose aspirations.

He arrived poorly prepared for the Setmana Catalana, where the bad weather brought about the onset of bronchitis, and only from afar could he watch the fight for victory between Zoetemelk, Merckx and his friend Agostinho. He followed that with the Tour of the Basque Country where he didn't feel much better, although he did finish third behind Lasa and Manzaneque. But there was no going back. The commitment had been made public. Christian Darras, the spokesman for Bic, had announced to the press on 8 April: 'As was planned, and according to his wishes, Luis Ocaña will take part in all three of the grand tours. But he has confirmed with the team that he will ride the Vuelta a España and the Giro d'Italia with a certain degree of tactical prudence so as to arrive in the best possible form at the Tour de France, which continues to be our number one objective, and his too.'

Ocaña was ill and in poor condition in Almería where the Vuelta was starting and where winter seemed to have taken root. It was cold and wet and every day got worse, as did his difficulties in breathing and with his lungs. Lasa was the favourite, as he was every year. The team owners looked more kindly on him than they did on Fuente, whose team mates, with the exception of Perurena, still hadn't forgiven him for his rebellion which had lost them their pay out in the Tour. And it was Perurena, leader again, as he had been two years earlier, who encouraged el Tarangu to attack in Los Ángeles de San Rafael on the first day in the mountains. In sub-zero temperatures the Asturian attacked on the Alto de los Leones and only Ocaña tried, unsuccessfully, to go with him, and he reached the finish with a lead of more than half a minute. That advantage, coupled with what he achieved the following day, over an uphill five-kilometre time trial, run off in an intense snow storm, on the same Ángeles de San Rafael course which Jesús Gil had just constructed and endlessly publicised, enabled Fuente to become race leader. On the following day, finishing in Ávila, in an atmosphere reminiscent of the Belgian Classics, with flurries of snow and a torrential downpour, Fuente was pleased to have another friend in his team, the hardman from Cantabria, Juan Manuel Santisteban. In temperatures that never went above freezing he was happy to pedal in a short-sleeved jersey. To protect himself from the cold the diminutive Fuente sheltered behind the broad back of Santisteban, who from time to time would turn round and say to him, 'Little Tarangu I would happily tuck you in one of my pockets so that you'd not be so cold'. Fuente told this anecdote years later in his autobiography *Cycles of Pain*, in homage to Santisteban, who was killed in a fall in the 1976 Giro.

And it was as leader, 24 seconds up on his team mate Lasa, that Fuente came into Oviedo, on the stage that ended on the Alto del Naranco, on *his* Alto del Naranco. Amidst all the delirium of the fans Fuente reached the finish alone, almost a minute ahead Lasa and with time to remove his right foot from its toe-clip and to cross the line that way to honour the doctor who, during the winter, had successfully operated on some invidious varicose veins which reduced the strength of his pedalling.This was the end of a stage which signalled the final break with Lasa. On the climb of the Pajares the Basque rider had infiltrated an escape group which had built up a significant lead, but it also contained Agostinho, the rival Kas most feared. Eusebio Vélez, who was directing Kas in this Vuelta, therefore opted for prudence and ordered Lasa not to collaborate. The break failed, the Agostinho danger was neutralised and Fuente rode triumphantly into his home town. Ocaña, who lost more than a minute, climbed the last kilometres of the Naranco amid a chorus of whistles, insults, jeering from the Asturian spectators. They hadn't forgiven him for the previous Tour, and above all they hadn't forgiven him for his veto that prevented Fuente riding in the Spanish team at the World Championships. 'French dog,' they shouted at him. It was complete, sad, bitter vengeance. It was Spain.

'You don't know how much I admire you, Luis,' his friend Perurena said to him the following day, after Fuente, at the start of the stage, had apologised to him for the behaviour of the Asturians and asked them for a show of applause in his honour.

'To me, you've never seemed more like a champion than you did yesterday, Luis. Neither in the Tour nor anywhere else. I saw how you were suffering and you don't know how those insults hurt me. And you'd had to fight alone and sick for 100 kilometres. I think so much of you, Luis, but why on earth don't you retire? Your bronchitis is getting worse every day; your coughing can be heard everywhere. You're putting the rest of your season at risk. Have you forgotten about the Tour? Have you forgotten about Merckx?' Perurena pleaded.

'I can't, Peru. Not even if I wanted to retire. There's something stronger than me that makes me carry on. I've got to get my revenge on el Tarangu. And, you know, I also need the money, Peru. I've got to finish so they'll pay me my fee.'

Ocaña never did get his revenge and, paradoxically, his attacks served to ennoble, almost aggrandise the stature of the Tarangu. The following day, for example, when Ocaña attacked on the Fito on the road to Cangas de Onís, all the time in Asturias, Fuente had a mechanical problem: his chain jumped, which immediately dropped him to the tail of the peloton. In a surge of anger he climbed through the field to get back to Ocaña before the summit. On another day, on the Urkiola, Ocaña did manage to get away from Fuente, but the next day, before the Vuelta's last summit finish on the Arrate, Ocaña and Fuente were marking each other so closely on the descent of the penultimate climb that their handlebars hooked up and they both fell. Ocaña was up quickly without injury; Fuente, however, took longer and when he started pedalling again the whole of his face was a bloodstained mess. He was such a moving and heroic sight that the Basque fans, who had prepared a less than friendly reception for him, believing that he had betrayed their idol, Lasa, could only cheer him emotionally. In the end he only lost ten seconds to Ocaña and six to Agostinho, with whom he had to fight for the overall victory in the 36-kilometre time trial at Anoeta.

Fuente, who began with a 2'–35" advantage, finally won his second Vuelta by a bare 11 seconds from the Portuguese. Agostinho's happiness at the news coming from his Portugal about the triumphant carnation revolution[1] was marred by this defeat which he never would accept. To the end of his days he insisted that somebody had fiddled with the clock so that Fuente won and he was robbed. Never again would Agostinho come closer to winning a grand tour.

---

1. Coinciding with the third stage of the Vuelta on 25 April, the song *Grândola Vila Morena* had been broadcast on Portuguese radio to give the signal for the start of the revolution.

The bitterness of Ocaña, who finished fourth overall, was no less than that of his Portuguese friend and companion in the Bic team. He reached the finish of the Vuelta in such a state that it was absolutely impossible that he could line up for the start of the Giro which began just four days later, on 16 May, at the Vatican after a blessing by Pope Paul VI, which made Fuente happy. In that Giro, Merckx's fifth victory, the Tarangu won no less than five stages, wore the pink jersey for a dozen days and ended fifth overall, only three minutes behind the Cannibal. And while the Asturian was rejoicing, Ocaña was trying to recover. He visited Doctor Colomer again who, just as he had done two years earlier, recommended some weeks of rest. This time Ocaña was too impatient to follow his advice. He was in too much of a hurry to prepare himself properly for the Tour. He reappeared, prematurely, in the Midi Libre, where his knees tortured him and the continuing bad weather damaged his lungs. In an unusually rare May snowstorm on the penultimate stage, he retired without reaching Millau.

Then he competed in the Dauphiné Libéré, which had almost always been an inspiration to him. So it proved this time, too. He was not the Ocaña of his great years when he fought with the best in his old, familiar Granier region and on the Luitel, but at least he was not the Ocaña of recent months, who suffered just to keep up. He ended sixth overall, and felt satisfied with his progress.

'I've suffered a lot to get to this condition before the Tour,' he said in *L'Équipe* two weeks before the start of the *grande boucle*. 'But I've improved more than I expected to, and I reckon I'm now at 70 per cent of my best form. I'm not anticipating that I'll perform miracles, obviously, but the essential thing for me is that I have a reasonable hope of getting to the Tour capable of competing with Merckx.'

On 18 June he turned up at the Tour of l'Aude to put the finishing touches to his form. Ahead of him at the feeding station Gan's Breton rider, Jean-Paul Richard, was fiddling about with his *musette* and unexpectedly fell. Riding behind him, Ocaña couldn't avoid him and came down himself. When he picked himself up he couldn't bend his arm and his elbow was bleeding. He had a fracture which would require at least a fortnight on antibiotics. He could start the Tour but he'd be so weak he'd have to retire within a few days. The sacrifice didn't make sense. To ride the Tour was out of the question.

To the perennial question which the press again asked about Ocaña's wretched luck – was it his luck or his own character – Bic answered unequivocally: it was his character. 'We have to make it clear,' Darras declared. 'We are very sorry for Luis, but in the end he is simply paying for the disorganised and unprofessional manner in which he has conducted himself throughout this season.' There was no more elegant way of Bic saying that it saw no future for Luis Ocaña with them. However, for now, they continued to recognise his immense publicity value, and the directors of the team (communications with De Muer having totally broken down) were going to demand he competed in as many races as possible if he wanted to earn his agreed salary.

Demoralised and ill, from one disaster after another, Ocaña ended the season almost mocked in some races, like in the GP des Nations where he finished in a despicable eighth place. One journalist wrote an article entitled 'The forced labours of Luis Ocaña' with the tone of an epitaph.

As for Bic, they neither renewed his contract not did Baron Bich see any point in continuing to support a cycling team. Bic disappeared with the departure of Ocaña, who would never again peer into Merckx's eyes and see that look of fear and defeat.

Part Three

1

23rd of April 1987. Benidorm. The humidity in the room is unbearable and, as soon as he gets to the hotel, Luis Ocaña strips off his sweat-soaked clothes and takes a cold shower. He comes out of the bathroom in his underpants and when he faces the full-length mirror on the wardrobe he breaks into tears. He was passing the mirror without looking, but out of the corner of his eye he saw a strange silhouette that he did not recognise – his own body. His breasts fallen, small folds of fat around his stomach, a yellowish colour, skin hanging from his arms, legs with no muscular definition, the legs of an old man. Not a single inch of his body carried a reminder of his once extraordinary physical vigour, his muscles as hard as stone, his magnificent shape, or of the determination which led him to ride beyond himself, to pedal to the point of exhaustion and to fall half-dead at the roadside, completely spent.

Sunk in his own darkness, Luis did not hear the door open. In cyclists' hotels there is no privacy possible. Everybody leaves the key in the door outside, everybody has the right to enter without calling. The person who had entered was the doctor, Pedro Celaya.

'I was looking at myself in the mirror,' he told him, 'and I didn't recognise myself. Is this me? Is this what I've become?' And in his underpants he sobbed. 'I'm 40 years old with the body of an old man.'

'Have you had your injection, today, Luis?' Celaya asked, before going silently out of the room and closing the door carefully so as not to make a noise.

Luis was alone again, still in his underpants. From the fridge in the room he removed a small ice-filled container in which there were vials of interferon. From his bag he then took out a small packet in which, carefully wrapped in cellophane, were a number of disposable plastic syringes of insulin. He measured with one of them his daily dose of the medicine and injected it into a fold in his belly. Some years before a blood test had shown up the hepatitis C virus, just as with a number of cyclists from that era, caused by sharing syringes which they used for injecting even the most innocent substances, vitamins or calcium. In Toulouse a Spanish doctor, Dr Luis Navarro, took charge of treating him. Synthetic interferon had just appeared on the market and was considered the best medication for keeping the virus, which couldn't be eliminated, under control and for providing the best protection of the liver.

'The main problem with interferon is its occasional secondary effect – a deep depression which can sometimes be associated with its use,' the doctor warned Luis and Josiane, who went with him for the consultation from time to time. And so, whenever Josiane saw him low, or sad, or feeling hopeless she would say to him, 'Don't worry, my love, it's only the interferon.' And Luis would not reply; he knew it wasn't that; it was something else.

The hotel was a tall, dark tower block in a narrow street. At the back, if you stood on tiptoe on the gloomy balcony you could see the calm sea. Luis sat down on the bed and the tears flowed – tears not of melancholy, but of depression and angry rage against the inevitable. These were tears of loneliness. Only after he'd developed a kind of fatalism was he able to understand all the misfortunes that assailed him. He refused to accept defeat, to give in to destiny; he used to smile and crack jokes like a blind optimist, but every day obstinate destiny reminded him that he was condemned to unhappiness. And he was sure it wasn't the interferon that had taught him that.

Little by little the half light, which was only altered by a dreadful light bulb on the balcony that it was impossible to switch off, blurred the outlines of the furniture in the room, and darkened the light as he, too, felt darkened inside.

Luis, now stretched out on the bed, insensitive to the rough, synthetic bedspread which covered it, was depressed even further by remembering his work that day. It was day one of the Vuelta; he was head of a new team. ADR-Fangio was a minor Belgian team of old sprinters with neither hope nor future, and novices with neither a past nor a future, which had been brought together by Wilfried Reybroeck, the brother of the magnificent Guido. These were men of the kermesses linked to Fons de Wolf who, in his first year as a professional, won five stages of the Vuelta, the Tour of Lombardy and Milan–San Remo, but whose promise was never fulfilled.

That was the measure of how far he'd fallen, Ocaña thought, Director to riders like that creep Luc Wallays. It had just been his misfortune to follow him in the prologue through the streets of Benidorm. Ocaña, at the wheel of the car, depressed and in silence, and alongside him Santi Durán, a journalist from *El Mundo Deportivo*, who reflected in his report (written in a distinctly comic-burlesque tone to avoid Ocaña's truculence) the few words spoken by the furious Director to his protégé. '*Allez! Mon Dieu! Tu arriveras hors delai! Aaaaahhh! Merde!*' he screams at him two kilometres from the end of the six-kilometre prologue when he sees the Belgian's total indifference at being overtaken by the Kas Swiss rider Alfred Ackermann, who'd started one minute behind. 'Have you seen how he's riding?' he shouts at the journalist. 'He's fallen asleep on the handlebars. I don't believe it…'

With that bitter memory in his mouth he fell asleep, only to be woken up some hours later by the aggressive, grating ring of the telephone. It was one of the mechanics. 'Luis,' he said, 'aren't you coming down for dinner?'

The days of the Vuelta were made bearable by the nights. That night he would again spend with his friend Julito – Julio Jiménez – who was there commentating on the race for the TV channel Cadena SER, together with Ramón Gabilondo. With Julito there was no need to speak, just dress up smartly and out you go. Off together to a disco to watch the girls dancing, smile naughtily, and anxiously because Josiane might appear at any moment, and then have some fun. Julito was a genius with a special talent for captivating young girls and Luis, in spite of everything, in spite of his pain at looking at himself naked, had kept himself in shape, slim to all appearances. How lucky that rogue is, Luis sometimes thought, and told him so: 'You're single and you're free, you don't have to be watching out for your wife or anybody, or be held accountable.'

'Ah,' Julito always replied with his dancing eyes, 'but don't forget that I have my mother, there in Ávila, always asking me when I am thinking of settling down and getting married.' But before setting out to conquer Benidorm with Julito he went down to dinner.

Luis usually liked to eat early, in the French manner, but being Director he had to stick to the time agreed for the whole team. That night in Benidorm, however, he was late going down to the dismal dining room, by which time his boys and the mechanics were already having coffee. He disliked the smell of the room, the buffet surrounded by dozens of hungry tourists, the noise. Turning his back on his team's table he glanced around the room and saw in one corner Celaya, alone at a table, enthusiastically digging into a salad. He sat beside him.

Ocaña had met Celaya during the Vuelta of '84, during his stormy period as Director of the Teka team. He was a Basque and as a young man he'd learned his job helping Fernando Astorqui, who was then the Vuelta's doctor. Some weeks after that, when Augustín Mondragón put Ocaña in charge of the resurrection of Fagor, Luis offered Celaya the job of doctor to the new team. Celaya accepted. Ocaña lasted one season in the post, but the doctor continued in Mondragón's outfit. Whenever they saw each other, less often now, they greeted each other and chatted. Luis found in Celaya's ironic, but kindly expression, in his way of listening and asking questions, an invitation to unburden himself.

Luis had few friends and Celaya was one of the few in the cycling world he rather liked and with whom he had a certain rapport. Nobody could put up with Luis and he couldn't open up to anybody, truly open up. Luis was prepared to invest a certain amount of confidence in those people he trusted, but he demanded too much from them in return. He insisted that he was always right, didn't understand that he wasn't always right, and didn't understand that he wasn't understood. He'd been like that as a cyclist and he continued to be like that as a Sporting Director. Some of those around him thought that the pain he felt, his pride, was just petulance. But nobody really knew him; he was a stranger to everybody.

They ate in silence. Afterwards when they had their coffee they began to talk.

'I don't understand cyclists nowadays,' Luis remarked. 'They seem to be afraid of me, but they don't do as I tell them. They behave like children who don't dare to say no to your face, but behind your back they do what they want. I don't understand why a professional, with a good bicycle, with good equipment, well fed, remains in the peloton on any hill, arrives outside the time control and doesn't always give his best. Do you remember De Wolf, that tall, strong Belgian we had at Fagor, with the best looking body I've ever seen on a cyclist? Well now I've got to put up with him here. Back then, at least he made an effort one day and we won a stage, but here... He's 30 years old and I don't know what he wants out of life... Belgians, French, Spaniards, Italians... they're all the same. If I could choose I'd go for the Colombians. They at least address me politely. "Good morning, Sir," they say to me every day and they respect me, not like this lot. I'm sure they laugh behind my back.'

'Eddy told you all that. Don't you remember?' Celya dared to advise him, while he stirred his spoon round in the bottom of his empty coffee cup, making transient little pictures in the dark dregs. 'The job of director doesn't fit with the temperament of a champion... You were like him, like the Cannibal; that's what you were like, and that's how I remember you from the first day I saw you and fell in love with your appearance, with your insatiable look in a race, with your style...You remember that day, the time trial day in the Tour of the Basque Country, so long ago... I had come up to see Anquetil, that phenomenon, and I discovered you, with that hunchback of yours cutting through the wind like the keel of a boat. And Eddy himself, Luis, the pair of you, you're the same breed; you couldn't fool yourselves. That's how I see the two of you. You're both the sort who thinks that a cyclist is not a true cyclist until he has plunged into the madness and has made that his method. And that, as that hopeless Austrian writer, Thomas Bernhard, remarked, is something that can't be taught; it's just something you've got, that madness, that lack of restraint, that lack of calculation. We are born with fear and caution. That's what our survival depends upon, at least for the majority of us. And the majority of cyclists, too, like the kids you direct, those who turn you to the point of despair. You want them to be like you, over the top and unpredictable. You demand they all have the same fighting spirit as you, and that is impossible. It's equally impossible you carrying on being a director: you'll never be any good at it because you'll never be normal. You'll never be able to teach anybody to be mean, small-minded, crooked…Look at today's bunch of directors, Luis. Look at what they teach them in Spain: they teach them to be shrewd, to act smart all the time, never to go crazy. When they're in an escape, they say to their riders: "Go to the front so it seems you're doing some work, but keep the changes moving; never be the fool who pulls harder than any of the others, but never be the smart arse who shirks his turn." And what do they learn from that? To learn to try and fool the rest, to be the smart arse.'

'Then I was the fool, and I want my riders to be the fools. I don't understand why somebody in an escape group doesn't pedal harder than anybody else. That's what they told me to do and that's what I did, and so that's what I want everybody to do. If not, cycling isn't worth the bother. And don't call me daft, Celaya, don't call me daft. I don't believe in that madness. When I did what I did, when I attacked to get rid of all the conformists, all those who only knew how to sit on someone else's wheel, all those who didn't dare take off by themselves away from the safety of the peloton all around them, I didn't do it because of a streak of madness. I did it because of a desire, because of an obligation. I needed to give it everything, to get to the finish with nothing left, to go where nobody else dared go. That's not madness, that's cycling. And I did my calculations, too, and I still do. I rode for money; I always did, not for romanticism. Cycling is that, too. The wheels don't go round if they're not oiled with banknotes. I haven't just fallen off the Christmas tree. But it is possible to be sincere and honest as well. I discovered that in the first Vuelta I rode.

'I'll tell you a story: I was riding for Fagor, in the first Fagor team, that of Perico Matxain, and one night, after dinner, when only the cyclists were around, they said to me, "We know that you've got aspirations; you're young and you're talented and you dream about winning the Vuelta, but Kas have offered us a lot of money to lend them a hand. So now you know: if you want us to carry on supporting you, you'll have to offer us more than them." And do you know what I did, Celaya? I told them to go and fuck themselves. Then I went off to talk to Pingeon, the Peugeot rider, and then on the day of the *etapa reina*, I destroyed the Vuelta, by myself and with Pingeon on my wheel. I destroyed Kas and Fagor and I showed them what it was to be a cyclist. I did that for pride, of course, but also for money. Call it character. Call it style. Things have to be done with style.'

'And that's not madness?'

'No, that's Luis Ocaña. That's being a man. And I'll tell you another thing, Celaya.' Luis now didn't need to raise his voice; he could talk in a whisper because all of a sudden he realised that the dining room had become practically empty as the hordes of strident, thick-skinned foreigners had marched out en masse just as they had entered. 'I had to hang up the bike in France, when I would have preferred to have done so in Spain, but in Spain they insulted me. The 2 October, 1977, an Autumn Sunday in Cannes I rode for the last time with a race number on my back. It was the Grand Prix des Nations, the first that Hinault won, the beginning of a new era in cycling when we earlier champions had been overtaken. Merckx only managed a few more months, till March of '78, before finding out that his body was no longer up to it. In that Grand Prix des Nations I did reasonably well, finishing tenth, and at least I took four minutes out of Poulidor, the old man who was giving me ten years and who also retired that day. But I would have liked to have made my farewell to all that at the Montjuïc hill climb. I said that to Sabater, the organiser, hoping he'd know how to reward me for the gesture, but what he did was to insult me. He offered me 75,000 pesetas, half what he was giving to others, as if I, Luis Ocaña were a Mister Nobody. I told him he could stick it up his arse. I went back to my estate in France and there it all ended.'

2

In the Autumn of 1977 Luis's strong, heavy boots sunk into the mud, leaving their lines of footprints between the rows of vines he ran his eye over. He was both proud and worried at the same time. A forgotten cloud seemed to have remained caught up in the bare branches of a slender poplar tree next to the road, and the wind blew out of a deep blue sky. The summer had been foul: rain, hail, floods, storms. The first harvest of his 30 hectares of *ugni blanc* and of aromatic *colombard* and *folle-blanche* had been a disaster. While he was riding in his last Tour, Luis, finally the landowner, dreamer, agriculturist, called Josiane every evening at the house in Bretagne-de-Marsan. He didn't ask much about the children, no more than was necessary. Nine-year-old Jean-Louis was already showing the signs of rebellion which he'd inherited from his father. In fact, one day when Luis took him to a criterium and the journalists asked him who his favourite cyclist was he told them it was Eddy Merckx, because he always won whereas his father only ever fell off. His father was on the point of giving him a slap there and then, but what he didn't understand was that in schools everywhere he, Luis Ocaña, was a nobody; in France it was all Poulidor and in the rest of the world it was all Merckx, and his son was a son of the world. As for seven-year-old Sylvie, she was the apple of her mother's eye. Luis's real reason for ringing was concern for his vineyards, his 60 hectares, 30 for vines and 30 of woodland, on his land in Caupenne d'Armagnac where, after winning the Tour, he'd invested all his savings from cycling. It was next to the Nagaro circuit, not far from Bretagne, and he would turn the grapes into white wine and then distil it to make armagnac, a liquor which would age carefully. It was the product of his own hands and sweat and tireless work, and that would be his life from then onwards. The fields, his fields. That's what it would be. He would work the land like his father had, but it would be his land, his own land, not working someone else's land.

Before buying the land which he'd suddenly set his heart on, way out in the country   and far from any village, with just two old, half ruined houses on it, Cescutti had advised Luis to build a hotel, a modern, 100-room hotel right in the middle of Mont-de-Marsan, next to the tranquil Midouze, the river which irrigated Les Landes. He bought the plot and put the plans in the hands of an architect. He even named it – Les Trois Rivières – and the cook would be his brother, Marino, who had been taking courses given by the chef Darroze in a nearby town, and the manageress would be his sister Amparo. Then, in the end he scrapped the idea. A hotel is a business, and if you want it to operate well, you've got to be there and not leave it in the hands of managers; you've got to be there in person, he decided. He was also thinking that his cycling career still ought to be a long one. He was 28 and had just won the Tour. The best years were only beginning. For that reason, and also because he was a son of the soil – he loved the land and he loved watching trees and plants grow and to see time passing – he stopped and finally decided to buy land. Initially just 14 hectares with a vineyard, but that autumn and winter, when he ought to have been devoting his time to honouring his yellow jersey, as you would a holy grail, and getting ready to repeat his victory in the '74 Tour, he spent it in the fields, his fields, his land. Operating the tractor, he ploughed an uncultivated plot and turned it into a vineyard. He took down all the farm sheds and old buildings and put up new outhouses. He got rid of the rusty old machinery, and the rust-coloured still and bought a new one. His savings fell by 200,000 francs, but his life became richer. He dreamed about armagnac. And when, in February, he went off to the Côte d'Azur for Bic's first team gathering of the year, he left in the hands of bricklayers, painters and tilers the initial renovation of the big house that would, years later, be his great mansion. And his children would inherit the land and the farm and the fortune, and would always be the children of a property owner, not of a poor, labouring woodcutter who had nothing to provide for himself and his family but his hands and his courage. And thus fate could be cheated, and he, Luis Ocaña, would do it.

Clustered around the vines, Ocaña planted evergreen holm oaks, the tree of Castille's barren uplands, of Priego's dry path and the slopes of the sierra. They did not take root. It was not the land that was at fault, generous and rich as it was, it was the damp air coming in from the Atlantic that killed them. He also planted a fig tree, like the one that had been on the little patio of his house in Priego, with its sweet smell of figs. The fig tree grew and became huge, but it would never bare fruit.

During his sad, last Tour of '77, Ocaña read the newspapers and watched the news broadcasts on television. The news and the pictures were alarming. The Gers, his river, the river that watered his land, bursting its banks, fields flooded, villages devastated. He saw pictures that frightened him: hailstones the size of pigeons' eggs covering the surface of what he supposed were lush fruit trees, expansive vines turned into stunted leaves, and devoid of any fruit. And in his mind were two conflicting feelings. There was the fatalism which would never leave him, the sense that he already knew what was going to happen, the conviction that no business he embarked on would ever be successful. That dejection fought against another, even stronger emotion – a confidence in himself, a belief that he, with his own strength and willpower could overcome all the disasters; it was an unfounded optimism. Josiane calmed him down on the telephone. She lied to him; she nourished his strength of will. 'Don't worry, Luis. I've gone to see the vines and they are not as badly affected as you're worrying about. Things are far worse in other places. Take it easy.' Ocaña ended up leaving things to chance – heads or tails. He never would insure the vineyards.

It was October, autumn, the time for reconstruction.

Ocaña was happy. He was a countryman, a cabinet maker again and a tireless bricklayer all at the same time. The great family home, like a small château in the middle of the wood was a ruin. It was necessary to take down the partition walls, relay the floors, rebuild the interior, dig out a swimming pool, pave the patio, retile the roof. And it had to be done quickly, or at least make one space habitable before Christmas, because that was when the new owners would be moving into the house in Bretagne-de-Marsan, which the Ocañas had sold to invest in the armagnac. Luis, the worker, felt like his father. He touched his calloused, hardened hands and felt as if he were touching his father's hands. He used to get up before daybreak and go to bed after midnight. He reconstructed the house and the small buildings that surrounded it, a garage for his white Jaguar, his De Tomaso Panther and his Mercedes, an outhouse for the big copper still, a storehouse for the barrels in which his patiently distilled armagnac would acquire its colour, and another for the bottles. He'd found his true life and he even forgot about María José, the beautiful, dark-eyed daughter of the ex-cyclist Jesús Martínez, who didn't live far away and with whom he sometimes passed his nights of insomnia. He also forgot about the Rothschild widow, the millionairess for whom he sometimes acted as a gigolo. Life, he decided, was what he constructed with his hands.

In the afternoons, when the light was good, he went out on the patio with his easel and oil paints. He played with the colours rather than the shapes, and he made a great effort with an unfinished portrait of his father, which he'd begun years before. He still kept his stern photograph – his serious-looking father, his eyes – in a corner of the easel, beneath the canvas he worked on.

Then there was his mother, constantly turning up, bringing him fried doughnuts, with onions and garlic, and making him migas[1], which he'd devour till he'd had enough. And on Sundays, the whole family getting together and setting up a large table in the middle of the patio, at the side of the half-built swimming pool. And there was the mother Julia, and her daughter Amparo with the husband who abused her, and Marie France and his brothers, Antonio, Michel, Marino. And Josiane who was an only daughter, and her mother who was an only daughter and separated from her husband, and grandmother who was also an only daughter. Josiane didn't like being in the middle of all that racket, but there she was, the hostess, with her children, Jean-Louis and Sylvie, such a pretty child. And they'd eat the stew and Luis ate for all he was worth. After filling himself with sweet, he'd open two bars of hard turrón and finish those off. He lived life to the full. And then he turned his attention to his family. They all had something to ask of him, and he, in turn, offered advice and money for their businesses,

---

1. Migas - traditional country dish made originally from various leftovers.

many of them hare-brained ideas which they suggested to him. He was the head of the family and everybody depended on him.

He lived in a cyclist's winter cap, well covered, warm and with earflaps. He went about in it, worked in it and felt attractive with it on, captivating, irresistible like some Alain Delon or Johnny Hallyday. Some afternoons, with that on his head, he would take his bicycle down off the hook and ride a few kilometres to maintain some minimum fitness. His agent, Daniel Dousset, had arranged some goodbye criteriums for him and even a cyclo-cross in Paris, and he didn't want to look ridiculous. He was Luis Ocaña.

'I am Luis Ocaña; I am one of a kind,' he told Juan Argudo, a countryman who also hailed from Priego, and who wanted to be a cyclist, and to be like him. Argudo was tall, very blond and chubby-cheeked and had an impressive looking body. Like the Ocañas, his parents were exiled in France; nine years younger than Luis, he had sought his advice and help in finding a way into the peloton. But he was no Ocaña, even though he used to train with him, had that same hunchback appearance on the bike, and even though he had undergone the same hardships as a child. Argudo would ride for Fiat in 1978, in a team that old Geminiani had put together, and in 1979 would go to Spain, recruited by Fernando Manzaneque into the Colchón CR team. In that jersey he would win the stage of the Vuelta that finished in Murcia after the Cresta de Gallo climb.

It was a happy life, a life to dream about, but an impossible life, too. It was as if it were condemned, as if each moment of happiness contained the seeds of tragedy.

Some nights when they went out Ocaña would wear his cowboy boots, and his cowboy tie and bomber jacket, and they would dance. They danced Johnny Hallyday; they danced rock and they lived it up. Sometimes they went up to Paris, lightning trips with Luis at the steering wheel driving recklessly, disdainful of risks. There Josiane bought clothes, jewels and perfume and they met up with the Anquetils – Jeanine, such a good friend of Josiane, and Jacques. And Luis used to buy all the Hallyday records, duplicate copies because he was anxious some might get broken or lost and he wanted to have them all. And they all went dancing, dining and drinking. They were all happy.

One afternoon in spring Luis said to Josiane, 'I'm going to go back to cycling; I'm going to go back to work. The farm isn't providing any money, only expenses – the house, the vineyards...I need to earn more, and the only thing I know about is cycling. I've got a job commentating on the Tour for television with Antenne 2.'

'I'll not let you go by yourself, Luis. I'll go with you like in the old days. I don't want to go back to being left alone in the house with the children and with the responsibility, like those Augusts when you'd take yourself off to the criteriums and I used to think – and I told you so – that the life of the wives was harder than that of the cyclists. If not the whole Tour, because my mother won't be able to be with the children all that time, and I'll have to take charge of the work in the vineyards, I want to be with you some of the time at least. I've also seen that this year the Tour is again starting close to here, from Fleurance, from Maurice's house. That will be a nice little excursion.'

In Fleurance, scarcely 70 kilometres from the Ocaña's farm, Maurice Mességué ruled. He was the healer with his wild herbs, their friend who prepared the herbal teas which Josiane, many years later, still maintained had given Luis the extraordinary health he enjoyed in his magnificent Tour of '73. Mességué was the Mayor of the town, and as such he'd regularly managed to get the Tour to pass that way. The Tour had actually started at his laboratories in 1977 and did so again in '79. Luis had been there as a rider in '77 at the start of what was to be his final Tour. In '79 he returned to Fleurance to begin his new career as a Tour pundit.

Josiane appeared at the Tour in Caupenne, and on Saturday 14 July, the Bastile Day holiday and a rest day for the riders; she was there again with the Tour in the Alps at the ski station of Les Menuires. Van Impe had won there the day before with permission from Hinault, who'd dominated the race as and when he wished ever since the Pyrenees.

That day Josiane found herself with the journalist, Chico Pérez, who'd also turned up there to watch the gymkhana which Toyota had organised for the journalists. Ocaña, of course, had decided that he would take part in the race to the top of the climb in all-terrain vehicles. It was a chance to have a good time.

'Come on, Chico, get in with me. Don't be a coward. You'll see how much you'll enjoy it.' Ocaña invited *Pueblo*'s special correspondent.

'Are you mad?' replied Chico, who liked him, and was close enough to him to get away with that kind of remark. 'I wouldn't get in any car with you, not even if I was paid a million pesetas.'

Josiane, next to him, blond, petite and beautifully turned out, smiled and agreed with him. She didn't need Chico, with his prodigious memory, and his relentless, rasping voice, to regale her with all the details of the crazy things her husband had done behind the wheel of a car, that he was disdainful of risks and so went looking for them at every bend in the road. But Chico had already started and now there was no stopping him.

'I've seen Luis blow up a Porsche, Josiane, the Porsche Commodore, which is so spectacular, so big that you can fit two bikes in the boot. And Julio Jiménez who, as you know, is also a rally driver, told me that he had Luis in the car one day when Luis told him to go quicker. He told him not to get the wind up but he'd be happy to take over and step on it. And Julio got out, gave him the keys, and off he walked – there's nobody who can stand it. And you know that well enough, Josiane,' Chico went on excitedly. 'You've had some accident or other with him.'

'Yes, alright,' she said, sweetly, able neither to conceal or cover up that other savage aspect of the man she loved. 'A couple of years ago we did have a collision. It wrecked the Mercedes but it wasn't Luis's fault exactly. We were on our way back to France from Gironella, in Barcelona, where the stage of the Setmana Catalana had finished, and close to Cervera, at a place called San Ramón, he went to overtake two tractors on a bend with good visibility. But the sun was in his eyes and in that moment of blindness he didn't see there was a lorry stopped at the side of the road and we crashed into it. Luckily for us we weren't doing more than 50 kilometres an hour and luckily the Mercedes was built like a tank and it protected us. But I hit my mouth hard against the windscreen and for several days my lips were swollen, and Luis hit his face against the steering wheel and broke his nose; he looked like a bad boxer. All it did was give us a fright, and thank God we had the Mercedes insured.'

'And that accident messed up the whole season,' Chico added. 'His last year as a cyclist in that Dutch team of Jan Raas – Frisol. What a disaster. He was so depressed.'

'Worse than that, I would say, said Josiane. 'What bad luck he had. Nothing worked out well for Luis. In his first race, the Tour of the Mediterranean, he had to retire because of a fall which put eight stitches in his knee. He was selected for Paris–Nice but his spirit was so low because he'd hardly been able to train, and he preferred to retire rather than grovel; in the Setmana Catalana, when it seemed he was recovering, do you remember that, Chico?' – and Josiane fixed him with a serious look so that he'd understand that she wasn't joking, that all those things that piled up on top of Luis that year were implacable destiny. 'Then a television helicopter turned up. flying low and generating such a gust of wind that it blew half the peloton over. The first to be knocked down was his friend Andrés Romero, that climber from Granada who also lived in Mont-de-Marsan and who Luis went around with, but as always happened it was Luis who suffered most: he ran into his friend's bike and he ended up with his back so purple that he could have turned up for one of our Easter processions without having to wear a habit. Then – and that's Luis for you, always such a brute on the bike – instead of getting into the relays with some of his team who'd been waiting for him, he leaves them behind and does 50 kilometres on his own to link up, and then he drops down exhausted the moment he's managed it. And so he retires before the finish, and so I drive down to pick him up in Barcelona… And he never did fully recover from that fall, because shortly afterwards the team made him ride the Vuelta, and then the Tour… And all that with appalling pain in his back. He could hardly get out of the saddle.'

Meanwhile, as they spoke on that clear Alpine morning, all around them could be heard the howl of revving engines, those all-terrains the victims of overeager and insensitive drivers.

'Yes. They made him ride the Vuelta because Raas removed himself from the line-up at the last minute and they didn't have another leader in Frisol. But nor did they treat him very well in the Vuelta,' said Chico, who that year suffered watching how Ocaña's so-called pride was punished again and again by his Spanish colleagues. 'Kas had some old scores to settle and they made him pay. I remember a number of days he escaped from the peloton, but they never let him get to the finish; they denied him the right to say farewell to the Vuelta with the honour of a stage win. That's bloody Spanish envy, for you. He never had known how to make friends, and nobody wanted to be his friend when he needed it most. You know, apart from criteriums, from the time he won the Tour in 1973, through to then, the Vuelta of '77, he'd only won one official race, one miserable time trial in the Tour of La Rioja in '75! He got away one day in the Vuelta on the stage to Igualada, but as soon as Menes and Ladrón de Guevara caught him, instead of working together they just sat on his wheel and then it was all over. Everybody was going wild about Freddy Maertens, that Belgian wizard who won 13 stages and the overall even though he was a sprinter. He wore the orange leader's jersey – yes, orange in '77, just like in 1935 – and Luis was forgotten about. But the worst of all,' Chico continued, irrepressible and encyclopaedic, and still pained, even two years later, by the mistreatment handed out to Luis – to Josiane's relish; she'd found a kindred spirit – 'worst of all was that day when the stage finished at the top of the Urkiola. It was the penultimate stage and the kind of day they call Dantesque – hurricane winds and rain like you can only get in the Basque Country, with its abrupt, narrow valleys. And there, alone, was the Luis of old. He was escaping at every opportunity, looking to say goodbye to the Vuelta in the grand manner, and quite right, too. And because they couldn't deal with him properly they ambushed him. Behind him, two from Kas jumped out of the peloton, Ladrón and Linares, and one from Teka, Elorriaga. When Luis learned of that he allowed himself to be caught, thinking that four of them would have a better chance of success. But when they got up to him, the two from Kas, as if they had already achieved their objective, stopped pulling, even though they still had three minutes. Then the peloton just gobbled them all up. That's Spanish cruelty and Spanish fans in equal measure. When they decide a person is finished, there's neither respect nor understanding; they are sent to the dustbin, to oblivion. A narrow-minded view of cycling in a country without nobility.'

'But Luis was not finished, not at all, Chico, and you don't need to get over excited, because I know you and I know how much you've always admired the grandeur of the great cyclists. Luis could have been weakened by the pain in his back and by all those years of giving everything – remember, he was 32 by then. He said it was the antibiotics they had stuffed him with to cure the bronchopneumonia when he was so ill in the '72 Tour, which had caused permanent damage to him and to his capacity to recover from the great efforts he had to make. I don't know about that, but I do know that mentally he was very strong in the '77, willing to suffer and to get back to being his old self. And what you were saying about the Vuelta is true, Chico, because he told me that. He told me he suffered like when he'd been at his best. In those escapes he'd felt like he had in those great time trials when it was Anquetil and Merckx at the same time, and he was best of all; when he was going with his arse on the point of the saddle and pulling on the handlebars and suffering so much that he didn't know if he was shitting himself or pissing himself – excuse me for talking ugly like that, but that's how he described the moments of maximum effort. And I remember his friend, Julio Jiménez, shared those feelings. With Julio, it was less lavatory talk and perhaps more mystical – but then he came from Ávila, the land of Saint Teresa. He used to talk about ecstasy and rapture as if his eyes, those disbelieving eyes of his, were turning round in their sockets, like he was in another world, swallowed up by a kind of dizziness. I don't know how, but climbing the Puy de Dôme, for example, he'd go into that state, beyond pain, and carry on pedalling without knowing how. And that's what used to happen to my Luis in the time trials. That's cyclists for you.'

'For me, Luis, like Anquetil, was perfection,' said Chico, more stylish, more aesthetic. 'They were pure style turned into cyclists, as if they'd managed to hang their head between their shoulders like the hare puts its head between its ears, looking for aerodynamic perfection – and finding it.'

'In that last Tour of his, Luis was strong and determined, and he was pleased that the Pyrenees came so early. They'd started from Fleurance, and already by the second day they'd reached Puy, after going over the Aspin, the Tourmalet and the Aubisque. The people at Frisol told Luis that they weren't asking him to win the Tour; they'd be happy enough if he finished in the top five, but Luis wanted more from himself. That day in the Pyrenees, I remember it perfectly. It was a Saturday, and Luis set out ready for everything, and got as far as the Aubisque with the leading group. It was a very long stage, more than 250 kilometres, but Luis was there, like in his best days, in spite of the back pain, with Van Impe, Thévenet and Zoetemelk, and even Merckx was hanging on. Then, however, five kilometres from the top of the Aubisque, the last col, it was as if he'd been given a knock out punch. He could hardly pedal. He lost more than 12 minutes. His Tour ended there. On the phone that night he told me he'd made an inexcusable mistake for a rider of his experience – a juvenile's mistake – he'd forgotten to eat properly and he'd been hit by a tremendous *pájara*...'

'Yes, he told me that, too, that he hadn't eaten, but don't be taken in, Josiane. Anquetil was there in those days, commenting on the Tour for the radio and the newspapers, and I remember word for word what he told me that night. "Don't be under any illusion, Chico." he said to me. "This is the end. I'm afraid that for our friend Luis, his time of splendour is over..."

'Well, be that as it may, despite everything Luis didn't abandon, he wouldn't let himself retire in his last Tour. And what purpose did his effort serve? To end up getting smeared, the victim of other people's scheming. Everybody was on something, shooting up or carrying pills of Centramina in the pockets of their shorts, but to punish the whole peloton they picked on a few in the last couple of days and declared them positive: Menéndez, Agostinho, Zoetemelk, Luis and some others. They gave Luis a 10-minute sanction, but that didn't matter, nor did the fine, but that his name was sullied. He said to me, "Ok, yes I took what I took, but many took more than that, including some of those who finished at the top, and they didn't do anything to them, and that goes against justice, against my sense of justice. There are as many injustices still being committed in cycling as there were when I started." And it's sad to end up like that, I think, Chico; he was a scapegoat…'

And so they would have carried on, interminably, the pair of them engrossed in the life and misfortunes of Ocaña, their Luis they admired so much, oblivious to what was happening around them, if they hadn't been interrupted by a thunderous noise and shouts of horror.

They looked towards where everybody else was looking, with enough time to see one of the Toyotas tumbling down the mountain, turning over and over, each time losing pieces of its bodywork to leave it sitting in an almost dried up pool, perhaps more than 100 metres below where it had left the road. Josiane and Chico looked at each other and in the panic of their respective glances they both knew they were thinking the same thing, dreading the same thing, and knowing they weren't wrong.

Chico descended more quickly, even though the soles of his trainers were slipping in the shortcuts between the tarmac-surfaced corners. He was a long-striding man, the son of a countryman, a lover of the country. Behind him, as if carried on the wings of her darkest foreboding, came Josiane. When Chico got level with the car, a shapeless mass of metal, missing its doors and windows, there were more people coming to the aid of the two occupants, and even a doctor, Dr Dazza. One of the occupants was Jean Sarrazin, a driver of one of the Antenne 2 cars. He was unconscious. The other was Luis; he was conscious, with a thin trickle of blood running from one ear and one eye completely closed.

'How are you, Luis?' Chico asked him in Spanish, his voice giving a squeak of anxiety. 'Say something to me.'

'I'm ok,' Luis replied, and Chico couldn't be sure whether or not he'd recognised him. 'We couldn't let them overtake us. They thought we wouldn't be able to get past them on the corner. We beat them, didn't we?' Ocaña tried to smile.

'Don't be afraid, Luis. I'm here with you.' It was Josiane, softly spoken, in French. 'Don't be afraid.'

She and Chico remained with Ocaña while the complicated rescue was organised. He was kept hydrated, a little at a time, and periodically given an oxygen mask to keep him awake. It was a long wait. There was talk of a helicopter, but it didn't arrive. The ambulance did but couldn't get closer than 200 metres to the stream in which the car had ended up. While the hot sun gradually sank to the horizon it was necessary to put together a stretcher to move the two injured men without them being jolted. As Sarrazin appeared to be the more seriously hurt, in a grade 2 coma according to Dr Dazza, and there were fears about his head injury, it was finally decided to move him by helicopter. Luis was taken by ambulance to the hospital in Moutiers, his body bandaged up like the invisible man. At his side all the time in the hospital was Josiane, just as she had been at his bedside in the clinic in Tarbes after his fall in the '71 Tour. Later, the doctor who'd given him the first dressings, came to give him the report.

'You are suffering from multiple fractures,' he told him, 'but take it easy. You'll be alright, although, because of the shock you're suffering from, we'll have to wait 48 hours before we can make a definitive evaluation. The fractures are located in the forearms; you've also received a severe blow to the face; and we are worried about one of your eyes. It will be necessary to operate on the fractures, but we need to wait a few days. Ah, and Sarrazin, he'll come through this, too. It's a miracle the two of you are alive. You've both been very lucky.'

Some days later Ocaña was flown from Grenoble to Biarritz and admitted to the Saint Vincent clinic at Dax – in Les Landes, back in his countryside, his light, where the renowned orthopaedic surgeon Jean-Claude Gardes operated on an arm and collar bone in two stages, during which time he required a blood transfusion.

While Ocaña was in hospital there were two pieces of news that July. One was the victory by his friend Joaquim Agostinho on the Alpe d'Huez stage, the day after his accident. Agostinho, the iron man, was 36 years old and finished third in that Tour, his best ever classification. The other news was the announcement by Kas, the oldest team in the world, that they would not be continuing in the peloton the following year; 1979 would be their twenty-third and their last season in cycling.

In February 1980 Ocaña had to go to the Barraquer clinic in Barcelona, where Alfredo Muiños, the Royal family's opthalmologist, would attempt to repair the left eye that had been seriously damaged in the accident. As he left the clinic Ocaña said that all his life he would suffer the consequences of that accident: his vertebrae hurt every day, and always would hurt; he couldn't hear anything in his left ear, and saw even less in that eye, and on top of that he had a metallic plate in his left arm. And then, since he didn't want the journalists, or anybody else, to feel sorry for him and because, in spite of everything, he remained an optimist with a sense of humour and capable of magnificent irony, he concluded: 'If I were not dressed in rags I would get the bike out again, with what they are paying them these days...'

Many years later, in one of those rare moments of peace between them, Josiane said to him, 'Your real decline, Luis my dear, began with that accident. You were never the same again. Before that you were Luis, with your strength, your vigour, and your energy, and that accident took away everything – except your desire to carry on being strong.'

In December 1993, five months before his death, a street in Priego was dedicated to him – Avenida Luis Ocaña – in the Priego he no longer recognised. There he was, elegant as ever, lightly clothed in spite of the cold coming down from the sierra in that sunlit winter, standing next to Josiane, wrapped up in a great cape. He drew back the little curtain with its Spanish flag, which hid his engraved plaque and spoke with such a strong French accent, his rrs smoothed off, so distant from the hardness of the stones, of the mountains and the winds of his own land, and ended his address roaring with laughter, happier than ever and ironic as always. 'Every year that goes by my assets increase; I have more streets with my name...' It was a nod in the direction of his decline, his joke a taunt against a destiny which every day put more pressure on him, and a direct grumble – 'I ask for bread and they give me honours, and honours are not edible.' His business was a ruin; armagnac had gone out of fashion and didn't sell. His debts were increasing, the rain and the hail continued to ravage his harvests which he, pig-headedly, refused to insure, and he carried on, not understanding cycling any more, yet needing cycling to eat. And he felt there was nobody to help him.

3

'I need the money, Julio, I need the money.'

Luis had not thought again about Benidorm, perhaps since the wedding of his friend Juan Hortelano, five years ago at least, in 1989. He'd been agitated when he got to the wedding in his white Jaguar. He ripped off the bridegroom's elegant pearl grey tie, removed from around his own neck the Texan tie, his trade mark, and tied it on Juan, black under the collar of his white shirt.

Then he unexpectedly said to him, 'But why are you getting married, Juan, if you are going to get divorced?' Let's go and have a night on the town in Benidorm without saying anything to anybody, and then you'll see how we laughed within a couple of years remembering how you talked about giving marriage the slip.'

He said it like he said everything, as a joke, but with a depth of determination and seriousness, so that it only needed the slightest doubt on the other's part for it to be turned into action. Juan, however, didn't have any doubt, although perhaps he had his regrets later, when with Luis at the wheel he and his bride got into the Jaguar, now turned into the wedding car. It took them from the church of San Fernando de Henares, where the bells rang out when the pair came out hand in hand under the shower of rice to the Miravalle restaurant, an impressive looking ship moored between Villalba and Guardarrama, where a great banquet took place. They arrived faint and ashen and with the bitter taste of sickness in their mouth because of Luis's reckless driving – another of his trade marks.

Now, on this humid and painful evening on 2 May 1994, Luis was sitting on a chair in the room of his usual hotel in Benidorm. Benidorm – so happy and busy with so many people in its skyscrapers, on its beaches, in its streets like ants in an overflowing anthill, so many beetroot red tourists and now so many retired enjoying their democratic right to cheap tourist holidays – why was Benidorm so painful to him? If he leaned out over the terrace on tiptoe he could even catch a glimpse of the darkening sea behind the white foam. It had been one more year on the Vuelta and one more year with José María García and the rest of the COPE lot, talking on the radio – his new job. Sitting down, with no wish to get up, without the strength to use the coming night to make something of the day, as he'd always done before. That, too, had come to an end.

When there was a knock on the door he thought it was the waiter with the French omelette together with a bit of salad he'd ordered for dinner, and he was about to reply that it was early and could he come back in a short while, when without waiting for a reply, the person who'd knocked gently on the door opened it and came in. It was Julio, It was little Julio Jiménez, his friend, a cyclist like him years ago and now a colleague again – and a rival, since he was still commentating on the Vuelta for the SER channel.

He couldn't any longer spend the night in the discotheques with Julio; those times of one-night stands were now over; he was not strong enough physically any more. Nor in spirit; his illness, his liver destroyed by the hepatitis, had ruled it out. He was in pain all over; his bones hurt; he suffered permanently from shinsplints; he could hardly sleep. Julio liked to visit him from time to time, to talk, to tell each other stories, or not even that, to sit beside him, just watching how the day invariably gave way to night.

'Julio, come on in. I was just thinking about Senna, about his death.'

'What a crash he had in San Marino yesterday, the poor fellow, he was a great champion. I think there's never been anybody like him behind the wheel, with his touch, with his ear for the engine of his formula 1…'

'No, there was nobody like him, nor was there anybody like me, Julio. He was a boxer, too, when he was at the wheel, like I was on the bike. There was no fight that wasn't worth fighting, neither for him nor for me. And we both had our moments of glory. Now he's gone, like so many have gone, like I'm going. I can see that; like they've all gone. This world doesn't belong to us any more, nor does it recognise us.'

'My friend Pierre from Carcassonne called me. You know, Campagnaro. He told me he was worried because you turned up at his garage one day with the white Jaguar and told him you wanted to leave it there to see if anybody would buy it...'

Julio had known Pierre Campagnaro since 1967, since Ford stopped sponsoring Anquetil. Geminiani set to that autumn of '66 and managed to convince Baron Bich to get into cycling. He persuaded him that there was no better way of letting the public know that Bic was not just synonymous with ballpoint pens, but was a commercial name, a firm that made lots of things. And that way the orange jerseys arrived in the peloton, and were worn by Anquetil and Julio Jiménez in their last years of racing, and after that by Ocaña in his early years. They were Geminiani's swan song and they were worn for one year, in '67, by Campagnaro. After he left he opened his garage in Carcassonne and that became the place all the cyclists of the south went to when they wanted to do some business with their cars. And although when Ocaña joined Bic in 1970, Campagnaro was just a legend, the name of a garage owner, he too made friends with the ex-cyclist and did business with him.

'Yes, that's true,' Luis admitted dismally to Julio. 'I want to sell the Jaguar.'

'But that Jaguar is so important to you. It's your life, Luis...'

'And Joaquim was so important to me, swarthy Agostinho, who used to look daggers at you – dark skin, jet black hair, and powerful. He was a rhinoceros; he had the body of a rhinoceros, hard, indestructible, and the blind charge of the rhinoceros which only he could do to the peloton. He loved me and I loved him, a warrior who understood me. He was an animal and I used to say to him: "Agostinho you are an animal, but what an animal." You told him to pull for 100 kilometres and he would pull for 150, getting stronger all the time. Even just hanging on to his wheel tired the rest of us out, and he carried on as if it were nothing. And he was like me; he was the son of a farm worker, landless too, and forced to emigrate. He said to me: "Luis, the bicycle is my plough and my fortune is the land I have bought with what I have earned by pedalling. I swore to myself that I would prosper in life, that I would climb up the social ladder, that I would own property, and here I am, Luis. And on my green, well watered land, which is so fertile that it doesn't need fertiliser, I will rear horses for the bullfights on horseback, not cows which are dirty and smell bad, but beautiful horses, like the aristocrats, and when I finish with the bike I will only ride on horseback." And he was close to me in my two greatest days of cycling – when I made Merckx crack, and when I won the Tour. And I've been mourning him for ten years; it's ten years now since a dog crossed his path at a finishing line, and that dog had his name written on it, it was his destiny. I had an argument with Agostinho one day, in a stage of the Vuelta. He had signed for Bic because he knew they were like Gods, and he was stolen from Gribaldy, and I took him with me to win the Tour. But before that we rode the Vuelta of '73 and on the Irache stage, an uphill finish, he goes and sprints past me, as he's my team mate. Perurena was some distance ahead and he won easily, and I was aiming for the second-place bonus against Merckx, and we're in the middle of that when I see another orange jersey, another Bic overtaking me. It's Agostinho and he leaves me ending up fourth, and without any bonus at all!

'I was absolutely furious, one of those fits of anger which used to scare people, which made them said that I was a *teigneux*, a bastard on the bicycle and the loveliest person when I was off it. But that day I felt like a bastard the moment I was off the bike. And poor Agostinho, he looked at me with total incomprehension on his face. "I only want to stop Merckx from getting the bonus," he told me. "But I didn't do enough." I had to believe him because I've never seen a team mate so self-sacrificing, so hard, so tireless, and so loyal, and yet I knew that in Portugal he was a great idol, a national treasure. There were dozens of Portuguese journalists who demanded great exploits from him every day and they drove him crazy. During the Tour, during my Tour, we often shared a room. One night he showed me a ceramic plate which he'd bought in a shop in Lisbon. On it was inscribed: For football, Eusebio; for pedalling, Agostinho; for the fado, Amália[1], and in this bar, good wine. "Do you understand, Luis? I am just one of the million Portuguese emigrants in France and Switzerland. I am their

---

1. Amália Rodriguez, famous exponent of the 'fado' a style of Portuguese folk song characterised by mournful tunes and lyrics.

hope: I left, I triumphed, I will go back to live on my own land." And we used to talk and he told me a little of his life during those nights of insomnia, on the eve of great days of riding.

'Agostinho said to me' Luis continued, "Viscount De Gribaldy discovered me,and the first lesson he gave me was this: 'Cycling is like boxing,' he told me one day, when he'd hardly got to know me. 'Cycling is not a game; it's a hard, terrible, implacable sport which demands enormous sacrifices. You play football; you play tennis, or ice hockey, but you don't play cycling and even less do you play boxing.' And when he said that to me, I remember it was in São Paulo, when he asked me if I wanted to be a professional cyclist in France, I replied that I understood perfectly well that in cycling you fight, that in boxing you do battle, but that I was not a boxer but I was a battler, a real battler. The first person who told me I was a cyclist I said to the Viscount, was the captain of my company in the war against the Independentistas in Mozambique." And Agostinho said that to me with that hard, sinister look of his that was so humane at the same time. "I had to do my military service there during the 60s, like all the sons of strong farm labourers, and it was three years. And there, in Matuluma and in Chicundi on the northern border, river patrolling down the Rovuma, and exchanging shots with the rebels, that's where I also met up with the bicycle. While others took five hours to ride the 50 kilometres on forest roads I did it in two hours. And the captain told me I had superhuman strength and that I was born to be a cyclist. Later on, again in Mozambique when they assigned me to the south and I spent the day on the beaches of the Indian Ocean, looking at the far off coast of Madagascar, I proved I had a unique lung capacity. I used to fish for octopus and squid and I could stay under water longer than anybody else. When I went back home to my village, which I would never have wanted to leave, Luis, because I've always been very attached to my area, although being Portuguese I've had to leave to earn a living, like you – a Spaniard who's never lived in Spain. When I went back to Silveira and Casalinhos, next to Torres Vedras, there, close to the sea, the infinite Atlantic, I ran into the cyclists from Sporting who were out training one day. I used to ride out into the country on an old iron which if it didn't weight 20 kilos didn't weigh anything. I grabbed it, accelerated and caught up with them. I could see they wanted to get rid of me, but they couldn't. I was 25 by then, and that's where my cycling career began. Afterwards I met the Viscount, Luis.'"

'What a character he was,' I said, interrupting Joaquim. 'When he was silent his look said it all, but at other times he talked and smoked a fag, and carried on talking like when he was pedalling, without realising what an effort all that rigmarole was. I met De Gribaldy some time ago; Geminiani introduced me to him. They are two of a kind, although they are rivals, two Frenchmen from the provinces who knew how to find in cycling a unique mode of expression and who have done unique things in cycling. When they met in Paris they often used to see each other in the Alcazar, that cabaret in Saint-Germain-des-Prés in which they set up their office, among the wine glasses and the showgirls, and I used to go there too from time to time because Johnny Hallyday spent time there meeting his friends. Then I think they stopped going there a couple of years ago when Jim Morrison, the musician with the Doors, died of an overdose in the lavatory in a club on the other side of the square. I told Agostinhoall this as if I were an open encyclopaedia, just as talkative because those are characters you like to talk about. De Gribaldy, who is a real aristocrat, with Italian blood, had been a cyclist – a bad one – then he began to set up teams in Besançon, almost for the love of it, to pass the time…And at that point Agostinho interrupted me to continue his story.'

'But, Luis, I'm sorry, but just to clarify something,' Julio interrupted in turn. 'In fact, Gem and De Gribaldy carried on going to the Alcazar after that business with Jim Morrison. They were very close with the owner, with Jean-Marie Rivière, who definitely had nothing to do with Roger Rivière, the cyclist who finished up paralysed on the Perjuret. He set up the Alcazar and Gem told me it could have come out of one of the detective films of Alain Delon or Yves Montand. "Those of Melville" was what Gem said, as if I'd understand that; those clubs were full of plastic – lots of light – see-through. Jean-Marie was an actor, or still is, because I believe he's not dead yet, and Gem introduced me to him once in his hotel in Clermont-Ferrand. You know you really haven't got to know Gem, although it was he who took you to Bic. Visiting Gem meant sitting down with a glass of whisky, or with a whole bottle alongside you, in the bar of his hotel on the Puy de Dôme, the Hotel de Suquets. And some famous guests – they are all his friends – come along to sit next to you at the table, and he starts recounting stories. He signed me up in '66 when he had the Ford team, because he wanted a true climber, and because I got on well with him from the moment we met. We spoke the same language. We both knew that in the '64 Tour which Anquetil won, it could really be said that he won thanks to me, thanks to me winning the Puy de Dôme stage and so preventing Poulidor, his big rival, from getting the time bonus.

'I was fine with Kas,' Julio continued, 'but the following year when I went to re-sign, Langarica, the boss, told me he couldn't raise my salary, so I took myself off with Gem to France to help Aimar win the Tour and to be with Anquetil. And I spent some months in Clermont-Ferrand in Gem's little hotel. Whenever I go to France I try to pass that way to visit him and also Lucien Aimar, who always invites all his friends to his race, the Tour of the Mediterranean in Toulon. And one night when we were chatting he started telling me your story, Luis. My last year at Bic was '68, two years before you arrived, and by then Gem had already cast his eye over Merckx, who everybody was talking about but who still hadn't yet won a grand tour. What Gem said to me was: "In 1967 I said to Christian Darras, the head of publicity at Bic, the one who took the decisions about the team" – Gem was really annoyed at how stupid it was that the marketing people, who knew nothing about cycling or about how things worked, were in a position to make these decisions – "I said to Darras," so Gem told me, "Merckx's contract with Peugeot is coming to an end; if you want someone to succeed Anquetil, because he's getting old and tired now, and hasn't got more than a year left, sign Merckx. I told that dumb ass Darras what Rik Van Looy had said to me: that Merckx was going to make people forget about him. That he'd be no more than a shadow from the past when that kid became what he was going to become. I told Rik not to get worked up about it, and that he was a living monument to cycling.'Wait and see, Gem,' he said to me. And when

I told Darras that, what he said to me was, "But your Merckx hasn't won anything." And I replied, "Wait and see, Christian." That was what Gem told me, Luis.

'Then he told me,' Julio went on. 'In fact he told all of us around the table, that finally Darras told him he was prepared to offer Merckx 250,000 francs a year. "But Christian," Gem replied, "Merckx is asking for 300,000, which is what Anquetil gets." To which, according to Gem, Darras replied, "In that case, drop Anquetil to 250,000." Since that was impossible, Gem couldn't have Merckx. That's what Gem told me, Luis.

'"But I had Ocaña," he said, and he told me that he'd spoken to you in '69 when you were at Fagor. He told me he'd said, "You are Anquetil, Luis, you are Jacques and you will be Jacques. You come with me to Bic, Luis. In a Spanish team you'll just fester away and give up hope. Listen to me, Luis. Come with me to France. If you stay in Spain you'll only race in Spain, and all your life you'll just be one more Spaniard. You have to be ambitious, Luis, you have to think about the wider world. You'll be an international figure, you must come to France, where you can be sure you'll ride in the best races, and in the Tour, of course, in the Tour which one day will have your name on it." That's what Gem said to me, Luis. Was that how it happened?'

'He convinced me, yes, but even before that Cescutti had persuaded me that I had to go with him. Cescutti was telling me all the time that I was Anquetil…As for Gem, his words ended up convincing me and above all it was the offer that persuaded me: no less than 30,000 francs a month! And that, as you well know, was a lot of money back then. But in the end, Gem never was my director.'

'He was chucked out of Bic in the '69 Tour, which was a disaster. Raymond Louviot had just died, you remember? The director who went everywhere with him, the deputy who was better understood, and he died shortly after that Tour of the Basque Country, which Anquetil won. Old Louviot, Laripette, as we used to call him, was killed in a car crash while he was making a reconnoitre of the Four Days of Dunkirk prologue. So the team was left in the hands of Gem and the other director, De Muer who, remember, had come from Pelforth with

Janssen as part of the deal and he only had eyes for the Dutchman in glasses and he didn't get on at all well with Gem. So, without thinking twice about it, when the Tour made the stage into his Clermont-Ferrand, he packed his case, stepped out of the car, and there you saw me. That's how it was, Luis, so I was told by Aimar, who did the best he could. And a little later, Anquetil also left the team and quit cycling. Jacques said this was as far as were going, and off he went to his château with Jeanine and Sylvie and all his women. They left the whole of Bic for you, Luis.'

'But don't complicate the thing, Julio. You were saying something about Gem and De Gribaldy in the Alcazar…'

'Well, just to go back, Luis. By then, Gem already had more businesses outside cycling than he had in cycling itself. He had hotels, bistros, brasseries, night clubs; he was a smooth operator in the hotel business, old Gem. And he was also a close friend of De Gribaldy. They were very similar, *bon vivants*, very cheerful but serious when it came to business and definitely when it came to cycling, but always with a dilettante air about them as if it were a hobby really, and their real life was after dark, chatting and friends. And they had all that in the Alcazar, where they also took impresarios and businessmen at night to convince them to get into cycling, to sponsor a team. It was De Gribaldy who persuaded Gem to get back into cycling and in '71 made an opening for him as director alongside him in the team which was then called Hoover – the vacuum cleaners. They weren't too bad a team – they had Agostinho and Mariano Martínez, and they rode in the Tour, remember? It was alright, but Gem got bored and went back home. However, he couldn't stay away from the steering wheel and the smell of liniment and cyclists and the talk in the peloton for very long. He couldn't live without shouting the odds and going on about his few noble truths, the essential truths of cycling, and one night in the Alcazar, at the end of '72, he had an idea which struck him as absolutely brilliant. At that time there was an old showgirl who used to perform around there. She was already 70, but what legs she had, Luis… the years hadn't touched them. Her name was Miriam de Kova, perhaps you've heard of her, Luis?'

'Yes, I think I know where you're going, Julio. The story is starting to ring a bell...'

'I think you've heard it several times. Well this Miriam was as bad a singer as she was immensely rich. She was the widow of a Greek shipowner with whom she'd lived in the United States, or so it was said around that time and that's what Gem told me, that Miriam, who was an American, was called "Yem", as if you were pronouncing James and we're drawing out the syllable and sweetening it to "Gem". She was filthy rich and had a longing for self-publicity, for being a celebrity and for selling some discs she'd recorded. One night, when the sun had already started to set over Paris, the time when many were already thinking about where to have their oysters and champagne for breakfast, the owner of the Alczar, Rivière and De Gribaldy convinced her that her best means of publicising her art would be a cycling team. "I will run it," Gem told her. "I have directed Anquetil, and I've also won the Tour with Aimar, and I promise you, Miriam, it will be a great team. We'll ride in the Tour and Aimar will be the leader. Although he's now 31, he is willing and able to become great again. And our friends, the Lejeune brothers, will provide us with our bicycles." The team was indeed formed, it rode the Tour, it signed up Aimar, but I can tell you Luis that it was the worst team in the history of cycling, as you well know.'

'Yes, I know Julio. They rode the Tour in '73, my Tour, with very striking, feminine pink jerseys, which carried the letters De Kova Lejeune, and I believe they set a record which nobody has yet been able to beat: the last five on general classification in that Tour were all from that team, all from De Kova...'

'And the showgirl got tired of pouring money into it, and by August the team had disappeared. It didn't even last a year. Gem went back home, but within a couple of years he decided to take the plunge again and set off for Portugal to direct Agostinho, who as you know had returned there when Bic folded. Then, years later, he ended up directing Merckx, when Eddy was past his best and – to his misfortune – at Fiat. What a climb-down for old Gem. But now that I've mentioned Agostinho, you were telling me a story about him, weren't you?'

'Oh, yes, Julio. I was saying that Agostinho, that night before one of the big stages of the '73 Tour wanted to tell me things about his life. "Luis," he said to me, "I began racing when I was 25 and I won the Portuguese professional championship – as an amateur. Then I did a good ride in the Worlds, at Imola, attacking at the key moment, although Adorni went off with the jersey. Then Gribaldy told me he already had his eye on me then, but where I fell in love with him was at São Paulo in a Tour of Brazil. It was December 1968, he'd taken his amateur team there and I remember it like it was yesterday. He came to see me at the little hotel where I was with the Portuguese team and asked me straight out if I wanted to ride with him as a professional in France. I was already almost 26." And he carried on riding till he was 41, and he would have gone on further if that dog hadn't crossed in front of him in the Algarve.'

'And now Joaquim is dead,' Julio said again. 'And he seemed so indestructible, immortal. However many falls did he have, and he got up from all of them...'

'He died on 30 of April in 1984 after ten days of stupid agony and medical errors. When he finished the stage – because after crashing into the dog 300 metres from the line, Joaquim finished the stage – he felt fine. He didn't know he'd fractured his skull; it was later when he realised that, when he felt lousy. They were late operating on him and after a couple of days they gave him up for dead, but his strong, hard heart, held out, Julio, and we were all believing in a miracle. I was telephoning the hospital everyday to find out if he'd regained consciousness. He never did,' Luis continued. 'I only ever saw him again in his coffin, looking so elegant in a tail-coat and a white bow tie when they laid him out for a day in the Basilica de la Estrella, the biggest in Lisbon. I was there. I went to Fuenterrabía with one of the directors of the French Federation and we got a plane from there to Lisbon. When we reached the church there was a queue going several times round it, kilometres long, married couples, old people with children in arms. What a send-off, what a funeral! Even Mario Soares, the Prime Minister, and President Ramalho Eanes were there. I also met Merckx there, and I took a taxi to Casalinhos de Alfaiata, his village, 100 kilometres away. In the whole of the province of Torres Vedras, all the businesses and the offices had closed, and there wasn't a school open either. There were such crowds and so many traffic jams – all of Portugal seemed to want to be there at the funeral to cry, and the little village and all around there was full to bursting – so after half an hour going nowhere, we decided to get out of the taxi and continue on foot to the cemetery of Silveira, some kilometres away. In fact, I wasn't really with it. The leg I broke in the accident in '83 was still giving me hell and I could hardly walk at any speed. We stopped at one house, and you won't believe this but it was Agostinho's house, with a cool patio protected from the overwhelming heat by a sunshade, some plants and a fountain. And there was a bicycle, Joaquim's bicycle. Without a second thought I borrowed it, and that way I got to the cemetery, with my tie flapping in the wind, and anonymous in the midst of so much mourning. It was a real effort, mind you, because it's all hills around there, and I arrived sweaty and out of breath, but I arrived on time. And I cried.

'I've only got a few months to live, Julio,' Luis continued without any change at all in the tone of his voice, like it was just a pause in his recollection of Agostinho, a monotone which seemed to have come out of the dark which now filled the room, in spite of that irritating light from the terrace which shone pitilessly on the other side of the glass and couldn't be switched off. 'Some months ago, before coming to the Vuelta, I had a consultation in Toulouse hospital. I've got no liver, Julio. I don't want to suffer like my father did, months of hopeless agony, a ridiculous fight like Jacques suffered, like Anquetil did, You remember – the cancer which ate up his stomach, and took his life? You were a close friend of his, you know how he went so terribly downhill, until there was nothing of him. So much pain.'

'Tamames told me something the other day. He told me that you'd said to him that if the analysis you were waiting for didn't go well, you were going to shoot yourself, and I couldn't believe him. You know what Tamames is like, a bit odd,' said Julio. He was trying to stay calm, and he did manage to prevent his voice from revealing the alarm and sorrow that had set his heart racing.

'I was like Jacques, Julio. I was like Anquetil. I had his shape, my upper body as immobile as his, hands gripping the handlebar as tightly, my chin on my chest and my gaze fixed on the horizon. I was just like Jacques, Julio, and I went through the same pain he did in the time trials, and pulling on the bars my body hurt all over. I reached my limit just as he did and then we went into another dimension. We were body and strength and vigour and we believed we could overcome our own destiny. Nothing was impossible for us, nor was it for you, Julio, when the road got steeper. After you put up with the initial pain you went looking for more until in the end you thought you were flying. And I was an Anquetil: I bolted food down like him, I drank like him, I boozed like him, I liked beautiful women who smelt of expensive Parisian perfume just like he did, and speed and convertibles and sports cars...'

'And Jacques suffered a lot, Luis, you are right. He had to give up everything that life had given him. A few months before he died he was in Santander with me. I took him to the Tour of Cantabria, where he was the Honorary Director in the first car. At night we went to the Rhine hotel or to other bars along the Sardinero beach to eat shellfish, one of his weaknesses. And it was terrible. He had hardly any voice and didn't dare to drink wine, a well chilled Galician Albariño I offered him – compared to what he had been. You know, when I met him in '64, when you were still in short trousers, he used to fill the bidons on his bike with champagne and breakfast on oysters and strawberries like he'd picked as a child in Quincampoix with his father. During a stage his *domestique*s were under orders only to bring him beer when they raided the bars... And they dined on langoustine and roasts, and like Geminiani, his kindred spirit, used to say, his body was a distillery, like you've got in your armagnac store, Luis, which distilled everything that went in through his mouth and transformed it into strength and grace. He was touched by grace was Jacques, you know Luis. And he also seemed immortal, but that day in Santander he said to me, "I've got cancer, Julito, I've got no stomach left. I've only got a few months to live." And his life was no life from then on, Luis, that's for sure. But there's progress all the time. Who's to say that there won't be a cure for yours? Who's to say there aren't new treatments and medicines which prevent the suffering, the pain, the agony, that can save you?'

It was difficult, now in the total gloom of that bare room, to continue talking with Luis, to endure his despair.

'I was with Fuente some weeks ago, with the Tarangu, and he too felt awful; his kidneys are wrecked. He told me he had to have dialysis every other day, but that night the two of us had dinner with Balagué and Hortelano in Bala's restaurant in Mieres and didn't leave till four in the morning. And we drank well and weren't affected by it, and we talked a lot without getting annoyed, we were in tune with each other, the Tarangu and I, knowing that if we had argued in the past it was because we were similar, two similar temperaments, two men who only knew how to die fighting, who used to finish stages dead on our feet because we refused to be calculating in our effort, it all came from our guts…

'We went there, Julio. I went with Hortelano in the Espace, because I'm done with sports cars; now I go in the van, I go as a travelling salesman with my cases of sparkling wine and armagnac, selling door to door. I've got to live, Julio… We went to see Balagué and to spend a bit of time with him, and to see if he'd buy my latest wine from me, a splendid fortified white. However, he told me it was very expensive, so he couldn't buy a bottle from me as it cost 10,000 pesetas, because what price would he have to sell it at? But we drank a bottle and we dined well and we talked and talked. Bala is a mine of information and memories. He joined Bic in Pérez Francés's last year, and was his best *gregario*, the only one who could put up with his bad temper, and then we got on well together and I regard him as a friend: he comes to my house to spend Christmas and I go to his. And there he began to remember old times, how he'd helped me in the Tour, although he wasn't in my team. How he'd started out with the Ferrys amateurs, "the best team in the world," he insisted. "We were the pure Spanish selection," he said. "It was Tamames and López Rodríguez, Luis. We went up north to the Tour of Bidasoa and other races, and you were there, with Aranzabal and Manzano, in the team which Labadie organised for you, and we did well; they were good fights. Then as a professional I saw straight away that I was no champion and I quickly learned to do whatever was demanded of me. And to do it well".'

'Balagué is definitely one of the good guys, Luis.'

'He also said, "You know, Luis, I don't know how they can talk, as I've heard them do around here, about you being a complicated person. You have a temper and you're strong willed and you're very Spanish, and you know we're like that in Spain; we always favour the foreigner. If it's someone who isn't one of us who has to win, we want it to be the foreigner, not a compatriot. And that's what we are like, Luis, as you know only too well. We're terrible." That's what Bala told me, and he knows me very well. "And sometimes you scare with your look and your voice, but you are clear; there's never any backsliding. One word from you and it's binding; it is as good as law. Do you remember the Vuelta of '70, Luis,?" he asked me. Of course I was going to remember the Vuelta I won I told him. "And I was riding for Werner, together with Tamames, who made you sweat blood, remember? And you asked me for help. 'The Bics are not good enough,' you said to me during one stage. 'I'll give you half a kilo[1] if you give me a hand.' No sooner said than done, Luis. I helped you; you paid me the money. Not like others, who ask, promise, then forget, Luis." And Bala had remembered that, while I had almost forgotten that story, but I hadn't forgotten the Marotías and our devotion to those frames which Marotías made for us in Aegría de Oria, that village in the Basque Country where he had his workshop. He was like a tailor, Marotías, he took your measurements and made you the perfect bike, although it always tended to be on the large size, which was as fashionable then as flared trousers and kipper ties and wide, exaggerated jacket lapels. It was made with Reynolds or Columbus steel tubes which we often picked up on the sly from Portugal where they were cheaper. Sometimes I saw him at work, as methodic and precise as a surgeon, slipping the tube into the lug, applying the blowtorch on the lug and when it was red, thoroughly red, fresh cherry red, since he liked to be precise, that was when the steel reached just the right temperature,

---

1. half a million pesetas

only then did he apply the silver or the metal which fixed the brazing. It didn't even need the lugs to be filed. The frame was perfect straight off. It was rigid and light, and it didn't flex or bend: we called it the Rolls Royce of frames. I always used Marotías from when I began in Fagor, where he made them for the whole team, and old Marotías, who was a Cantabrian who'd gone to set himself up in the Basque Country, treated me like royalty. Later, in Bic, I used the frame painted in the orange of Motobecane, which was the team's official bike and with their transfers. When I called him, Marotías would appear from wherever I was riding, driving through the night with a frame in his car and my mechanics had it fitted out by one or two in the morning with a Campagnolo groupset – gears, chainset and rings. And to reduce weight by a few grams, my mechanics drilled the chainrings, the brake levers and parts of the derailleurs with a very fine, accurate drill. They were artists; they knew how to do it perfectly so that nothing was broken – on a climb a gram is a ton weight. One of them, who lived in Toulouse and worked in the Airbus factory, managed to get some titanium screws to put on my bike to lighten it further.

'I always rode Marotías bikes, well, almost always because in my final years I met Jean-Pierre Doléac, another artisan who started making magnificent frames in Muret, just next to Toulouse, and they were more close fitting. Fashion had changed and you didn't have to lower the saddle almost down to the crossbar to be able to reach the pedals, and I used a Voltaire saddle instead of the Brooks that everybody had. But Jean-Pierre only made bikes for a short time; he couldn't compete with the big manufacturers. He was so good that he set up a business to make aeroplanes and he's still there – a real engineer. Fuente told me that he used a Marotías as well, although his team, Kas, had their frames made by Faliero Masi, who had his workshop under the terraces of the Vigorelli velodrome on the via Arona in Milan. Faliero, who was very famous, and even embarked on making mass-produced Masis in California, also made Eddy Merckx's frames when he was with Faema and Peugeot. Then Merckx wanted to change to Marotías but he didn't get along with the old man. But Fuente, yes, Fuente was a devotee of Marotías, and of Rudy, who made our shoes for us, also to measure, in Bera de Bidasoa. And Balagué also told me that he was able to go to Marotías thanks to me. "It was because I was with you that the old man took any notice of me," Bala reckoned. "Because he had so many orders he took almost a year to make a frame for anyone who didn't have any influence. I remember that Fulgencio didn't stop nagging him about when his bike was going to be ready, and every time he called Marotías, he'd put it back further; the old boy was a bit of a character, Luis. But he made an exception with me, because of you. I remember one night he brought the frame to your house in France; he had to deliver one that you'd ordered and that was the easiest way to do it. It was already daybreak when I got back into Spain, so pleased with the new frame in the boot. Going through the frontier at Hendaye they searched the car and they thought the frame was being smuggled, and they wanted to take it away from me, but the chief customs man turned up and he was a cycling fan. He recognised me and let me go through, The only thing he said to me, Luis, was 'You don't have a racing cap, do you?'"

'But I've always heard,' interrupted Julio courteously, 'I've always heard that in the '73 Tour you rode some stages on a bike made entirely of titanium. A superb and extremely light frame; I don't know who told me that it only weighed one kilo, two hundred grams. Who made the titanium one? Was that Marotías as well?'

'The business with the titanium bike was another story altogether. It was in the February of '73, and we were in Seillans, in the Var, in a little village there, very pretty, very provincial, where De Muer always took us to prepare for the new season. As usual, what we spoke about most was equipment, whether there was anything new, what Campagnolo had brought out, if there were any lighter wheels…and there we were talking about all this in the cafeteria of the Hotel de France, when an English journalist behind me cleared his throat. "Ehem. Ehem. Excuse me for butting in on your conversation but I think I must tell you of something which will interest you greatly." Very well mannered, in very correct French, but with a distinct flavour of English. "What would you think," he went on, "if I told you I knew somebody who could make you a bicycle which, complete, fully set up, weighed 7.8

kilos? That I was mad, right?" And confronting our protests, us telling him that he was talking about Vitus aluminium frames, the journalist shouted that they would only allow you to contemplate a 9 kilo bicycle and that they were used by De Gribaldy's team, and that the lightest steel bike was almost 10 kilos. Then the journalist, whose name I can still remember – Peter Duker – pronounced the magic word: titanium. "I know a firm in Birmingham where they can make a titanium frame to measure. It's expensive, because the manufacturing process is complicated, but I guarantee that it is the bike of the future. Isn't titanium used for aeroplanes and especial ships? Titanium is lighter than steel, stronger than aluminium, and as resistant to corrosion as stainless steel." And he began to tell us that a friend of his designed these frames; he was an engineer who specialised in suspension bridges and that his qualifications were in brazing without lugs. "But to braze titanium," he told us, "special conditions are necessary. If you come to the factory and see how they do it, you will think you are in a place for dealing with radioactive material. The problem with titanium is that it corrodes very easily when heat is applied, so it has to be brazed in a special chamber. It's a completely isolated room in which the tubes are left prepared and from which all the air is extracted, and then it is filled with argon, an inert gas. In one of the glass walls there are two circular holes which end in rubber gloves, sealed to the glass so that not a breath of air can enter. And that way the frames are brazed, each one taking no less than four hours, although what they're doing mostly now is motor-cross chassis…" That's what he told us, and also that the firm was called something like Speedwell. It was simple enough to give him my measurements for a frame, and then I forgot about the whole thing.

'But in June, in Lyons, before the start of the Dauphiné Libéré, the journalist Duker turned up in our hotel, together with the engineer, whose name, if I remember it, was Hugh Kirton, and he only spoke English. They'd brought with them a frame, wrapped up in a fabric bag. "Tell the mechanics to set it up," they asked me, and Claude and Robert were excited by the lightness of it – it weighed exactly 1.26 kilos – and set to work. Next morning, very early, before the start of the day's stage, I tried it out. "I like it and I don't like it," I told them. "I like the lightness and the responsiveness of the bike. I don't very much like the angles of the tubes; it worries me a bit because I can see it bending, and I don't like the ends of the front forks, their design, they give me the impression that at any moment the wheel is going to come out. But the forks, not having a crown, all made from one piece, strikes me as really beautiful." We hardly said any more. They picked up the frame and went back to England. Four days later, when the Dauphiné returned to Lyons, they appeared again with a new frame. They must have worked day and night during that time. The next day I used that frame in the final time trial, and it turned out to be magnificent, spectacular. I won the time trial and took more than a minute out of Thévenet, who'd been leading up to that point. And so I won my third Dauphiné. And I took the bike with me to the Tour and, with it being so light and rigid, I used it in all the mountain stages. And I used it when I crushed Fuente and everybody else on Les Orres, Julio. Then they made one for one of my friends at Bic, the veteran Agostinho, of course, and also for Leif Mortensen, and I even heard that Poulidor had got himself a titanium bike. But not long after that carbon came in and other makers discovered other alloys that were almost as light and much less complicated, and they began to churn out bicycles like sausages, and that was the end of titanium.

'Did you know, Julio, that Vallugera committed suicide? Vallugera was the only journalist who understood me, who didn't judge me for the most showy, the most superficial thing, but for what he saw within me. And I, in turn, understood him, although I hated the smoke from his Tuscan cigars. He was different from the rest. He created the Montjuïc hill climb and the Setmana Catalana and he liked me as if I were his little brother. And when the Tour gave him the long-service medal I was the one he handed it to, he didn't want anybody else to have it. He put up with life till he was 54. I don't think I'll live so long... My father died at 48, which is what I am now. Anquetil died at 53, Agostinho at 41...I have read somewhere that living to 50 is enough to do everything that it's possible to do in life, everything we need to do, that from 51 onwards we become bad and narrow-minded, we lose our personality, some of us become cowards. That's why, so they say, a lot of people commit suicide at 50, or around that age: it's because they have a sense of shame in carrying on living; they know they've no longer got anything to do.'

'Oh, Come on, Luis,' said Julio, irritatedly, or making out as if he was. 'Why on earth are you bringing Vallugera up now? He died nearly ten years ago! And to change the subject, tell me Luis, what are you going to do after the Vuelta? You'll go home, have a bit of a rest and recover, make yourself strong like we all want to see you...'

'After the Vuelta I'll pass through the house to change my suitcase and go straight off to Italy, to the Giro. Once more with COPE.'

'But how are you going to go to the Giro, Luis, in your state, with all the pains you've got? If you can hardly get through the stages, if you haven't got the strength to get up off the bed? If you don't get well...'

'I need the money, Julio. I need the money. I can't just pass up the Giro. And anyway, Josiane has sorted out all the tickets and reserved my hotels. It's all fixed now.'

And as if written by a dramatist, at that very moment they heard someone knocking on the door. 'Room service. I have your omelette Señor Luis...' and before either could reply the waiter came in, pushing a little table into the darkened room and instinctively switched on the light, which dazzled and disconcerted the two who were talking, turning their shadows into bodies, and transforming intimate night into broad daylight.

'No, don't switch it off. Leave it just like that,' Luis said to the waiter, who, as he left the room had tried to restore the darkness.

'Doesn't it strike you, Julio, that time goes more quickly, as if our short-term memory, our memory of what we've just talked about here, Julio, is shortened and abbreviated? It's as if it could do away with the insignificant moments of our recent past, as if they were accelerated, like the videos nowadays. It's not only the tape winding more quickly but also jumping tiny fragments, certain scenes.'

And before his visitor stops getting up because, discreetly, he wants to let him eat by himself, he begins to tell Julio another story.

4

'I didn't ride for love or for passion. I rode for money. Mind you, once I was riding I wanted to be the best; I wanted to destroy everybody, because that was in my nature, Julio, my personality, what the press and my team mates called, 'Ocaña's strong personality'. I did have a strong personality, very strong; I never just went along with things. I had the personality of a champion and if you talk to Eddy Merckx, he'll tell you that: the Cannibal always used to say, "my two rivals were Fuente and Luis, not Gimondi nor Motta nor Maertens, but those two crazy Spaniards." Wait, Julio, don't go yet. Have I ever told you about Juan Hortelano? I met Juan Hortelano (the father)…well, no, he met me rather in 1962 or '63. I was a kid and he a Spanish cyclist who'd emigrated to Pau with his family to ride in a French team. He was, as I remember him, tall, blond, slim; he looked like a Hollywood star with those bright blue eyes. I was riding in a race in some village around there and I broke my bike, and he was there because he was racing later with the professionals, and seeing that he spoke Spanish, my father, who'd come with me that day, went up to him and asked him if he could lend me his bike. And he did. Well, obviously he did, otherwise there wouldn't be a story.

'A few years later, when I was becoming known, I went to race in the Madrid velodrome, and there was Juan Hortelano. Juan Hortelano Poderoso was his full name, with that magnificent maternal surname, and he said to me, "You don't remember me, do you?" And I said that I certainly did, that I never forgot someone who'd helped me. I shall never forget him, neither him nor his wife, Milagros Peñalver, the sister of some cyclists, who loved me like an older sister. We talked and we saw that we had a lot in common. Although he lived in San Fernando de Henares, in the suburbs of Madrid, he too had roots in a village in Cuenca, Atalaya del Cañavate – do you know it, Julio? And he too was the son of a victim of the reprisal after the Civil War – he'd been an officer in the Republican army. This won't alarm you, will it, Julio, what with your father being a driver for one of Franco's generals?'

'Calm down, Luis,' replied Julio. 'You know me well enough and you know that with all the places I've been to and got to know, and the freedom and the the good things that came from democracy, and sexual freedom and the happiness of pretty young girls, and their carefreeness when I was riding in France in the 60s it would have been difficult to believe in Franco...'

'Juan has another brother who was a cyclist, Amalio, the best trackman in Spain, king of the Six-Days, and, I believe, a regular companion in your adventures, like Anquetil was, like so many were. And Juan has a son, also called Juan, who was born right there in Pau in those years when his father was working there. And you know him, too, although not as well as I do; he's my friend and he helped me. He was also a cyclist but a poor one. He tried to be a director but he didn't have any success with that either. But it's perhaps thanks to him and to his huge generosity, that I'm still here.'

5

One day during the Tour of 1982, after the Orcières-Merlette stage, Felix Lévitan summoned Luis Ocaña to his hotel. The meeting intrigued Luis, who still had his contract with Antenne 2 to comment on the race. Lévitan was one half of the professional Goddet-Lévitan marriage, which for decades had dictated everything that happened and ought to happen in the Tour. While Goddet, who also wrote epic reports for *L'Équipe*, dealt with what could be called its purely sporting aspects, Lévitan was responsible for its economics – the sponsors, the need to generate a bigger income every year. It was his idea for the Tour to finish on the Champs Elysées, which occurred for the first time in 1975, and also for the temporary return to national teams instead of commercial teams (so that the sponsors didn't overshadow their own riders). The last idea he had thought about was to make the Tour an 'open' race – opening its doors to the great amateur teams like the Soviet Union or the Colombians, so the business would be more worldwide.

Luis still didn't know about this when, on his way to the Tour organisers' hotel, through the same Orcières-Merlette streets in which in 1971 he had killed Merckx as surely as El Cordobés kills the bull in the bullring, he tried to guess the reasons for the meeting. He wanted to believe that Lévitan had in mind him using his recollection of that year to criticise the Spanish performance this year, because it had been dire. Only one Spanish team, Teka, had been invited. Only ten Spanish riders had been on the start line in Basilea, and of those only the climber, Alberto Fernández, had made an impact, although that had been limited when up against the current giant, Hinault, and his Dutch acolytes, Zoetemelk, Winnen and Van der Velde. Marino Lejarreta, who had been awarded the last Vuelta, was an hour down on general classification, and the second best of the Spaniards. If he presents me with all that, thought Ocaña, I shall tell him that he's right, that Spanish cycling is cycling from a different period and of a different kind. In his time, when he went to ride the Vuelta a España, he was up against almost impossible opposition – riders like Tamames, Linares, full of strength and resources – such that he was only able to win one Vuelta. But then those same riders went to the Tour, two months later, and ended up at least an hour behind the leaders. And I'll also tell him, he thought, that during the last Vuelta they had told him about their hopes for the future; they'd told him, and he'd seen with his own eyes, so he had asserted it publicly that Echávarri's boys in the Reynolds squad, Arroyo, Laguía, Delgado had cycling in their legs and were keen to show it in the Tour. Although in the end, Arroyo had had the Vuelta taken away from him because of doping, Reynolds had won five stages. And so, Ocaña thought, 'If Lévitan asks me, I will tell him that the Spanish team he must invite to the next Tour is Reynolds.'

Ocaña was wrong. Old Lévitan, well mannered and courteous as ever, hardly said anything to Luis about Orcières-Merlette's golden past, or the present obscurity of Spanish cycling. He spoke to him about the future, about Colombian cycling.

'Next year,' he said, 'we will have an open Tour and we want the best Colombian amateurs to compete in it. We believe they deserve that opportunity. They won the Tour de Pourvenir a couple of years ago; they are spectacular in the mountains which is what the public likes, and their presence would allow us to open up markets in Latin America where we'll have great business opportunities. We need, however, a European expert to guide them through this adventure, somebody who really knows the Tour. And we thought about you, Luis. In addition to all that, you speak their language and you also have an attacking way of thinking which I like and which will sit well with those Andeans. Do you know anything about them, Luis?'

Luis said that he did, that the year before he had attended the RCN Classic, one of Colombia's major races and he'd enjoyed and admired it. 'I saw riders who don't exist any more in Europe, climbers who can fly,' he told the old boss of the Tour, whose eyes were popping out like Tío Gilito's when he dived into his swimming pool of gold coins[1]. 'I saw kids, knee-high to a grasshopper and slim as matchsticks,

---

1. Tío Galito – a Disney cartoon figure, Scrooge McDuck, based on Ebenezer Scrooge, and very rich.

who ride tirelessly, kilometre after kilometre over dirt roads full of potholes, at incredible altitudes, up never-ending hills, who can also ride at 60 an hour on the flat. And they're fearless. And I'll tell you something else, Monsieur Lévitan,' [he was a man you always had to treat respectfully; you never missed out the Monsieur]. 'I have seen something of me reflected in them because they show the same spirit and fierceness I did when I was in my prime. They are like me; they came out of poverty, they want to live from cycling. Their enthusiasm is boundless. I like them as riders, as people, as team mates, and make a note of these names, Monsieur Lévitan: Lucho Herrera, who still isn't yet 21, and wins everything over there and climbs like I only once saw Fuente climb; then there's Fabio Parra who's a bit older, more serious, more of a *rouleur*, but he too can fly in the Andes.' And then he told Lévitan that he didn't need to be asked twice, because he would even volunteer to take part if they decided to take the plunge in Europe.

In what remained of '82 and in '83, Ocaña went back to Colombia from time to time. He felt he belonged to the peloton again; he had finally got back into cycling. And he was back for the same reason he'd got into cycling in the first place, for money, to pull in enough to shore up the farm production, to deal with all the expenses, all his cravings, and the family's. And he was back because he also wanted to show how things should be done, how his kind of cycling, which made him unique, had not completely died during this period in which he saw it distinguished only by careful calculation and mediocrity. And that's what he told Lévitan, and that's why he accepted the challenge.

In June 1983 Belisario Betancur received in his presidential palace, the Casa de Nariño in Bogotá, the detachment of cyclists that would come together to conquer the Tour in the name of their country, and to hand over to them a Colombian flag as a symbol which they would have to stab into the heart of France in the Alps and the Pyrenees. There were the directors of the Federation, and of Varta, the battery firm which had agreed to meet the expenses. And there was Luis Ocaña, just as elegant as only he knew how to be on the grand occasions, and there too were his colleagues in the management of the team:

Martín 'Cochise' Rodríguez, the first Colombian cyclist to achieve international renown, *gregario* to Gimondi in the great European races, amateur hour record-holder and world pursuit champion; and Rubén Darío Gómez, nicknamed the 'Lynx of Pereira', who as a cyclist had beaten the great Efraín Forero in a Tour of Colombia. The ten riders finally selected were Alfonso Flórez, whose victory in the 1980 Tour de Pourvenir was an historical first, the veteran Patrocinio Jiménez, Samuel Cabrera, Cristóbal Pérez, Edgar 'Condorito' Corredor, Alfonso López, Rafael Tolosa, Abelardo Ríos, Fabio Casas and Julio Rubiano. It wasn't possible to nominate Herrera, as Ocaña would have liked: he was then 22 and the Tour didn't want to admit riders under 23.

Some weeks before the beginning of the Tour Ocaña set the team up in a hotel in Nogaro, which was used to receiving sportsmen, since its cliental consisted essentially of racing drivers and motorcyclists who came to compete on the Paul Armagnac circuit. Ocaña lived nearby, which was convenient for him and it wasn't far from the Pyrenees, where they went regularly during their stay to get some idea as to what was awaiting them – the Tourmalet, the Aubisque, the Aspin and the Peyresourde, the Pyrenean giants which were so different from the much longer, much higher cols they were accustomed to. Ocaña was enthusiastic about what he saw.

His enthusiasm didn't last long.

The early stages of the Tour run over the flat plains of the north, where the rain, the wind and the Roubaix *pavé* were very hard for the Colombian riders, as well as for the Spaniards in Reynolds, making their Tour debut. The stories of the first stage for both groups were comical: attacks in the neutralised zone, crashes, clumsiness, fear. On the third day there was a team time trial over 100 kilometres. Ocaña's Colombians were inevitably last. That night they didn't sleep, beset by nightmares about what they could look forward to the following day – the *pavé* of Roubaix. It was cold, the sky was grey and the Pyrenees were a long way off. Chaos reigned, and the first disagreements surfaced. Ocaña and Conchise spoke the same language, Spanish, but from a cycling point of view they didn't understand each other. Nor could the Spaniard tolerate the Colombian journalists – more than 40 of them – who, according to him, didn't leave them alone for a minute, hounding them in the hotels, at the start, at the finish, demanding their attention and preventing them from concentrating on their job.

According to what all the European reporters were repeatedly saying, half in admiration, half in jest, three radio stations – Radio Caracol, RCN and Radio Todelar – were transmitting colourful broadcasts of each stage, spearheaded by Caracol, the star radio broadcaster of the whole Tour with a nine-hour live programme, starting an hour before the start of the stage. They had available a team of five technicians, a pilot, four drivers, eight radio announcers and journalists, and four interpreters. And they moved about in three mobile units, a motorbike and an aeroplane which served as a radio relay. A studio rented in Paris served as an intermediary in the operation. Via satellite, the Colombians covered every minute of each stage and the unfolding story of the 'pedallers on their little iron horses'.

'It's them or me.' said a wishful thinking Ocaña. To the press he declared: 'Every day we have to face up to an absolute invasion. The situation is really getting beyond a joke. If there are no signs of better cooperation I shall resign, although I can't see how they'll get along without me.'

In the end it was them, and Ocaña was the one who felt marginalised and not listened to. The 'beetles', as the Colombian cyclists began to be called, preferred the advice of their compatriot technical staff, the directors they'd known all their life, and rode senselessly on the flat stages, wore themselves out before the mountains, and didn't achieve their objectives. Two of them, the best two – Patrocinio Jiménez, who made life difficult for Van Impe in the battle for the Mountains jersey, and Edgar Corredor – finished in the top 15. And Luis Ocaña, who stayed away from the project once the Tour was over, relied on both of them for his next cycling venture, and his next inevitable conflict.

6

At the end of September 1983, Ocaña was more preoccupied by a telephone call which he hadn't received at his house at Caupenne than by the grape harvest which that autumn would be non-existent. Worse than any other year, the hail in August had devastated the vineyards, ruined the season and increased his debts. The call which Luis was impatiently waiting for was from Bernard Hinault.

'I don't understand why we haven't had news from Hinault. A week ago he said that within 24 or 48 hours everything would be sorted out.'

In the kitchen, after dinner, with a bottle of Coca Cola on one side and a bottle of cheap whisky on the other, from which he took long alternate slurps, Luis wanted to share his worry with Josiane, his patient accomplice in a project that could change their future.

It all began in the summer, during the almost catastrophic Tour with the Colombians. It was a race that resulted in the divorce between Cyrille Guimard and his star, Hinault, who'd won four Tours with him but, exhausted and injured after an extraordinarily hard Vuelta a España, had been forced to miss the Tour. In his absence, Guimard had discovered the tremendous potential, the strength and ambition of Laurent Fignon, and had decided to construct the Renault team's future around the Parisian. There was going to be no room for the Breton. No sooner had his manager, Daniel Dousset, told him the story than Ocaña moved quickly. He called his friend, Guy Merlin, and told him they had a great opportunity in front of them to establish a team with Hinault. Merlin gave him the green light and Ocaña set out, without realising it, towards another disaster, another clash with a reality that he couldn't see. As if it were his fate, or his own ignorant ineptitude.

Guy Merlin and his brother Roger were two builders who had made a fortune putting up huge apartment buildings in the dunes on the cold Atlantic beaches of the Vendée, south of Nantes. Great believers in the publicity value of cycling, they chose the Tour as a basis for getting to the masses who were eager to own an apartment right next to the beach. Their banners adorned the roads of the Tour at the beginning of the 1970s and their graffiti dirtied the tarmac. A number of times they managed to get the Tour to have a stage in their urban development known as Merlin Plage, presented an apartment to the winner of the Tour and even, in 1974, together with Flandria bicycles, sponsored the team that Guimard had ridden for. And, as if that weren't enough, they'd made friends with Ocaña. Now, with him and with the promise of Hinault, they were ready to make a return to cycling.

'And remember, Josiane,' Luis continued in the kitchen, 'how enthusiastic Hinault was when I told him about the possibility of the team: Merlin as sponsor, Philippe Crepel, who rode with me at Bic, as manager, and me as director. We met at the beginning of September in Paris. I told him what I could do; he told me what he required and we reached an agreement. We drank champagne to seal it. "I give you my word as a Breton," he told me, ending up getting quite emotional. "In two days at the latest I will call you to confirm the agreement." And as soon as the word got out that I had a sponsor, (as you know, Josiane, in this little world a secret doesn't remain a secret for ten minutes) I began to get called with crazy proposals – from the Italian Malvor, from Teka, and even from Kelme; they called to offer me their set up. They'd welcome me, Merlin and Hinault – and even without Hinault they'd be happy with an agreement. I said no to all of them because I had Hinault's word. And here I am and he hasn't called.'

The person who did call the following day was Dousset, a man Luis trusted and had total faith in. Although now retired from business, old Daniel Dousset was still one of the people best informed about what was happening in that little world of cycling. There was nobody who didn't know Dousset, nor who, when he was at his peak, wasn't afraid of him. After confirming that life in the velodrome didn't bring you in more than enough for mere survival, and that he definitely had a talent for fixing races and moving about in the mire of betting, Dousset set up his office in his wife's bar in Paris after the Second World War. It was conveniently located close to the Velodrome d'Hiver, the heart of cycling in France. From there he began managing riders' careers and subjecting teams and organisers to his strong arm tactics. His real strength came from the post-Tour criteriums, which for many riders represented their major source of income for the year, more than their salary or prize money. Dousset was not the only agent, but he had the best riders and in the '60s he ruled over everybody. His squad was the Geminiani squad; it contained Anquetil and Darrigade, the most brilliant and spectacular, and the most magnanimous. His main rival was Roger Piel, whose figurehead was, naturally enough, Poulidor, taciturn, tightfisted, a farm worker, but not a labourer; he was the son of a small property owner and was tied to the land. Julio Jiménez, friend of Anquetil and Geminiani, also made his money with Dousset, and for Ocaña the most natural thing in the world was that he should end up in Dousset's stable. Guimard no; Guimard in Mercier colours, like Poulidor, was a Piel man.

'Hinault has deceived you, Luis,' said Dousset over the telephone. 'I've learned that Hinault has signed a contract with a very doubtful business character called Bernard Tapie, and also mixed up in it is your friend Crepel, who has been signing up riders. He's now got Arnaud, Marc Gómez, Le Guilloux... And as director they are reckoning on a Swiss who rode with De Gribaldy, but who hung up his bike years ago, Paul Koëchli. They've fucked you, Luis! Well and truly.'

Instead of phoning Hinault immediately, Ocaña put the telephone down and waited. He knew that if the news had reached Dousset, it wouldn't be long before it became public, and the Breton would have to call him to tell him that he had tried everything but it was impossible, that there was no place for him in the new team. The call was not long in coming. Luis listened attentively; he heard what he expected to hear, and replied with a calm, measured fury. 'You're a fucking crook, Hinault. You've laughed at me; you only wanted me because I had a sponsor; the moment you found another you dropped me. But Bernard, just remember, I even got to announce everything I did for you, that all you needed was a quiet environment in which to relaunch your career, and I was able to provide you with that...' And Luis let it all out on the phone, and when he hung up he didn't feel the relief he thought he would, but the emptiness of distress, the nothingness. 'And now what do I do?'

Hope against hope, incapable of understanding the logic of the changes that had happened in the world of cycling, Ocaña still wanted to believe he could persuade the Merlin brothers to carry on even without Hinault. 'I have Bernaudeau,' he told them, 'and I can get Arroyo, the best Spaniard, a sensation who is going to win the Tour one day – remember he was second this year. And also the best Colombians will come with me, Patrocinio and Corredor...' The Merlins would not be swayed; they didn't even mellow when Luis reminded them of the great party they'd paid for in the Folies-Bergères when he won the Tour, to which he invited more than 1,000 people, among them Marie-Jo, who was his private little pleasure. How he'd made them enjoy themselves that night, which ended with them walking down the Champs Elysées, glass in hand, in the early hours of the morning.

'No,' they said.

The only door left open to him was one that he hesitated to go through, the one offered by Teka's manager, Santiago Revuelto. He was a man to be feared, a man of great truths and measured words who created mistrust. He had promised Ocaña six million pesetas. Revuelta ran Teka and simultaneously organised the Tour of Cantabria and never stopped quarrelling with the Spanish Federation. He was forever talking about great signings, which never came to anything. There were riders like Arroyo who preferred to ride for other teams for less money than believe in Revuelta's promises and to put up with his intimidating personality. Ocaña was fundamental to Revuelta's plans, which involved going back to the Tour again, taking with him the two Colombians whom Lévitan liked so much, and being welcomed and on first name terms with the Tour's organisers.

'And I won't bring you Lucho Herrera, who is the best in the whole of Colombia because he's still very young and his federation won't give him permission,' Ocaña told Revuelta at Barajas airport one November day in 1983. That day Patronicio Jiménez and Edgar 'Condorito' Corredor had committed themselves to ride for Teka and to move with their families to Santander. They both announced they were doing this on account of Ocaña, because they'd also had good offers from French and Italian teams.

Teka had been founded in 1976, on the skeleton of the Monteverde team, with its base in Santander and with money from the German maker of ovens and sinks. Before Ocaña, Teka's long line of directors had included the home-grown Julián San Emeterio, Miguel Moreno, Txomin Perurena, who had just finished his career with Kas at the age of 36, Antón Barrutia and finally José Antonio González Linares, who'd been the absolute ruler and had given up half his throne to Ocaña only with the greatest reluctance. The agreement with Revuelta displayed the judgement of Solomon: Ocaña would direct the team abroad, especially in the Tour, and Linares would take charge in the Spanish races. Teka was a team of the transition towards modernity, between the days of Kas, Werner and Fagor towards the splendour of the 1980s with Reynolds, Moliner, Kelme and finally ONCE. And there embarked Ocaña, who neither knew nor understood the intricacies of Spanish cycling, so small, so treacherous, so complicated that it was to overwhelm him. His beginning was not a very glorious premonition.

7

One cold, sunny Saturday in January Luis Ocaña arrived in Santander. Sitting in a wheel chair he spoke to the 24 riders who made up the Teka squad at the team presentation, the great Spanish team. They applauded him, emotion overcoming any wariness. Rather than imagining a cripple was going to direct them towards their conquest of France, they preferred to think that it was a great champion who had directed his words to them, and although the wheelchair had come as a surprise, it would nevertheless not be permanent. And even the famous comic actor, Andrés Pajares, who Revuelta had got to introduce the event, was sufficiently moved to forget his joke.

Ocaña's temporary disability was due to another car crash. A month earlier, on 22 December, two days before his 17th wedding anniversary, a lorry had jumped a stop sign on a local road near Nogaro and the car that Ocaña was driving crashed into it. Again he escaped by a miracle, although with some broken bones and more injury to his already damaged left eye, in which he was now almost blind. Josiane was close to the truth when she remarked, 'Oh Luis, my dear, when you went on a bicycle you often fell off, but you never broke anything; now, in a car, in every accident you break half your bones.' To which Luis invariably replied, 'but I'm alive my love, I'm still alive and with you.' The most serious harm was to a knee and to one eye, which sent him twice to the operating table, put him in a plaster cast and a wheelchair for some weeks, and rekindled the fear that he would finally lose the sight in that eye, whose circulatory wall would need to be reconstructed.

His continuing physical decline did not affect either his unrealistic optimism, or his capacity for self-deception. His was the optimism of willpower, a denial of pessimism, of feeling, of premonition. Like a porn actress who is engaged to appear in a film just to show off her breasts, but who is then told she has a future in dramatic art, Ocaña was given his contract at Teka only because of his prestige in the Tour, but was told he would be a great *director deportivo*, as great as he had been as a rider, which was never going to happen.

In his first big test as director of a cycling team, in the Dauphiné, a race which, as a cyclist, he had loved so much, his failure was total. His Colombians collapsed, unable to cope with the climbs. And this wasn't a question of racial inferiority, or it didn't seem so, because this Dauphiné of '84 was the Dauphiné of Martín Ramírez and of Pacho Rodríguez, of Reynel Montoya and of Pablo Wilches. In the hard, burning Alps the beetles cut down the haughty Hinault, who wanted to make his comeback with La Vie Claire, together with Lemond who was beginning to shine and the emerging Roche. And Ocaña's Tekas? They were invisible, and in the Tour the situation would get worse.

After the Dauphiné Ocaña brought his Colombians together in Nogaro. They were given some medical tests, and the analysis revealed they were anaemic, their haemoglobin was low and they were lacking in iron. They'd found the cause of their weakness in the Dauphiné, but not the reason for their physiological problems, which could not be solved before the Tour. In the Pyrenees, on the first mountain stage, Corredor abandoned and Jiménez held on as best he could. Not even Pedro Muñoz, a serious-minded Catalan climber whom Ocaña liked and had confidence in, resisted the lure of abandoning. Ocaña believed in Muñoz like he believed in himself, because he saw him as somebody marginalised by the mediocrity of official cycling in Spain, because he was cold and kept his mouth shut, and was not very well liked by his team mates and, on top of that, he was capable of standing up to Revuelta and speaking out loud to him. Ocaña thought, 'This one's like me; he's a rebel.' But he wasn't a rebel at all, and when the moment of truth came Pedro didn't give Luis what he was expecting. Luis despaired, and called him a buffoon. He called them all buffoons because none of them gave him what he expected, without realising that he was expecting the impossible, that cycling had changed. Muñoz went under and Ocaña publicly ranted against them all. He couldn't carry on in Teka.

8

'Open your eyes, Luis. In Spain your ideas are worth nothing; They're not worth twopence.'

Luis was in Spain, in Madrid, on that hot mid afternoon in August. He was in the noisy, dusty, dirty Plaza de Atocha, in the shadow of that ugly scalextric, sweating and shouting over the metallic counter of the Brillante bar to make himself heard. He was wolfing down a squid sandwich and when he put it down on the bar to take a swig from a little bottle of chilled Mahou beer he looked at himself in the mirror facing him. He felt well; he felt strong. Beside him his friend, the young Juan Hortelano, was trying to make himself understood between the various noises – the cars, the customers, the glasses against the metal, the CD player, above the mixed fumes from car exhaust pipes and cigarettes, over the mixture of smells of stale cooking oil and half burnt diesel from slow old Pegaso lorries.

Luis liked being there. He liked Danny Daniel and his 'For the love of a woman' which was playing at the time on full volume. He knew it from memory and was singing it to himself and singing it with feeling. He liked the cheesy lyrics and he liked the squid sandwiches and the pork stew and the rice with cod which Milagros, Juan's mother, always cooked for him when he dropped by her house.

Juan was a strong kid of just over 20, and Luis trusted him, confided in him, and accepted his advice. If there was no pork stew, it would be raw onions and tomatoes. Whenever he went to Madrid, and recently he'd had reasons for doing so, he stayed in Milagos's little house in San Fernando de Henares, a village in which they were beginning to build those large blocks of flats, and destroying the character as fast as they could. But in Jardines Street, which was short and quiet, Ocaña could still park his Jaguar outside the door and walk into the house, shouting, 'Milagros, give me some old stockings' and go out with a bucket of water overflowing with foam to wash the car. He wore high boots and overalls which Juan senior lent him, and the pupils from the school opposite went out into the street to watch him and to enjoy seeing the care and pampering he lavished on his white Jaguar coupé, which was always sparkling. And none of them knew they were looking at Luis Ocaña; none of them even knew who Luis Ocaña was, and to Luis Ocaña that didn't matter a bit. And when he was satisfied after washing, drying and polishing his white car, Luis went into the house in this village surrounded by monstrosities to eat some gachas[1] at Milagros's kitchen table.

And after that he said to her, 'Can you give me the telephone directory?' and he then asked for a biro. 'I'm going to give you a note of Marie-Jo's number. She's a friend of mine from France, a brunette, the daughter of the cyclist Martínez, who came to watch me in one race when she was little more than a girl and we started seeing each other.' And as he saw a sign of worry on Milagros's kindly face he reassured her: 'My love – and you know that very well, Milagro – my only love is Josiane, and she'll never stop being so, but sometimes I need something more, something different, another passion. You know what Josiane says to me, that I am Gemini – that deep down I am two Luises in one, one luminous and one sombre, one who likes blondes and one who goes for brunettes. And perhaps she's right, but Josiane will always be my love, and you know that, Milagros. Josiane tells me, "Luis, you are the sun and the light and your smile is worth everything, and when you are happy I wouldn't want to be with anybody else in the world; I'd only want to spend the rest of my life listening to you laugh." That's what Josiane said to me, Milagros. She also said, "But when you are dark, Luis you are frightening; when you dress only in black, your black shirts, your trousers; when you paint about death and cemeteries and you recite Espronceda's poems[2] to me. You frighten me, Luis, like this dark, black, heavy furniture for a medieval castle that you've made for our house, makes me unhappy." Josiane also tells me that, Milagros.

'My life is a continuous conflict, a quarrel, a fight. And sometimes I think I always choose the worst solution, the clash, the confrontation. Do you know, Milagros, my son can't stand me? He looks at me and

---

1. Gachas – simple, traditional dish based on toasted flour.
2. José de Espronceda – C19th Romantic poet.

I see myself in his big, mysterious eyes, a well into which I wouldn't dare go, in his big hands, in his contempt for authority, in his rebellion. I see him like that and I see myself as I saw my father, his bad temper, his hitting, his discontent, his arrogance, his singular, unquestionable authority against which I rebelled, Milagros. Jean-Louis believes that he despises me, but he is still very young – he's 16. He believes that he is like me, that he will grow up to be like me, and he wants to make me angry. He doesn't want to ride a bike; he prefers to play rugby. And I have always refused to go and watch him play. He doesn't say anything, but I can see in his face he feels bad that it is like that. I went for a ride with him and when I accelerated a little he was finished. He said he didn't want to ride; he didn't want to be like me; that he liked motorbikes.

'When I go home he shouts at me. "Before when you were always away from home I missed you. I wanted to be with my dad. Now that you're here all day I don't need you. I just want you to clear off on some journey." Jean-Luis has a revolting, very long mane of hair; it is his pride; he calls it his personality, and it makes me feel ill every time I see it; it's so dirty. One day I waited till he was asleep, took a pair of scissors and I cut off his mane. I can't stand the squalor of it, Milagros. When I get back home after some trip I'm afraid of it. I'm afraid of meeting my dirty son, with the tools carelessly thrown about the workshop in any old manner, the neglect, the doors of the bodega and the distillery, and the walls which I always leave whitewashed, dirty. The rafters no, not the wood. The wood isn't painted. Wood is wood, like the 50 banana trees I planted at the end of the patio to the house, a stretch of shade. It's the worst thing about coming home, coming up against reality, the laziness of my workers. My moody son.'

'In Spain, Luis,' Juan junior carried on shouting between bites of his squid sandwich. 'In Spain everything is more complicated than you think. Here the directors are also managers and have a lot of strength, a lot of power. And you, Luis, you are a danger to them: they think you're going to take something away from them, you a Frenchman who knows nothing about Spain, who doesn't know the cyclists here.'

'In Spain, Juan,' Luis belched after swallowing a good swig of Mahou and then replied, 'In Spain there's a lot of stupidity. Look at what happened to me with Teka. Before the Dauphiné I went to Santander to talk to Revuelta. And there he tells me he's fed up with Linares and he wants me to run the team by myself, that everything is a disaster and he has no faith in Linares. And what do I do, naïve as I am? Do I accept that and they bugger up things for Linares? Is that what I do, Juan? No. I'm loyal, and I tell Linares about it; I tell him to take care because Revuelta has put him on the black list. And what does Linares do, Juan? What does he do, that idiot who only thinks about saving his own arse? Does he thank me? Do you believe, Juan, that he thanked me, that fool? Absolutely not. What he does is to take the story to Revuelta; he goes and tells him that I am a pain in the neck, what a bastard I am, that I am creeping first to one then the other.

'And how does it all end, Juan? After the Tour Revuelta calls me again and shows me the door. "Good bye. Nice to have known you," he says to me. "What a disappointment you've been. You are a traitor and a liar and on top of that I find out that before the Tour you cleared off to Italy to negotiate the clothing of your new team for next year, and that during the Tour you were signing up riders for Fagor, who tell me that you will be directing them in '85, and that you are going to take Pedro Muñoz and Patrocinio Jiménez." And in passing, he says to me, "I'm informing you that instead of the six million pesetas we agreed upon, I shall be paying you only half, and don't complain because that's not bad for the five months you've effectively been working. You were a useless bit of crap who couldn't support himself and I saved your life."

'That's what he said to me, Juan, and you know, the only person who's ever supported me was my father. I invited Revuelta to my house and he spent three days there; I treated him like you would any guest, and he could see how I lived. Then he insults me by saying he hired a cripple whom he felt sorry for, and as you know, Juan, I had the accident a month after I'd signed for him, and it was he who called me, and I only replied to him when Hinault let me down. And I didn't miss a single race due to that accident. I started off in the Paris–Nice because I only managed to get the official driving permit by then. I didn't mess things up. And he sacked me, Juan, he sacked me.

'Do you know what I said to him? I told him what I thought of him and of the team he'd put together, and of his way of running it. I told him the only nice thing, the only good thing was the team bus; he'd dressed us like clowns with that hideous tracksuit; we looked a ghastly sight. He didn't give us suits; he didn't give us ties. I come from France, Juan. I'm used to riding with the greatest, of being the greatest. I was the only one who had the nerve to take on Merckx, the only one who put him on his knees, and here they carry on as if they don't know me, as if they don't know who I am. Here the people in charge of cycling were never more than middle ranking riders, and they look down on me. Who is Mínguez, Juan, and who is Carrasco, and Linares and Moreno? Who are they? Where do they come from? Linares was the best cyclist out of that lot, but he was a brute and a fool without any class.

'Echávarri, yes I knew him. A little fellow who spent one year with Bic, the year I arrived, and he rode a Setmana Catalana in my team, in '70 I believe, when Mendiburu retired. I thought I'd never seen him, but then he reminded me that we had met a couple of years earlier when I joined Fagor in '68. First of all they took us to Aránzazu, the sanctuary there in Oñate, and that famous priest, Cesáreo Gabarain, turned up. He was a singing priest from Guipúzcoa, who was in the Marist School in Madrid and he recorded records and everything, and he became famous with "Fisher of Men". He was called the cyclists' priest because he used to go to the Vuelta and he liked cycling a lot. He married Perurena and even set up an amateur team. He was in the team get-together there and he brought with him some young kids so they could see real cyclists. And in the Setmana, two years later, Echávarri told me that he was one of those kids who looked at us, full of admiration, their mouths wide open, and he even reminded me that he had a Seat 600 and that he dropped me down to Oñate one afternoon. Echávarri is a little different from the others because he respects me. And in fact, I told Lévitan, remember, that he should invite Reynolds to the Tour. Echávarri appreciates me for what I've been; he recognises what I've done and admires me as a cyclist. He knows what it all takes, and that nobody ever gave me any presents.

'But everybody now believes in a tightfisted kind of cycling, of careful calculation and of taking advantage of other men's work, of traps and trickery, Juan, but it's not like that. Cycling is for brave men; cycling was Merckx; it was me; it was Anquetil and Fuente, and cycling is Hinault and Fignon; it's attack until you drop and don't think about tomorrow. Spanish cycling is behind the times. It has no future. Where has all this come from? What have they gained as cyclists? What are they? When I talk and argue with Guimard it's a train crash – he is Guimard, one of the greats, although I row with him; and Thévenet and Zoetemelk, too. Those people are worth something.'

'You're in Spain, Luis,' his friend Juan again reminded him. 'You ask me how somebody who's been such a poor cyclist can be a director, and I say it's the other way round: only poor cyclists can be good directors because they develop their intelligence to take them where their legs can't. Do you remember what Miguel Moreno said to you? He told you that winning with bad cyclists is very difficult, but screwing it up for everybody with one bad cyclist is very easy. He told you that and I don't know if you understood it, Luis. If you continue thinking the way you do, you'll never fit in here. Here the fight is about survival, Luis, not for grandeur. It's always been like that, ever since the Catholic Kings in the fifteenth century. In Spain all that matters to us is survival and honour. And what do you do, Luis? You come here and you impose your personality in front of everybody, not like a shield but like a spear, and what you've managed to achieve is unanimity: everybody in Spanish cycling is against you. You are a very complex person, Luis. You don't have any tact, or diplomacy; the only thing you're good for is confrontation. And up to now, as a director, it's only with the Colombians that things have gone reasonably well for you, because they respect you and obey you, but not with the others; you haven't known how to win them over. You'll not make a good director, Luis; you're like Maria Callas, who never could teach singing. For you, cycling comes from the gut; nobody taught it to you; you rode according to how you felt, and Callas sang the same way;

her technique flowed from her heart. And the only people who can become good directors are those who were poor cyclists, because only the weak become astute and clever, and they'll learn how to win, and they'll teach how to win. Your character is your destiny, just as it's shaped your past. Your character for having challenged the best, your temperament for not knowing how to deal now with people who aren't seeking to crush nor be crushed.'

'That's worth nothing, Juan. Nobody anywhere in Spanish cycling knows who I am, that's the problem. They could have asked; they could have spoken to Guimard – just look at what he did as Hinault's and Fignon's director, or with Thévenet, who eventually dealt with Merckx. You know, Juan, more than once Thévenet said to me: "Yes, I beat Merckx, Luis, but you beat him before that, in '71, you had him on his knees, and if it hadn't been for your crash you would have carried away all the honours, and deservedly so." And he also said to me, Juan – fix this in your memory, remember his generosity because I've not seen it anywhere else – Thévenet said to me, "Luis, you are a proud nobleman because you're not content simply with winning. You have to do everything with daring, with a sense of the heroic, destroying your enemy. Sometimes I wonder about you, so Spanish in spite of thinking of yourself as French, because you are Spanish and you want to be Spanish, Luis. I sometimes think that if you were an object" – that's the way Thévenet once put it to me – "you would be the torero's muleta, with which he wants to subdue everybody, including Merckx. You've been the only one who has had the tenacity to do that; the only one who hasn't just talked about it; you've done it. And when you beat me in the '73 Tour, you took a quarter of an hour out of me, like Merckx would have done. You only wanted absolute victory. Winning by two or three minutes didn't interest you, Luis." That's what Thévenet told me one day during the Tour last year, when we happened to meet in the hotel, he as director of La Redoute and I with the Colombians. "You were Luis," he said, "and neither before nor after has there been anybody like you in the Tour. On just one day in the '69 Tour Merckx was a rider from another age, from the time when they destroyed the entire peloton behind them and won by minutes. But you, on the other hand, Luis, have been that twice – in '71 on Orcières-Merlette when you annihilated Merckx and everybody else following you, and in '73 on Les Orres in your duel on the Galibier with that great fighter, José Manuel Fuente, perhaps the best climber of all time, who's hardly ever mentioned now, forgotten by everybody." And I said to Thévenet that I excused him for calling me a nobleman and a torero, like everybody else did, and that, in fact, it was he who associated Spain with those principles of hopeless bravery and exaggerated pride, and I also told him that in the end I made my peace with Merckx, but that I'd never forgive him for not taking part in that Tour. There are always people who insist that I won that Tour because Merckx wasn't there; there always has to be a "but" in my life. But Thévenet pacified me. "Merckx preferred to ride the Vuelta because he was given a financial offer like none of us, including you, have ever received in our lives," he said, "but I'm convinced, Luis, that even if he had been there you would have won that Tour. Remember that Vuelta, the '73, Eddy beat us thanks to the time bonuses, but it cost him dear, and I remember that day on Orduña when you stripped the Cannibal naked with your tremendous attack."

'And I also spoke with Guimard, Juan. He was one of those who was fast in a small group, but he was never a great climber, and in spite of that he dreamed about winning the Tour. But the year when everything was going best for him he forced his knee too much, got injured and had to abandon. That was the end of his cycling career, there and then. Four years later – think about that, Juan, you who said great riders couldn't be great directors – as a director he won the Tour in '76 with Van Impe.

'That '72 Tour was bad for me, as well. I fell on the Aubisque and I carried on as best I could until pneumonia forced me to abandon in the Alps, when I was fighting with Guimard for second place. In the end it was Gimondi and Poulidor, two veterans who never made a move, who ended up second and third. And Guimard also came to talk to me one day, a long time afterwards: "Luis," he said, "you almost had the '71 Tour won. Merckx would never have won that Tour if you hadn't crashed on the Menté. That dark day when the road turned into a river of mud, I was on your wheel and was able to save myself with my quick reactions, but I don't know what would have happened if you hadn't fallen. You can't re-write history, that's true, but it's also true that neither champions nor anybody else have the right to talk about bad luck. Bad luck doesn't exist, because luck doesn't come about by pure chance, Luis. There are always dozens of little details which mean that in everyone's life, everyone's sporting career, things happen this way or the other way. In '72 if I myself hadn't had the problem with my knee Merckx wouldn't have won either, and you fell on the Aubisque stage, just when I had attacked on the descent… Life is as it is, Luis." That's what Guimard said to me. Behind his glasses there is a penetrating, intelligent look, and beyond the strong wine on his breath there is a head that thinks. "I know, too, why you defied Merckx, just you and not anybody else," he said. "You did it because you were, because you are, an arrogant, anarchic little bugger who won't accept authority and won't submit to anybody. And you're like that because your father was an authoritarian who used to harass you, Luis, and when you attacked Merckx in the Alps, really you were going for your father. That's how I see it, and how I used to see it and I can say that to you fearlessly because you yourself have told me about how hard your childhood was. And not only was Merckx your father, he was also that boss in the carpentry, the one you threw a hammer at. Luis, you've always had your principles and the more anyone tries to oppose you the more aggressive you become, and the worse you become, worse in the sense of arrogant. So then, Luis, you have the fierceness of the nobleman, and forgive me for bringing up the Spanish stereotype because, as you know, for us, for us French, Spain is Carmen, Bizet's Carmen, with bullfighters, jealousies, and absurd deaths over nothing. And that was you as a cyclist, and that is you as a director. That is the essence of you and that is your strength, and that is the very reason for your lack of restraint that makes you the first to explode, Luis."

'And Juan, what Guimard said to me, and he said it to me a number of times, nobody has ever said to me in Spain. Why's that? Why don't they like me in Spain? And Guimard knows what he's talking about; he knew how to tame Hinault's pride and ferocity and Fignon's aggression – don't forget that, Juan. And he didn't stop there. "I love you, Luis," Cyrille said to me the other day. "I love you because you are a courteous loveable boy and because you are the only rider who questioned Merckx's authority, not only his authority as a rider, but also his dictatorship, and that of his director, Driessens, and that of his manager, about the way cycling works. You were a magnificent rider but unfortunately you lacked one true cycling quality: you lacked riding skills. You don't have a great palmarés, much less than Merckx, but for me you undoubtedly have a much more attractive image, because you, Luis, you got across the emotion of the moment, the essence of cycling, while Merckx was cold, unemotional. You were all emotion, like Hinault was, but not Merckx, a cannibal."

'And Juan, so you can see that Cyrille was being sincere; he wasn't seeking to flatter me, look at what he also said, one night when we moved on from the wine to the whisky (and for me the Coca Cola, too). "But Luis," he said, "You never were very much a cyclist; you were never really into it; you weren't one of us. You didn't come to the track, nor to the cyclocross, and that's the reason you often fell: you went beyond your level of bike-handling skills and you took excessive risks. I can remember that now and again you'd say to me, before starting some stage, 'Today, Cyrille, I have a feeling that something unusual is going to happen to me; I believe I'm going to fall.' And inevitably, as I remember, that unusual thing ended up happening to you. Apparently you were an optimist, Luis, but you never had a positive premonition." That's what Guimard said to me one boozy, but honest night. He talked about my father, and he said something I've never forgotten: he reminded me of something which I already knew but would have liked not to have known. He told me I was a determinist, and I, as you know, always want to rebel against a destiny which I know is going to swallow me up. He said, "You are your father, Luis. Everybody is condemned to repeat, to be like their father. You, too, and also you and your son, and me and mine."'

'Yes, Luis, you are right about all that, and I'm not going to take any of that away from you,' said Juan, the mediator who didn't want to get embroiled in deep metaphysics. 'You have been great and were great, and in this little country we don't know how to recognise you for it, but you're not going to deny that Revueltas was partly right in what he said. You had already made up your mind to move to Fagor, and in the Tour you had been talking to Kelly and LeMond, who gave you the brush off.'

'But, make no mistake, Juan. Yes, I had done some work for Fagor, but I hadn't ignored Teka. If they kicked me out it was because of Linares's stupidity. The rest was just excuses. Don't get confused. A couple of months ago, Henri Labadie called me. He's a good friend, as you know and he's always helped me ever since my amateur days when he used to organise teams to race in Spain. It was always Aranzabal, Manzano and me, together with him, and we won the Tour of Bidasoa, which made me well known. He's always given me whatever I asked for, and he also had me in Super Ser. Well, Labadie called me from his office in Bayonne – as you know he's the Zeus distributor in the south of France – and he told me that Agustín Mondragón wanted to resurrect the Fagor team with Zeus bikes. I told him that I was with Teka and had a contract. A bit later Mondragón called me; he reminded me of the old days, how bad he felt about the way I left that Fagor team where I began, and he wanted me to go as the new Fagor director. "It's not going to be a Basque Fagor, nor a Spanish one, Luis, but a French team, registered in France and the majority of the riders will be French. It won't be long before Spain joins the Common Market and we need to establish our brand on the other side of the Pyrenees. And it's a good moment to return because at long last Spanish Television is broadcasting cycing live. I've got a budget of 150 million pesetas and I want a big team, really big. We'll need a Spaniard, I suppose. What would you say if we brought in Pedro Muñoz with you?" So I had him and Patrocinio. And we would also have Bernaudeau and De Wolf and a new Irishman called Early. And so I go to Fagor, although I'll not have the big names I wanted. And I'll show what I am worth since I consider this will be the first time I'll be working as a real *director deportivo*, with full responsibility. All this is in my hands. In Teka, remember, I was no more than a chauffeur.'

'Be careful, Luis,' Juan warned him while, at the same time, he threw into the wastepaper basket the serviette he'd used to wipe the last taste of battered squid from his lips. He made a gesture to the waiter: two coffees.

'Be careful, because Fagor and Spain have changed a good deal since fifteen years ago. Fagor is no longer the Fagor of Pedro Matxain, with whom you could sort things out with a couple of words. Fagor is now the symbol of the Mondragón Co-operative and Mondragón is also Eroski and Caja Laboral. Fagor are co-operatives with thousands of Basque workers, and they all have feelings and an ideology. Don't forget that, Luis. Be careful about what you're getting into. Do be careful.'

In Fagor, in the disaster that was Fagor in 1985, in his fleeting moment in the team, Luis was never careful. The year 1985 was one day of ambiguous glory and 364 days of misery.

Glory came on one of the last days of the Vuelta a España; the misery was endured daily, although a couple of days were especially hard to swallow. On one of them, the real Ocaña, the Luis we all know came to the fore. There are people, so it's said, whose nature softens with the years, who were once hard and sullen who become at least a bit more polite; and there are people whose temperament seems to be engraved in blood and fire in their genes – immutable, indifferent to the passing of time. That was Ocaña, and they told him so, those who, in spite of everything, loved him. "Luis, be reasonable, Luis, think before you speak because then you'll realise that you're wrong. Your pride stops you from rectifying what you've said and apologising, and the only person who loses is you, Luis." But, pushed by his own unique sense of what was true, Luis neither thought nor calculated. He spoke the way he pedalled, looking straight ahead, with no thought as to where he was going to end up, nor how.

From a sporting point of view, the year didn't begin badly. Pedro Muñoz won a stage in Paris–Nice and finished fifth in an overall classification that was dominated utterly in those years by the untouchable Sean Kelly. Then, in the Tour of the Basque Country, where the young Peio Ruiz Cabestany was the revelation, Muñoz had another stage win. A few weeks later, in the Vuelta, everything would slip from his grasp, but before that – one great day.

It was the stage from Albacete to Alcalá de Henares – 252 interminable kilometres, as straight as the crow flies, over La Mancha, and the promise of a strong wind. The previous night, in the Parador of Albacete, Luis and his friend Perurena had planned it all. In the overall standings, behind Robert Millar, the leader, came the Colombian, Pacho Rodríguez, at 13" and, at 1'–55" Ruiz Cabestany, the leader of Gin MG-Orbea, the team that Perurena directed. More than four minutes down was Pedro Delgado, also in Perurena's team.

'You won't remember, Peru, because by then I believe you were already in hospital recovering from a fall which had split your head open, but in 1970, in the Vuelta I won, we in Bic organised a curious strategy on the stage which came into Madrid, from Calatayud. There was a lot of wind that year, too, and it was a very long stage. The night before we asked the masseurs to prepare us some special provisions. We told them to cut a number of water bidons in half and fill them with rice cakes and jam sandwiches and the usual chocolate bars. And some kilometres before getting to the feeding zone, De Muer brought his car up close to the tail of the peloton and gave the bidons to a water carrier who shared them out among the four or five in the team, among them the strongest of our *rouleurs*, Johnny Schleck, that tremendous Luxembourger – do you remember him? – Roger Rosiers, a Belgian who thought that God's only mistake when he made the Earth was to allow any mountains, and Anatole Novak, a Frenchman as big as a lorry and, with his 85 kilos, almost as heavy. And when we got to the feeding zone, while everybody else was braking to get their bags, we went to the front and attacked as if our lives depended on it. In the end it all came to nothing because we were caught by Tamames and his Werner team, but we enjoyed it hugely. The stage was run at more than 40 per hour and we arrived in Madrid an hour ahead of schedule. The finish was in the Retiro, where you once won, Peru, and we were so early there were hardly any spectators there. As if that weren't enough, even the podium girls hadn't arrived, and they had to ask for volunteers among the few who were there to give the bouquet of flowers and the kisses to Schleck, who had just won. And the poor fellow had to do without the official girl who arrived a good deal later, all dolled up and straight out of the hairdressers.

And as he told the story, Ocaña felt like Napolean on the eve of a battle, applying his strategegic principles: knowledge of the terrain; the direction of the ambush; concentration of troops at the most unexpected moment and the effect of surprise.

'And what are you aiming at, Luis, that we do the same tomorrow? But what do you believe the others will think? What will your boss think? You're Fagor; I'm Orbea. It's fine for me because I can do something with Peio, who's a good *rouleur* and could strip Millar of his yellow jersey, but you, what do you get out of it? After Pedro Muñoz retired – what a leader he was, by the way – you haven't got anybody for the overall. There'll be trouble for you, Luis; they'll say you sold the stage.'

'No, don't worry about me, Peru. If all goes well one of the Fagors will win the stage and I will tell them all the truth, that I did it to help you. I'll say that you've been my friend for years, since I first joined Fagor, and you gave me a marvellous welcome. I'll say you are one of the most honourable people in Spanish cycling and it's a pity there aren't more like you. I'll also say that I did it because I felt it was a shame that such good lads as your Cabestany and Delgado, with such a future, couldn't win the Vuelta. Along with that I'll say that I'd already given you a hand during the Tramp stage, when Millar and Kelly made that ambush and Cabestany lost the yellow jersey, with no other Spanish team willing to help him and Perico Delgado. That's what I'll say and I won't lie because it's true. What's more, if that's not enough, we are crossing the plains of Cuenca, my territory, and there I've got the right to make a mark on the day.'

The following day, now in the province of Cuenca, a few kilometres after passing through El Provincio, on the way to the feeding zone at Las Pedroñeras, where they grow the best garlic, on a never ending straight road, Ocaña and Perurena closed up to the tail of the peloton. From his Fagor car Ocaña handed six doctored bidons to one of his six surviving riders; Perurena handed out the hidden food to three of his:

Delgado, Cabestany, and Zúñiga. Once into the feeding area, the nine attacked en bloc, relaying each other. They were joined by two strong Russian *rouleurs* – and nobody else. There were 170 kilometres to the finish at Alcalá. For more than 70 kilometres those eleven riders kept the peloton at a distance, but finally they gave in. Unluckily for them, they didn't have a crosswind but had to face it head on – it was an impossible task. And nor was Kelly infiltrating the group something that they had bargained on. In Alcalá, where Flequi Juárez won, after a lone escape, the only thing being talked about was Ocaña's ploy. Not since his time as a rider had he received such accolade: great strategy; revolutionary; historic... 'I didn't invent the feeding station attack, but after 20 years in cycling I've learned that trick and some similar ones,' Ocaña told the press, finally vindicating himself with some achievement. "We are now in the era of computers, but computers don't race 10,000 kilometres every year."

In spite of that failure, Perurena would end up winning that Vuelta, but not with his fellow-Basque and leader, Cabestany, but surprisingly with Delgado. Two days later on the mountain stage, in his own territory, descending the Cotos, he teamed up with the tremendous José Recio to dramatic effect. As he was more than six minutes down, Millar, the leader, stayed in the peloton keeping watch on Cabestany and Pacho, the men closest to him. With the connivance, at long last, of all the Spanish teams, Delgado won the Vuelta. His ploy put Ocaña's strategic cleverness in the shade for ever, but it didn't dull the friendship between Ocaña and Perurena.

Nor did the events of the following two days.

Coming into Salamanca on the Vuelta's last Sunday, with the whole city waiting with admiration for the triumphal entry of Delgado who had defeated the sinister Scotsman with the earring, Ocaña accelerated his car until it crashed, with the din of scrunching metal and breaking headlights, into the car ahead of him in the line of directors' cars – Echávarri's Reynolds team car. The noise of the crash was as loud as the 'Shit, merde!' with which Millar had replied to the journalists who'd asked him the day before for his opinion on the Delgardo-Rocio manoeuvre which had lost him the Vuelta. The Navarran director got out, surprised and somewhat concerned that it was nothing more serious than Ocaña daydreaming. Could he have fainted, perhaps? Ocaña also got out, apoplectic, and hardly giving Echávarri time to speak, started yelling at him.

'Were you daydreaming, Luis?'

'No, I was not daydreaming! I did it on purpose and I'll do it again a thousand times! And it's a pity nothing more was broken. You can't behave like the Spaniards do, giving your riders a lift, giving a ride up to the peloton in your slipstream every rider who drops back or wants water or gets a puncture. That isn't cycling, that's cheating on everybody.'

Echávarri was astonished. He understood that his easy going manner, his discretion would not be enough to bring an Ocaña who was absolutely livid back to reason; it must have been other worries that had made him lose his sanity. It made no sense explaining to him that what was upsetting him so much was a common, courteous practice which did no harm to anybody, and even less on a day like that, the last stage of the Vuelta, the parade and the party.

'Look, Luis, this is not the time to discuss it. Better if we talk about it later.'

That afternoon in the Hotel Regio, next to the city's baroque Plaza Mayor, and renowned among the bullfighters from the Salamancan countryside, Echávarri talked with Miguel Gómez, in charge of Fagor's public relations.

'Look, Gómez, this is what happened. During the stage, Luis accelerated and hit me with the car on purpose. As you'll know I have to send a letter of protest to his boss because that is not normal. I'm not doing it so much for measures to be taken against Luis – we all know he has an explosive nature – but so that they will have a word with him and ask him to calm down, because he'll be the first to be harmed by it.'

A month hadn't passed when Echávarri and Ocaña met for the first time since the incident. It was 9 July. Luis was 40 that day and he and Josiane celebrated it in a hotel in Éibar, where the following day the Subida a Arrate hillclimb would be taking place. They were drinking champagne and Echávarri came over to congratulate him. They drank, they offered toasts, they talked about this and that and, finally, Echávarri, the prudent Echávarri, dared to touch on the subject.

'Regarding what happened in Salamanca, Luis, I imagine you'll have thought about it and understood...'

And Luis, volatile, genial, always Luis, cut him short.

'Yes, José Miguel, I certainly have thought about it. And I'll tell you one thing. If we were ever in the same situation, I would do it again!'

At the beginning of the Tour some weeks later, without even waiting for the sporting disaster that was about to happen, Agustín Mondragón spoke to his closest associates: 'I am extremely sorry because I like Luis very much and he is a fine person, but I am going to have to dispense with him; the riders have rebelled and they say it's him or them.' To his disappointment, Mondragón came to the conclusion that Ocaña was not the right person to direct his team. On top of the blackmail by the riders, there were public outcries brought about by his volatile director, such as the crash with Echávarri, as well as other private rows, one an uncontrolled verbal and ideological outpouring from Ocaña which a flushed Mondragón suffered in silence in the team car. This was during one stage of the Vuelta that Mondragón had wanted to cover in his team manager's car. Over the radio, on the hourly news bulletin, there was a report of an attack by ETA, and Ocaña, thumping on the steering wheel and without a thought to the possibility that his Basque companion, director of a co-operative which was the pride of the Basque country, might see it differently or feel injured by it, started shouting: 'Those ETA sons of bitches, if I got hold of them I'd hang them up by their bollocks in Salamanca's Plaza Mayor!'

Ocaña was done for, but he didn't know it, or didn't want to know it. In the Tour, Pedro Muñoz in whom so much hope had been invested, went from one failure to another. The absolute control of Hinault and Lemond overwhelmed all their rivals, nullified any will to turn things around, to rise up against them. It was the same with Ocaña, who admitted to the press: 'I am sorry about the position Pedro Muñoz is in, but it's terrible for Fagor. In this Tour my hands are tied by bad luck and I can't find any fighting sprit. This squad isn't up to much, but next year we have ambitions to improve it. I've spoken with Lucho Herrera and Cabestany, and it might be …'

The following year the director of Fagor was a man called Pierre Bazzo, a French rider from the team who, at 32, swopped the handlebar for the steering wheel and took the place of the sacked Ocaña. About him, Bazzo, there had been plenty of talk in the peloton during the previous Setmana Catalana, because one day he asked the race doctor, Pepa Beltrán, for some pills and as she refused to give him any, Bazzo spat loudly and fully in her face. The next day, accompanied by Ocaña, dragging him by his jersey, Bazzo went to apologise to the doctor. The big names who signed for Fagor under Bazzo were Eric Caritoux and Martín Ramírez. The team continued to be a shambles and a waste, and would continue being so until its disappearance in 1989, hastened by the signing of Stephen Roche. When he went to Fagor in January 1988, together with Robert Millar and Eddy Schepers, the Irishman was 28, wore the rainbow jersey of World Champion and was burdened with the honour of having won both the Tour and the Giro the year previously, and with an incurable injury to the tendon in his left knee which had been operated on in Paris in November. He also contributed to the common good by bringing with him a couple of others, a manager and a mechanic, whom he wanted to be well nourished from the common good – that is to say, the Fagor bank. The manager was none other than Crepel, the man who had betrayed Ocaña in order to sign on with Hinault at La Vie Claire. Roche wanted him to become the general manager of the team; the mechanic came from his time at Peugeot, Patrick Valcke, for whom Roche demanded the post of director deportivo. And when he was asked how he intended to make his mechanic a director, like Caligula making his horse a Consul, Roche replied that Patrick, his friend, was more than a mere mechanic and told them the usual story: on the day he resolved to win the '87 Giro, he was in an escape group while his Carrera team leader, and the *maglia rosa*, Roberto Visentini, were further back. The team car, with Davide Boifava at the wheel, came up to him. 'Stop!' Davide shouted to Roche, who looked towards the back seat where Patrick was surrounded by wheels. 'I looked at Patrick and said to him, "What do you think?" And he replied to me, "Listen, if you've got the balls, show it!" And I dropped the chain on to a smaller sprocket and went on ahead.' When he retired from cycling, the betrayed Visentini opened up a funeral parlour. 'I don't want to have anything to do with the living,' he said.

In January Fagor convened all the riders for the official squad photographs. When Roche learned that Mondragón wouldn't agree to Crepel and Valcke directing the team he told his companions that there would be no photo. The 16 foreigners withdrew from the pose; only the two Spaniards remained: the eternal Pedro Muñoz and Gaxento Oñaederra. Mondragón played his card – all or nothing: 'These are the terms and you either accept them or you all clear off, for good.' The riders took themselves off and the clever Crepel, according to Sean Yates, another of the Britons in the team, began to inform the media that he had a team – 16 magnificent riders led by the incomparable Stephen Roche – but he needed a sponsor, because Fagor didn't deserve them. Within a few days Roche met Mondragón, who gave in, yielding once again, as he had done when he sacked Ocaña, to the blackmail threat of his riders. Valcke would be the new *director deportivo* and Crepel the general manager. Fagor remained a disaster. Within a few weeks Valcke was dismissed. In his first year in Fagor's jersey Roche only rode four second-order races. In April he had to have a new operation on his knee tendon. On that occasion it was performed by José María Villarrubias, the surgeon of the stars, of Ben Johnson and Diego Maradona. In his second year there he finished ninth in the Giro and abandoned the Tour. In his two years with the team, the Irishman, the great world figure, managed just four victories, all in 1989: one stage and the overall in the Tour of the Basque Country, a stage of Paris–Nice and another in the Four Days of Dunkirk.

Echávarri and Delgado, two inquiring minds, the two eternal students, together again at Reynolds, successfully applied the tactic of the surprise attack at the feeding zone, which they learned from Ocaña in Albacete. It was in '88, during the Alpe d'Huez stage, counting on Indurain as the spectacular driving force at the point of launching it.

Beforehand, all the riders had covertly collected their food bags from the team car. By then, Delgado was 'Perico of Spain', the Segovian having become the great idol and the personification of guile. By then, Ocaña could only be heard on Spanish radio as a pundit, not in a leading role as commentator. He had already become something of an outcast.

Ocaña's professional decline and, inseparably, his personal one, became increasingly unstoppable. Little by little he began to break with everybody around him, as if he only found pleasure in his own company, as if only that intimate relationship gave him any satisfaction. Following Saint Francis of Assisi, he believed that only beauty could save the fallen man, to which he was predestined. Following his own thoughts he came to believe that true beauty was in the fallen, or at least that was where he found it.

As the peloton didn't want to know anything about him, as he continued to need a salary to deal with the losses from his vineyards; the armagnac wasn't selling because young people didn't like it, preferring whisky and spirits with mixers, just as he did. Luis, lucid when he was pessimistic, began to picture himself as an old bottle of armagnac, magnificent, splendid, but which nobody liked and was now unfashionable. Ocaña accepted the offer from the SER channel to commentate on the Vuelta and the Tour, and began a new radio career. In April '86 the channel of the Gran Vía filled the pages of the newspapers with enormous advertisements which announced, in big letters 'Ride La Vuelta With Ocaña'. And in smaller letters, lower down:

> Follow the Vuelta a España with Ocaña. In this edition Joaquín Durán has signed up for the SER team a first-class *gregario*, Luis Ocaña, our star commentator, so that you can hear and experience, live, the end of each stage through the eyes of a legendary cyclist. And with the support of the most complete team, 25 people, four mobile units, three motorbikes and SER's helicopter.

The advertisement promoted SER and inflated Ocaña's unbelievable optimism, his incredible capacity for self-deception.

For the first time in many years Ocaña was smiling again. He felt he was a star; he felt unburdened of responsibilities; he enjoyed travelling across Spain, and enjoyed the evenings with the wine and the women, together with José Manuel Fuente who commentated on the Vuelta for the rivals, for Atena 3 Radio, and with Julio Jiménez who that year was with Radio España.

'I will have a terrific and very peaceful year,' he told the journalist, Javier de Dalmases of *El Mundo Deportivo*, during the Volta a Catalunya.

'I shall be doing what I like doing. What I enjoy. I've never been so relaxed as this year, and next year will be the same. I continue to think about bringing out a team and I have two French firms waiting on confirmation, but the team would be for '88 and I'd only work with them to get it going. Whatever happens I am not going to drop the radio commentating. It's exciting. If I wanted a quiet life I'd stay where I am, but I've got a return match with myself after what happened at Fagor. That was a catastrophe for my morale. I have overcome it thanks to having a very composed nature, but I am sure that I'm right for this work and my challenge is to prove it to everybody else. There are two kinds of director – those who take charge of everything and those who are chauffeurs. That's not for me. In my new team, as I did at Fagor, I will assume all responsibilities.'

Two months later, ADR-Fangio, the sad Belgian team from Louvain, announced they had engaged Ocaña for stage races. All his dreams and designs on returning to the top went no further than that, a Belgian team which exasperated and depressed him, as did the world around him. He began to feel a sad, wounded survivor as those close to him disappeared. In January '87 Viscount Jean De Gribaldy killed himself in a road accident; in February his friend Antonio Vallugera committed suicide; Anquetil died in November. The only relief was in July. He went to the Tour, not as a director of a lifeless team, but as a reporter and columnist for *El Mundo Deportivo*. In his pieces he got excited about Perico Delgado, and he admitted to feeling devastated when Roche beat him in the final time trial. In none of his reports did the old champion convey either envy or spite, but pure admiration. In the autumn ADR downgraded him: he wouldn't be *director deportivo* as from 1988, but would be 'in charge of the organisation of the team abroad, public relations and spokesman'. In the same note in which his appointment was announced, the team pointed out that none of their riders had managed to complete the Vuelta in '87 under Ocaña's direction. They all abandoned.

9

Over the restaurant table, and the plates awaiting the arrival of the hors d'oeuvre – prawns and ham or stuffed hake, the specialities of the house – and over the glasses half filled already with glinting, dark red Rioja, Juan Hortelano spread out a newspaper – it could have been *El País* – and began to read out loud. Opposite him sat Luis Ocaña, who was fiddling with an enormous model boat, more than a metre in length. It was the frigate which had given the restaurant in which they had just started dinner, its name – San Fernando – and it occupied the space to their left, as if it had been reserved. It was one night at the end of April 1988 and it was raining in the street, and when the door of the small restaurant opened a drop of water was blown in with some force. The following day Luis had to take a plane to Tenerife, where the Vuelta a España was starting that year.

'What a lovely boat this is. Why don't you ask the owner of the restaurant if he'd sell it to me?'

'And what do you want it for, Luis? You'll put it in your house and straight away forget you've got it. It'll be one more bit of junk in your life.' Juan showed his impatience, as if Luis, and his distraction, was making him irritable. 'Come on, leave the little boat alone, and listen.'

'Look,' Ocaña interrupted him, indicating with his finger, almost touching the back page of the newspaper his friend was reading. 'Look, that advert Butano has put in: "García is off to the Vuelta" and a massive photo of García in a helicopter. And look, Juan, he's also put: "And with him, Luis Ocaña and a team of 22 people working flat out so that no detail of the race is overlooked. With following cars. Motorbikes racing everywhere. And even a helicopter, to be up with the front of the race. Everything very well set up on a mobile 16-metre screen. If you want to be well informed, stay with us. Stay with Antena 3." Since Fuente has gone with the Asturian team, Clas, Butano has signed me up. He gives me more than SER, but I liked the advertisement they did last year more, and in this one they have got at Perico to provoke Unipublic because he preferred to ride the Giro rather than the Vuelta as preparation for the Tour. At least they put my name in big letters. And I'll have to put up with García, who's furious with Perico and Echávarri.'[1]

'Where they've put your name in big letters is where they shouldn't have put it,' replied Hortelano, who was not prepared to allow him the slightest excuse, even if he was his friend. 'Look at that, what a headline: "Luis Ocaña: 'Le Pen is peace'." Listen to this and don't interrupt. I'm going to read it aloud so you can hide your face in shame,' and Juan Hortelano, his friend, read it. He read it without pausing, almost without pausing for breath, or for the occasional sip of wine, and without looking at his friend, who made out as if he were not listening:

To everybody's considerable dismay, the cyclist Luis Ocaña [winner of the Tour in 1973] supports Jean-Marie Le Pen.

Like many old immigrants, he says: 'For those who are not involved in politics, Le Pen's programme is for peace. I am not interested in getting wrapped up in politics and I want to be left alone. Everybody keeps saying that Le Pen means dictatorship. That is nonsense. Do you imagine a president, sitting down in his armchair in the Élysée, abolishing the right to vote and the French just standing there with their arms folded? Dictatorship in Europe is finished, and a good job too. Le Pen only wants to clean up the country, and he's right.

Le Pen wanted to get together with sportsmen to talk about their problems, and a number of champions were invited. I was the only one who went and a few days later I was asked if I would agree to sign the list in support, and I did. Some people have said, 'Luis, are you sure he knows you're a foreigner?' Of course he knows. And so what? My country is France, and my region is Gers. That's where I like living and where I'll always

---

1. There was a constant struggle between Unipublic, organisers of the Vuelta and Echávarri, director of Reynolds, then Banesto, first over Delgado then Indurain. Unipublic wanted these stars in the Vuelta, whereas the riders came to regard the Giro as better preparation for the Tour.

live. My wife and my children are French, from Les Landes, but I am still Spanish. Perhaps if I hadn't been a public figure I would have adopted French nationality, like my brothers. But in my case that's impossible; everybody knows I'm Spanish and a little piece of paper is not going to change anything. I've never asked for any favours or indulgence. Everything I've done I've done by myself. Like my father. And believe me, I have never been given any special favours. Having said that, I don't see myself like the Spaniards, but rather more like the Italians from around here. I go back to Spain from time to time because of my work, or to visit the family in the village. It's sad to see how things have broken down there in recent years. If you go there in a nice car you can be sure it will be scratched. If your wife goes out wearing jewels they'll be ripped off her. In the squares you see young people full of drugs, and not only in Madrid, but everywhere in the country. Don't get me wrong – I don't miss Franco's times, but the fact is that during his period, if you didn't get mixed up in politics, you could walk down the street in peace. That's all changed. Freedom, for me, is the right to work, not just the right to go on strike. A man out of work loses his dignity. Every man needs to find a job and if he works 50 hours a week he should be paid for 50 hours. But how many want to work nowadays? They won't convince me that the smart alec who demands a 35-hour week is not a bloody crook. When you are healthy and want to get somewhere, you've got to roll up your sleeves, damn it. I've sweated as an apprentice, on a bike, on the tractor. My house, my vineyard, my car… nobody gave them to me. Accidents, hail, taxes…there's been no shortage of those on the list. The most silly thing in recent years is schooling up to the age of 18. There are those who are born to study and others not; they are real mules – not clever but damn hard-working. Before, those who didn't like school could leave at 14 and go out to work. Now, at 18 you know all about cigarettes, drink, girls and you're not interested any more in lending somebody a hand. It's like on the bike. Before, if you rode well you left work to become a professional, you were still a little wild and you pushed others aside. Today, in the cycling schools, the youngsters learn to be economical with their efforts, make use of others and wait for help. They learn to be a con artist, so when they sign their first licence they are already professional down to their fingernails. I'd willingly die the day after my last race if I could begin riding again. It's not that I'm unhappy with my present life, but I'll never again experience those emotions I had on a bike. I am scared. When I say that I support Le Pen because he represents peace, it is because I am scared. Not for me but for my family. I am scared that one of my family will be attacked; I am scared that vandals will clean everything out of my house while I'm away. I'm scared that in one of the big department stores a friend will get shot in the head. Or that somebody hurts my children.

Look, my mother was robbed last week; she had her bag yanked away from her in the market. She's a good woman. Isn't that disgraceful? It's stupid to blame everything on the Arabs or the Africans. But even if they don't represent more than ten per-cent of the attackers, they should be deported. The French shouldn't let themselves get annoyed by them, as the Arabs don't want others to get annoyed by them in their country. When a neighbour comes and buggers about in your garden, you kick him up the arse. That's natural, isn't it?

People say that Le Pen is xenophobic. That's a real obsession. I've not heard anything xenophobic in what he's said. The day I hear Le Pen denigrating immigrants I'll insult him, just as one should. But this isn't the case. He's only against illegal foreigners, petty thieves and terrorists. That's all. When my father came, in 1957, there was work for everybody and jobs the French didn't want. Today there isn't the work and the French have priority in their country. I don't believe Le Pen sincerely believes everything he says. Especially about religion. But that doesn't matter; he's the only person who does talk about it, and I like that. I am very much a believer. All the other candidates go on and on about 1992 and Europe. Le Pen is the only one who still talks about morality and traditions. I know that it makes you look old to be linked to old principles, but Luis Ocaña laughs at appearing old.'

'I am not asking you if you said that, if you uttered those words, which seem like a speech from a meeting, because you evidently did,' Juan continued. 'No one, no newspaper, could have invented it for you. And *El País* is not the only one to publish it. It came out here a week ago, but friends from France tell me it came out there in a blaze of publicity, and it was on television, as well. What I want to ask you, Luis, is something different. Do you actually believe what you say? Have you thought about the consequences? What do you think your father, who got out of Spain because the Fascists were starving him to death, would think about it? Or your uncle Sorio, who fought in the war against everything that Le Pen represents? Do you know what they'll think of you in Spain, a country that's just discovered democracy? My uncle Amalio, who goes to Republican demonstrations whenever he can and reads Haro Tecglen[1] every day and cuts out and saves his columns, what will he think? Are you aware of something, Luis, my dear Luis? You intervene in the French electoral campaign when you're not French and cannot vote in France…and what about your brothers, Marino and Michel, who are Communists, what are they going to say to you? How are they going to look at you now?'

'The Spaniards? You think it matters to me what they think in Spain? You think I'm of any interest to them about anything, that they care about me, recognise me? My brothers don't worry me; they already know what I think, and my sister Amparo thinks like I do, and Jean-Louis has left home, Juan.'

'How old is he now, 15, 16?'

'Go on. He's already 18, legally an adult. There's nothing I can do. Sylvie is still at home; she's only 16. And she's got a boyfriend, an Italian hairdresser, and when I see him in the house I want to vomit. Do

---

1. Eduardo Haro Tecglen – leading Spanish journalist and critic of Franco's regime.

you know he even wears an earring in one ear, the poof. I had a terrible row with Jean-Louis. As soon as he saw me on television talking about Le Pen he refused to talk to me. "I can't live in the house of somebody who thinks like that and boasts about it," he said to Josiane. Whatever he had to say to me he said it by telling his mother. Then she reports it to me. She told me that Jean-Louis poured everything out to her, like never before. She'd never seen him so worked up. He said things had always been very bad with me. "Up to the age of 10, while he was a professional, the most I saw of him was a month and a half in the course of a year, but afterwards I saw too much of him." That's what Josiane told me he'd said. "The fact is he never goes out of the house, Mum. He's always doing things, always asking, always demanding, always telling me off. Look, Mum, look how bad he is sometimes with his liver; and hooked on the interferon drug. And even so, he's up at five o'clock every day, as if time is running away from him, as if every minute were precious and he can't bare not to live it. And as soon as he sees me, he calls me nancy boy, Mum. 'Look at that hair' is the first thing he says to me. 'And I don't want to see you with that earring in front of me. Take it off right now".'

Jean-Louis spoke to Josiane, in French, the language he always used with his mother. With his father, he spoke in Spanish, sometimes in French, or more often than not he didn't speak at all.

'Sometimes, Mum, I can remember some good moments, though not often, when I felt happy, holding father's hand, going with him into the country, out walking, or playing bull and bullfighter – his occasional obsession with bulls and with Spain. I remember one day, the first time I went on a motor bike, which was with him, he driving and me on the pillion. At first I tried to hold on to him round the waist so as not to fall, but he made me let go of him. "Boys don't hold on to each other," he shouted at me. But those moments of nostalgia are rare compared to the bad moments. Think of that day when he cut my hair while I was asleep, or of how he threw my packet of tobacco on the fire so I wouldn't smoke. And his moral lessons. That's what I could put up with the least, trying to give me those lessons. Mum, you know that Dad, like all the country people loves rugby, and you know

I've been playing rugby for seven years, and not once has he come to watch me. However, remember, one day he put me in the car and drove a long way, to the Arán Valley. We went through what seemed to me to be a steep, narrow alley, a bit spooky, and from there he pointed out with his finger a school run by priests. It made you afraid, just looking at it, dark and cold on the mountain – that's how it seemed to me that clear winter night. "You see that?" he said. "There in that school I spent two years studying and suffering. Would you like to go there too?" And we returned home. We didn't say a word for the whole of the journey. Father is very impulsive and he works too much. I've put up with two years working with him on the farm. Suffering. It's all the same to him whether it's raining, snowing, or scorching… He's pig-headed and he's got great big hands. Father is very peculiar; I've never seen anybody the least bit like him, and he's not somebody you expect to see every day. The only things he worships are cleanliness and order, and Spain seems to him to be dirty.'

'That's what Josiane told me; that was his confession, Juan. He's a rebel is Jean-Louis, like me, who hates authority and hates me,' Ocaña continued. 'I called him and shouted at him for the last time, "If you want to carry on living in this house you'll do what I tell you," and he answered me by slamming the door. I don't know how long this separation between us will last. You talk to me about Spain and about democracy, Juan, and I'm going to tell you something about Spain.' Luis was silent for a moment while they began to serve the dinner on the table, now free of the newspaper. 'I'm going to talk about Spain, about the dirty, ugly Spain, that we know today. Do you know I've sold the house which I built in Priego on that plot of land the town council gave me?'

To Juan came the memory of an old photograph, in black and white. Luis is in the foreground, elegant in suit and tie, one of those very tasteless ties, wide and with gaudy patches of colour which he wore from time to time. His hair perfectly cut and combed with the parting on the left and his fringe falling like a dark black diagonal curtain over his forehead. He hasn't even left those very long, very Spanish sideburns and his cheekbones are accentuated under the smooth skin of his face. He is looking straight out at the camera with his big, dark eyes and he's smiling, almost laughing, a childlike laugh showing his regular teeth, a melancholic laugh as if it hid something he didn't like, and he is leaning on the crossbar of a bicycle which he's holding with his hands. And behind him, some distance off, there is a gully with high, vertical walls, almost a cliff face. Further off still is the village of Priego, with its graceless lump of a church on the edge of the cliff, and the little houses attached to it. Juan remembered having seen the photograph, big and ostentatious on the wall of some bars in Priego. The photo, taken from the edge of the Madrid road must have been taken after the Vuelta he won, the '70 race, when Luis then felt himself a champion. And Juan also had, superimposed in his memory, another amplified photograph, this one in colour, of the silhouette of Priego, taken almost from the same spot, against the light. Now Ocaña is not in the foreground, but filling the space his body occupied it's possible to see a new building, with such an ancient appearance that it seems it ought to have been there, at the end of the Chica Bridge even before the solid-looking church. It looks like an old medieval fortified tower, cylindrical, made of stone, and with dark windows irregularly placed along its height and length, and with battlements which could have been taken out of a catalogue of Exin castles[1]. Alongside it and almost invisible, its foundations practically touched the gully from which the highest branches of the poplar and chestnut trees appeared. They could have been a second tower, only much lower.

This is the house that Ocaña had built after winning the Tour, when he thought he could live in Spain, or at least Josiane would put up with the two of them spending long periods of time there in the village, their village. It's a whimsical house that came out of Ocaña's imagination and ideas, almost Daliesque, sitting on the edge of a cliff, like the whole of his life. This was Ocaña's romantic vision, and so profoundly Spanish – always on the knife edge between life and death.

One happy day he invited the cycling press and Spanish Television cameras to be shown around it. The journalists still remember their

---

1. Exin Castles: a construction toy for children, similar to Lego, only for building castles.

astonishment at the sight of the spectacular bath on the ground floor, excavated from the solid rock, and its gold taps.

'Yes, I've sold it. I was fed up, sick of the fact that the washing machine and the television were stolen every winter. Whenever we went to spend a few days there it was the same story. You open the door and there's a disgusting smell of crap and pee the robbers have left, or from people who had got into the place to get drunk. You imagine that. We used to pay for it to be cleaned up and then we had to go and buy a washing machine, a tele, a fridge… all the domestic goods they'd stolen, and then report it, for all the good that did. It was unbearable. What's more, Josiane couldn't put up with being in the village for more than three days in a row. She found it suffocating.'

'It seems, Luis, as if the whole of your life consists in breaking bridges with everybody, in isolating yourself, in having rows. It seems that you're only looking to be on you own, as if you didn't need others. You're running out of friends, Luis. Do you know that Pérez Francés has called his dog "Ocaña", just like you called yours "Merckx"? There's nothing nasty about it, he says; it's to remind himself of you. What friends do you have, Luis? You have me and my family and we think the world of you, like one of our own, and you have Aurelio Soler, little Julio and Balagué, and a few more.'

'So many have betrayed me, Juan, that I can't trust many people. I know that neither you nor your family would ever do wrong by me. With you, no Juan. With you I don't quarrel. You understand me. You know what goes on in my head.'

'Don't be so sure, Luis. I understand you, and I love you. I know you are impulsive and visceral, that sometimes you don't think, or you do think, but you think too late. When you claim that you only say what you think, you don't appreciate what it is you're saying. And I know that you're arrogant, but I sometimes wonder… You are not a normal person, Luis.'

'I detest people who doubt me, Juan, just as I adore those who adore me. I'm not normal, Juan. I know that, as you know it, as Josiane knows it, although sometimes it seems I don't want to be understood. No, I'm not normal. A doctor in Barcelona once told me that. He was

Doctor Colomé, a specialist in bronchitis who examined me to see if I had recovered from the pneumonia which had forced me out of the '72 Tour. "You are unique, señor Ocaña," he said to me in his consulting room on Calle Muntaner. "You have the body of an athlete and the soul of an artist. In spite of having had tuberculosis as a child, which makes you very susceptible to lung infections, your pulmonary capacity is astonishing. It's more than seven litres, I've never seen anything like that. Not even Kubala[1], who had the biggest lungs I've seen, is close to you. And you're just like your lungs, strong and sensitive." That's what he told me, Juan, almost 20 years ago and I've never forgotten it. And Josiane was with me and could confirm it.'

'Yes, I already know that, Luis. I know you are a sensitive brute. I'm fully aware of that. Luis you are Alfredo di Stéfano and Luis Miguel Dominguín[2] rolled into one. You are like them, people out of the mould, from a different time, a different age, a different everything. You are from a different time in life and in sport. You are not made for this rhythm, for this life. You are special. You are a quite unique person, and life hasn't treated you well.'

In spite of having to be dressed in a ghastly, ostentatious tracksuit – the uniform of García's team – Ocaña, who only felt good in a suit and tie, looked in good shape during the Vuelta, which was won by Sean Kelly, who'd been allowed to ride even though he'd tested positive in the Tour of the Basque Country some weeks before. And he also looked good throughout Perico's Tour, which he covered in a Volvo, combining commentary for Antena 3 and public relations for ADR. Perico's win made him immensely happy, without the slightest element of insincerity or envy.

'I found it odd that Spain should have won so few Tours, only the Eagle's and mine,' he said.

In September, a couple of months later, when the grape harvest began and the trees were turning yellow and the sun caressed

---

1. Ladislav Kubala, legendary Hungarian footballer who played for Barcelona FC in the 1950s.
2. Famous Argentinian footballer who played for Real Madrid in the 1950s. Famous bullfighter of 1940s and 50s.

everything, Juan Hortelano invited Luis to a snack in a wine bar where they burned the sheaves and grilled lamb chops on the embers.

'I've invited you to offer you a job, Luis,' Juan said, as he finished off a bone with his teeth, leaving not a scrap of meat on it. 'I've found a sponsor, a manufacturer of doors from a village in Toledo, and I'm going to bring out a team and I'd like you to be the manager. There are five million pesetas to do whatever you want, although you'll have to put up with the owner of the factory. And you'll also be able to continue on the radio with Butano.'

10

Puertas Mavisa was Luis Ocaña's final team. A small team with small ambitions, which rarely rode outside Spain. Luis hardly had to do anything. He advised Juan, who was the director. He looked for riders for him in Luxembourg and Switzerland. He wore the team jersey and attended the presentation and appeared in the photograph. During the Vuelta he gave interviews, and spoke about his life and work. To Luis it was worth it. It earned him some money. He spent time with Juan, and together they travelled through Spain between races in his Espace delivery van. He carried his sparkling wine and French white wine, which he tried to sell from bar to bar, without much success. He was with Juan, who accompanied him through his emotional outbursts, neither an accomplice nor a guardian – but a friend. A friend who understood him thoroughly.

'Let's go to Nogaro, Juan.'

'Are you mad, Luis? It's 11 o'clock at night. We're going to sleep here and we'll go in the morning. It's 400 kilometres, Luis.'

'No, let's go now. If we set out now we'll be there in time to see the fight.'

The keys of the Jaguar coupé fell loudly on the tablecloth, landing next to the bottle of whisky from which Luis had been drinking during dinner. They were staying with Juan's godparents, who'd retired to bed and left them by themselves.

The Jaguar sped along the roads, empty that moonlit winter's night in December 1989. Luis drove silently, concentrating, his gaze fixed on the road ahead, just like when he rode a time trial. At a cross roads they were stopped by a couple of gendarmes. Luis got out of the car and they proceeded to shout at him.

'Are you crazy, how can you go at that speed, 180, 200, at least, on these narrow roads, and at night?' They were serious and they talked nonstop. Luis, who had no time for authority, nor for the moral advice it offered, became impatient.

'Are you going to fine me or not? Because if you're going to fine me, fine me, but don't give me any more of this rubbish, and if you're not going to fine me, sod off.'

'You are mad señor Ocaña; you are not right in the head,' the policemen replied. They had recognised him, a man they considered beyond help, and decided to let him go.

During the fight, transmitted from Las Vegas during the early hours of the morning, Juan dozed on the sofa in front of the television. Luis, next to him, didn't miss a punch.

'Look, Juan, look at Mano de Piedra,' he urged him, trying to wake him up with his elbow[1]. 'Look at him, 40 years old and he's come back to challenge Sugar Ray Leonard. That takes some balls, and some hunger. He's some man. Ten years ago, in his last fight, he threw in the towel in the eighth round, shouting, "no more, no more". When he returned to Panama, his people, his country, they called him "chicken". They shouted that at him; they sang "no more" to mock him. They humiliated him and he suffered a lot, like they humiliated me in Spain before I won the Tour, and afterwards when I didn't win it again. It seemed as if victory was a moral virtue, as if just winning it made you somebody respectable, a man without defects, an example of how to conduct yourself that everybody ought to follow; on the other hand, if you lose, you're a degenerate, a waster, irresponsible. What a world! And everybody knows that to win you've got to be a bastard, and to lose too, because it's impossible to be a cyclist, or any sportsman, or have an ambition to be the best at anything without being a selfish bastard, Juan. If you win, you're good, untouchable, you receive tributes and nobody dares to criticise you; if you lose, it's open season and everyone thinks they've got the right to insult you. Wake up, Juan, wake up! It's finished. Leonard has beaten him again, although this time he went the 12 rounds.'

'It's over now, is it? Then I'm off to bed.'

'No. What are you doing, Juan. I need your help. I've got to fix some tiles in the swimming pool which were broken during the summer. I need you to hold the lamp.'

---

1. Mano de Piedra (Hand of stone): Panamanian boxer, regarded as one of the greatest of all time.

'But, Luis, it's four in the morning. You're not going to go out there in the cold…'

'I'm isothermal, Juan. I don't feel either the cold or the heat. Do you know that I always shower in cold water? Even in winter.'

At four in the morning and freezing, Juan gazed at Luis preparing a trough of tile adhesive in the kitchen, and then they went out on to the patio with a ladder and a lamp screwed into a holder trailing several metres of cable. Luis leaned the ladder against the wall of the empty swimming pool and descended into it. Juan switched on the lamp and went closer to the edge, leaned over and lit up his friend, who was removing the old broken tiles with a hammer and chisel.

'Ah! Bugger it!'

Juan leaned over further, concerned, but had to move away because Luis was blindly coming up the ladder and holding a finger which was spurting blood.

'What a cut I've given myself.'

'Let's go and get that fixed and then get to bed, eh? It's very late now, Luis. You can't see properly and you're going to do more harm to yourself.'

But his friend didn't hear him, or look at him. Juan saw him walking off towards a corner of the garden, as far as the hedgerow, where he undid his flies and urinated straight on to the wound.

'Come on. Let's keep going. There's something I don't think I've ever told you: I never liked cycling; what I really wanted was to be a bricklayer. I wanted to be a bricklayer, but I became a cyclist because one day, working in the carpentry workshop, the boss, who was a real bastard, started insulting me, and I threw the hammer I was working with at his head. Pity I didn't hit him. He was a right son of a bitch. Have I told you how I learned to swim, Juan? When I began to take cycling seriously, Cescutti said to me, one day, that in winter I had to swim because swimming was a very good exercise for cyclists. At that time I didn't know how to swim, but I didn't tell him that. The next day I took myself off to the river – this was in winter – I went with a fairly long length of rope to the Ardour, where the water was going down pretty high because of the rain of the previous weeks. I tied one end of the rope to a tree and coiled the other end round my waist and threw myself into the water. I had to do it twenty times, but in the end I managed to swim.'

When he finished repairing the swimming pool wall, Luis insisted on making something to eat. They had sausage and eggs in the kitchen and only then did he allow his friend to go to bed.

'You can sleep for half an hour and you get up as good as new,' Juan grumbled, 'but I'm human and I need eight hours at least.'

He hadn't even had four hours when he was woken up by the cheerful songs coming from Luis in the courtyard. He leaned out of the window to see his friend washing the car, bringing out the brilliance of the white cellulose of the coupé with a yellow rag as he sang to himself.

When Juan went down into the courtyard he noticed that the yellow rag had the letters HD embroidered on it. He looked more closely and realised that what he thought was a rag was a very thin yellow cycling jersey.

'You don't use a Tour *maillot jaune* to wash the car?' Juan asked, in wonderment.

'Why not? What's it worth otherwise? I don't keep anything from my career. No cups, no trophies, nothing. I've given away everything, or left it somewhere or other, Juan. Once, when I was a kid, I won a race and the prize was my own weight in turkeys. They forked out more than 20. On the way home I was giving them to people as presents. I kept one because I'd promised my mother, but when I was nearly home I saw the village idiot, and I gave it to him. So then I had to go to the poultry shop to buy one, so I wouldn't arrive home empty handed. I told that story to Jean-Louise and he turned nasty – "I'm fed up hearing your moralising stories ." What a character, my son.

'As for the Tour jerseys, I only wanted to keep one properly, the one I gave to my father after I won my first Spanish Championship. The Tour ones don't interest me. And do you know why? Because the race I remember best was that Championship in Mungia. It was a surprise victory; nobody thought I could win it, whereas in the Tour it was predestined, there was no merit in it. I've spoken with Jean-Louis again.'

'How? Has he come home? Don't tell me you've made it up between you.'

'Well, I wouldn't say that, exactly. Nor have I spoken that much with him. Before the Tour I called Leblanc to get him to hire my son for the setting up of the barriers, so that he could know what hard work is like. At the same time I spoke to him to tell him that if he wanted to work in July I knew where he could do so. I also mentioned that I knew Josiane was secretly sending him money and that that was going to stop. And he agreed to go to the Tour. He hasn't done badly, the little bugger, from what Jean-Marie tells me. You know, Juan, that Leblanc was a team mate of mine at Bic; he was there a number of years and only rode one Tour. He was an honest *gregario*, who enjoyed giving everything he could for the team, although that didn't amount to much. He was an intellectual, a university type who also played the clarinet, and he joined Bic because he came from Lille, like De Meur did, and he came with him from the Pelforth team, but what interested him most was his studies. For him, being a cyclist was a hobby. He was a dilettante, daddy's little rich boy, who dreamed about finishing the Tour, and he managed it. And he didn't do badly, either. It was in the '70s. We won a stage with his friend Alain Vasseur and Jean-Marie kept guard on the peloton admirably. Afterwards he became a journalist and ended up as the boss of *L'Équipe*. We've never lost contact and as a cycling journalist he admired me, admired what he called my 'audacious side', my passion for attacking. And now they've made him Director of the Tour. I rang him after the race was over to ask him if he'd seen Jean-Louis, and he told me, yes, every day. "And he's like you, exactly like you – stubborn as a mule and won't accept orders. And what a head of hair. I asked him why he didn't get it cut, and you can imagine what he said, that he'd quit the Tour before he got his hair cut. I looked at him and I saw you, Luis," he said to me. Anyway, Jean-Louis began putting up the barriers, but on the second day the man who carried the slate-board on the motorbike had an attack of sciatica and Jean-Marie, who felt some compassion for Jean-Luis, put him in as substitute. "He was the most envied bloke out of the whole crew. Everyone would have paid millions to be in his position, and have a front row seat to watch the attacks of Perico, LeMond or Fignon in the mountains, but he didn't give a damn. I saw him every night, because we gave him a room in the Tour organisers' hotels and when I asked him if he was enjoying the race he told me that he didn't understand what was happening, he didn't like cycling, but he did enjoy going on the motorbike. 'And what I like most,' he said with a grin, 'are the hostesses, how easy it is to pick one up, the parties at night...' So, like I say, Luis, he's your son for sure. And of course, I didn't get him to cut his hair." That's what Jean-Marie told me and on the one hand I was happy, and on the other it hurt me. Do you know why I bought this land, Juan? Do you know why I invested all my money in the vineyards and the house and the armagnac, and everything that is leading me to the poor house? Before getting into land, my sister Amparo advised me to invest in something secure, profitable, buying flats, or car parks, or commercial premises. And I didn't take any notice of her.

'Nor did I want to take any notice of Manuel Manzano. Do you know we made our peace in the end? We hadn't spoken to each other since we were amateurs, in fact I didn't take him to Fagor for that reason, because I wasn't speaking to him, and now I don't remember why. After finishing with the bike he set up a machinery hire business, and I passed by there looking for a cement mixer. And almost without saying a word to each other we shook hands – you know what we Spaniards are like – and we were reconciled. We don't see much of each other, but our paths cross from time to time, and he used to ask me about my business. From the first day he was convinced that I had made a mistake. "A man like you, at your social level, doesn't need to invest in making, but in selling. With your standing," Manzano said to me, and that's how I remember him, "with the popularity you enjoy, you don't make; you buy and sell. Land makes you a slave. You work like mad, for nothing. You're killing yourself working in a sector that has no future. Armagnac won't bring you in a fraction. I heard you nearly killed a careless worker the other day; he'd closed the barrels badly and almost wasted the harvest. You have no control over the hours you put it. I know you work on impulse and you're a country boy, Luis, and I know that the land is stronger than you and all that, but like this you are heading for disaster."

'Amparo told me; Manzano warned me and I took no notice of them, Juan. And do you know why? I thought my father would be proud of me, a land owner, he who never owned a square metre of land, he who earned a living and raised us all only through his hands, only by hiring out his hands and his calluses to a landowning master. That's what I thought. That's what I thought about my father, who couldn't care less about me, but I did also think about Jean-Louis and Sylvie. They will be my heirs, I said to myself, and I imagined them here, where you and I are standing now – Jean-Louis returning from work and Sylvie in the office, there in that little house, looking after the accounts and talking to the suppliers. And look what I've got: Jean-Louis ignores me and Sylvie goes to the hairdresser, besotted with the Italian boyfriend. I've forbidden her to bring him into the house because I couldn't look at him, and if I did see him I'd beat him. Do you know the other day he wrecked the little car I gave her as a present, a Honda like her mother's? And Sylvie has stopped speaking to me, too. "You are not my father," she yells into my face.

'You don't know what kind of a family I've got, Juan. When my father died I became in charge of everybody, my mother, my brothers. I wanted to be the head of the family, to advise them, help them, and I've done all that, in my way. With their financial problems, and their marital ones, too. And they've all been complicated. One day I had to go to Paris with a pistol to get Marino's wife back – she had run off with someone else. And I threatened Marie France's husband that I'd kill him if he left my little sister. Some months ago when I was at the Tour I called Amparo, my oldest sister, to congratulate her daughter Sonia, who'd just turned 18. It was 12 July, a date I'll never forget because she was born on the very day I crashed going down the Col de Menté. It had such an effect on Amparo, hearing the news on the radio, it brought forward the birth by a couple of weeks. Her children are all very close to me. The first one she had – she got married at 17 to get away from the house – she baptised on the day of my wedding, in the same chapel, at Labastide. But that day I was telling you about, after talking to Sonia, Amparo came back on the line. "I've got divorced," she told me. "My life has changed. I've finally left the drunken bastard and I've got another man. I'm not going to be a nun, Jesús, I'll be at your house for Christmas, as usual, but with my man. His name is Alain." That's what she told me. I was tired, and I told her she ought to stop that stupid stunt. She owed it to her husband that they shouldn't separate. But she's a hard woman, Juan. She's like me, hard and very strong; she can deal with everything that's put in front of her. She set up a restaurant in Bordeaux, the "Don Luis", she called it, and it served 250 meals every day. She was the boss and it went well, and what's more she made the opportunity to study and everything, as well as look after her three children, all from her own strength of purpose. That's Amparo, Juan. In the same telephone call she said something to me and I let her say it because she is Amparo; I wouldn't permit it from anyone else, only from her. She and I went cold and hungry in the Arán Valley, and we survived the coldness and the harshness of our parents, and their lack of love. She spoke about Josiane. Amparo doesn't get on well with Josiane; she thinks she's cold and self-centred, and very jealous, and spends the day criticising my brothers. "But look how Josiane is," she said to me. "She saw me the other day with a diamond ring my husband had given me, and the next day she bought one exactly the same. I am a woman, Luis, and I know what women are like. If I found out that my husband was cheating on me with some other woman I wouldn't have allowed it either. You're good looking, Luis, very good looking, and you speak very well and you know how to chat up women, Luis. You have that gift. They all fall for you. I want to tell you something, and don't take it as a piece of advice. I know you'll never take any notice of me because you're pig-headed and only know how to do the opposite to everybody else. I'm like you, and that's why I know you and know how you think. I've seen you working in a plaster cast after one of your car accidents, Luis, driving the tractor with just one arm, or pruning the vine shoots with your hands cut. I've seen you doing that. You are an animal, Luis, and we both have the same character; we are both like our mother. I know the kind of stuff you're made of. And when some arsehole says something about you to me I tell him he's not fit to lick your boots."That's what Amparo said to me, Juan.

'And she also said, "I want to tell you that there always comes a moment when you have to say 'enough'. You have to know how to say 'no'. If you don't love Josiane, tell her so. Tell her that it's ended and separate, but don't play one against the other. You need love, Luis. You need someone who will give you the affection your parents didn't give you, the affection you've never had. And Josiane is cold, Luis. She doesn't give you what you need." That's what she said to me, Juan. And I told her, "Do you know what the problem is, Amparo? The problem is that I love Josiane like nobody else on earth. I love her. That is the problem, Amparo."

'And they didn't wait till Christmas to come to the house, but at the get-together I arrange for all the Ocañas every year on All Saints Day. I opened the door to her man, Alain, of course. We drank an armagnac and we became friends. And afterwards we eat the stew my mother had cooked and I ended up scoffing a whole jar of jam. Do you know something, Juan? I really fancy some tripe, some of Milagros' tripe; it's the best in the world. Why don't we go to your house and have some? If we go right now, we'll get there just in time for dinner.'

'You are crazy, Luis,' Juan repeated more than once, as the car sped towards Madrid. In Burgos, where they stopped for petrol, Luis told Juan to call home and say they would be there in a couple of hours, and to buy some tripe and cook it. 'But are you crazy? You really believe you can prepare tripe in two hours? First you have to clean it thoroughly, keep it for a day, and then it has to be cooked slowly. It takes hours.'

'Ok, then, tell her to prepare a paella with cod, or whatever. I'm hungry.'

There were also days of silence. There were journeys when neither of them said a word. Journeys in the Fiat, Madrid to Pau, in which Luis sat in the passenger seat and took charge of the radio-cassette. The tape of Danny Daniel grinding on when Luis rewound it rapidly, looking for 'For the Love of a Woman' and then 'The Waltz of the

Butterflies', which he listened to over and over again, while he nodded his head or sat up tall in the seat.

Those kinds of days occurred least often.

11

'Don't give me that about the Pink Panther, Juan. There's never been anybody in films like Louis de Funes playing the part of the stupid policeman. I've never laughed so much in my life. I just love to sit on the sofa and spend the afternoon watching his films when they put them on the tele. What a policeman! And do you know we have something in common, Juan? Do you know his parents were Spaniards who emigrated to France? Well, they emigrated – that's one way of putting it. It's more that they went to France in search of freedom. So they could get married, to put it simply. I have read that his father was rich, an aristocrat from Seville who fell in love with a servant girl from Galicia, and because they were not allowed to get married they took themselves off to France. And from that dramatic couple has come the funniest guy in France. Can you believe it? That's life. And with that terrible surname, as well. Do you get it? You know – de Funes, Funesto[1]. You know something, Juan? I am going to commit suicide. I'm going to get rid of myself.'

Luis Ocaña, who was driving the Espace, had changed the subject of the conversation, without the slightest variation in the tone of his voice, and without making the slightest gesture. There was no snapping of the fingers on the steering wheel, nor any shifting his gaze from the straight, continuous white line on the tarmac which the headlights illuminated, and gave some shape to a night as black as only a dirty, moonless February night can be on the Madrid road from Cuenca. In the back, the bottles that filled the unsold boxes clinked over the potholes: the sparkling, the white, and the armagnac from his own bodega, Armagnac Luis Ocaña, *hors d'age*, the very best from his bodega, everlasting.

Luis carried on driving as if he had not opened his mouth, as if he had not said a thing, but Juan would never forget that just a kilometre

---

1. A play on words; 'funesto' = dreadful, terrible. Louis de Funes was a highly popular comic film actor in the 1960s and '70s.

further on, the headlights and a tiny lamppost would reveal a town entrance sign, which read Perales de Tajuña.

Then 45 minutes to reach San Fernando. These thoughts passed mechanically through his mind while he digested what he had just heard, interpreted it and tried to react to it. But Luis didn't stop talking in the darkness, broken by the green lights of the dashboard reflecting on his tired face. And Juan, who felt as if all his happiness in life had been abruptly taken away from him, remembered, unwillingly, a phrase he'd once read in a book. He was not much of a reader, but that phrase was easy to recall as it was the opening line of *El Malogrado* [*The Deceased*], which he didn't understand at the time; it was about a 51-year-old pianist from Vienna, and it was written without a single full stop. He didn't get beyond the second page. But the book began with this phrase: 'A long anticipated suicide, I thought, not an act of momentary despair'. And he thought about life, and how it would be to live like that, thinking every day about ending it, and putting a date on it. And he thought about Luis, his friend Luis.

'I've had a really dirty trick played on me in France, Juan. I sold a character 3,000 bottles of Floc de Gascogne, the fortified wine I'm making to open up a spirits market and he hasn't paid me. He doesn't intend to pay me. And nor for the 1,000 bottles of sparkling, either. He's ruined me. And the Inland Revenue is asking me for a million francs. I'm going to lose everything. A few days ago I was in France at the funeral of a friend who had committed suicide,' Luis continued, quietly, dispassionately, as if it were a matter of no consequence. 'And in the church they played Ravel's *Bolero* and the *Concierto de Aranjuez* on the organ. It was so lovely, Juan. I want that for me, at my funeral, I want them to play that music. I'm telling you this so that you can arrange it.'

'Bloody hell, Luis. Can't you talk about something else? Can't you carry on with your jokes, talk about girls, or cars or whatever? And you have to come out with death. But what rubbish you're talking, Luis.'

Finally Juan found something to say, albeit not very original. 'You say that I understand you and sometimes I believe I do, but so many other times I don't know what the hell you're on about, because you're a very complicated person. You're so extreme. You jump from white to black so easily you leave me flabbergasted. You are like Spain, Luis, and forgive me if I'm starting to get a bit deep, but you are like the history of Spain in the twentieth century – a contradiction and a tragedy. You have been the regime's sportsman, even going to shake Franco's hand, but at the same time you were opposed to them; you were an exile from the regime. And in France, out of loyalty, you say, and out of a sense of justice towards the France that fed you all, you go and become a supporter of Le Pen. And here, remember how you used to call Samaranch,[1] that life-long Falangist, every name under the sun. You said he didn't want you in any Spanish team because he said you were more French than Spanish, and a Communist on top of that, and that you didn't become naturalised only because you wanted to avoid French military service. You have lived in one Spain which has now come to an end. Those of us who are here haven't experienced the hunger you did, nor the miseries you went through and we haven't fought like you against poverty. You are from a different period, Luis.

'You really do know how to spoil my day, Luis. Here we are, happy, off to see my mother and have a good time for a few days, enjoy ourselves, and you come out with those things, Luis. It's not fair.

'It's ever since you started reading Larra and Bécquer and Espronceda[2], and writing sinister poems and painting those skulls. You're so indiscriminate – you paint Christ, a nude woman, a skull; it's all the same to you. Ever since then, ever since you became a romantic and dressed in black, you've become impossible to live with. You talk about death as if it were a game. You talk about killing yourself like someone talks about going to watch a game of football or going to spend a few days on the beach. And I don't know what you went to Paraguay for, Luis, but you've been very strange since you've come back. You've become superstitious, which you never were before, and you wear those necklaces as if you had joined a sect.'

---

1. Samaranch: President of the Spanish Olympic Committee, then Rresident of the Inernational Olympic Committee.
2. All three, C19th Spanish Romantic writers.

'I went to Paraguay, and you know that Juan, because I needed money, and because I wanted to breathe. I couldn't be with Josiane in the house all day, pestering me, what with her demands and asking me for money all the time. So when Lucien Bailly, the Technical Director of the French Federation, told me that the Paraguayans had called him and asked him to recommend a trainer for their youth teams and he'd immediately thought of me, I didn't hesitate for a second. After the obligatory discussion with Josiane, who didn't want me to leave her for so long, alone with the farm and the workers, and with all the work falling on her, I set out for Asunción. And no, Juan, it's not that I was changed when I got back; it's simply that I was tired. There's a lot of things I don't understand any more, Juan. No sooner had I got back from Paraguay, than there was an article in a French paper: "Ocaña ruined". It spoke about my problems with the tax authorities, with the fine they'd given me, about the vineyards, my debts and the armagnac. Sure, no doubt about it, bankrupt. But to see that was like being given a punch in the stomach. Everybody was talking about it, talking about me, but nobody offered any help. I'm not going to go around begging; people already know what's happened. And nobody, not even those who claim to be my friends, helped me find a way out. It seemed that people were happy to see things going badly for my business.

'Some days after that I went down to Cuenca with Josiane, and to Priego, where the people in the village made a tribute to me. Tributes and memorials and streets named after me; that was all they did; nobody gave me a penny. You can't eat honours. They've organised a race with my name, here in Cuenca – the Trofeo Luis Ocaña – and I like to come here every summer and direct it and to greet Indurain, Rominger, Escartín and so many generous cyclists who come to ride it. It's very well situated because it takes place before the Worlds and serves a bit like a rehearsal. It's spectacular with its final over the cobbles on the climb up Alfonso VIII, the Plaza Mayor and San Pedro. And I walk through Cuenca's old town eating a wonderfully rich tortilla sandwich, and then another one with anchovies in vinegar and oil, and people greet me and slap me on the back, and they love me, Juan. But I don't get a penny out of all this. In fact it costs me money.

Honours I don't need, Juan. They are not important to me.

'On that day, the testimonial day in December, a newspaper from a few days earlier came my way, in which Linares, that fool Linares, was talking about me. He says in the paper about how I must have been doped during his time, because when they, in the Kas team, were going full gas they couldn't catch me. But it's quite the reverse; it's the opposite question that I ask myself, Juan. I've never understood how I was only able to win one Vuelta a España, how riders, who were so mediocre that every year they would lose at least an hour in the Tour, were able to beat me in the Vuelta. I don't understand it. Tamames, Linares, these people…how could they have beaten me if in the Tour people laughed at them? I am not telling you, Juan, that I never took anything, but I've never needed to go up to the eyebrows to win.

'And I'll tell you something else, Juan, if I gave a positive in Spain during those years, that positive would have been right. They wouldn't have covered up anything for me. They never accepted me, that bunch of mediocrities, they never wanted me in Spain. I was always riding at a disadvantage in Spain, and there, anti-doping was a joke. The first Vuelta where they put in controls was the 1970 race, and I was the very first to take it, because I won the prologue in Cadiz – that prologue which ended in the football stadium, the Carranza stadium, where poor Pijnen fell. In the gate of the stadium there was an ambulance and I go in there to pee, bending back next to the stretcher. And in the papers the general secretary of the Vuelta, Albéniz, came out with some statements saying that because of having had to put in anti-doping controls, some teams had withdrawn from the Vuelta. He cited the Salvarani of Gimondi and Balmamion and Bracke's Peugeot and Planckaert's Belgian team. "This anti-doping innovation has done us few favours," said Albéniz. And now Linares comes at me with this. Fuente has also come out, talking frankly about everything he put in his veins, and when they asked Linares he says No. He's not going to talk if they don't pay him money. That's Spain for you, Juan.'

'Don't get bitter, Luis. Don't get bitter. My mother is waiting for us at home, with a surprise for dinner. She doesn't want me to say what it is, but it can't be bad, Luis.'

'You are seeing me black and mournful, Juan, right now, but I am the sun. I was the sun of the pelotons, the warmth and the generosity, the light which gave the races their life and emotion. I was all of that; I was the cycling that people loved. And afterwards a black storm cloud shrouded the sky.'

In San Fernando, in the besieged little house on Jardines Street, increasingly displaced by those ugly, shapeless tower blocks, Milagros was waiting for them with some tripe, which tasted glorious, and Luis finished off a stick of bread wiping the dish clean so there wasn't so much as a drop of the red sauce left, utterly content. With the meal over, he got up from the table and said, 'I'd like to go out on the town, Juan. I'll change my shirt, then let's go.' A few minutes later, Luis returned to the living room still in the same shirt he'd been wearing and with a black one in his hands. He showed it to Milagros. 'Look', he said. The beautiful, shiny black silk was full of tiny little holes, as if a moth had had a feast. 'Look at what Josiane has done to me. These are definitely not moth holes. This has been done with a cigarette. She's ruined my shirt, burning it with a cigarette...

'I wouldn't know how to live without women, Juan. Without seeing them, without touching them and feeling them. Without smelling them. What have they got? Why?'

Luis didn't like the roadside pick up clubs: the girls coarse and ordinary; the smell of the lorry driver's sweat; the ugliness of those places. When he crossed Spain with Juan and their cases of wine, they never stopped at those places, but when they went through Madrid it was always possible to go up to D'Angelo, in the Castellana, or better still, to the Pigmalion, very close by, in Pinar Street. Luis liked their Parisian and cosmopolitan atmospheres, their leather sofas around the edge of the place, up against the dimly lit walls, and the mock stained glass with a medieval theme in the dark windows. Above all he liked their women. Elegant, refined, smiles rather than loud laughter. On one of the sofas Luis spoke to Juan about women. Just the two of them, they still hadn't let any of them come and sit with them.

'But, you know, Juan, it's not like it used to be. My body doesn't function so well now. Have I ever told you about the night I beat

Merckx, really thrashed him? Have I ever told you that he was left like a dropped fag end, incapable of doing a thing? Well, you know that we never really got on together since I wouldn't put up with his authority, his dictatorship; you know it got up my arse that he always wanted to impose his rules about everything, about races, criteriums, teams… Above all, what really sickened me was the meekness of all the other riders: everyone submitted to whatever he said without a complaint; "Yes, Sir," they all said and they were content with whatever he left for them. That Tour of '71, when I had him on his knees, we stopped talking. And it went on for two years without a word passing between us. We'd run into each other in the hotels, on the trains, in aeroplanes, in restaurants, without even saying "Good Morning". I really didn't like it, but I put up with the situation; it was Eddy who finally broke the ice. It was in '73; I won the Tour and I still couldn't forgive him for not riding that year. It took the shine off my victory, even though I won it in the way he won his, I won it à la Merckx, taking half a dozen stage wins, and a quarter of an hour out of the second man. And that must have made him think, because in September, in the Paris–Brussels he came up to me and said things couldn't go on like that. "One day we'll have to go out, you and me, and make peace over a drink." Ten days later we met up in Lausanne. We were riding on the Sunday in a race called À Travers Lausanne, but we were already there on the Saturday. It was the perfect opportunity. We went out and began to drink in a bar and it was a real competition to see who could hold the most. On that field, Juan, you know I've no rival; I can cope with alcohol better than most. Eddy, on the other hand, was a little softie. After that we went to a whore house – he's already half-cut – and began competing again. He fell asleep with the first. I sent him the second and he told me there was nobody who could wake him up. I, of course, carried on a little longer.

'We got back to the hotel at six in the morning, he snoring beside me in the taxi. It was a total victory for me. By a knockout. At ten in the morning we were riding the criterium, which consisted of two parts – a road-race and a time trial. Both very short, just five kilometres, but on streets that went straight up and down, really steep. Well then, with the biggest hangover of his life, (perhaps the first, he confessed to me later), Merckx beat me, and not only me. He beat everybody in both sections, and the best were there – Gimondi, Poulidor, Thévenet, Fuente... I finished fourth. Eddy showed me there that he had a capacity for recovery like few others. And from that day we were friends. Eddy has done well in business; he sells a lot of bicycles, Juan. He's always had a better instinct than me when it comes to dealing with money, but always, whenever I've asked him a favour he's helped me out. Thanks to him a lot of doors were opened; I sold armagnac in Belgium; he came with me to the trade fairs and stayed at my side. And from then on Eddy was part of my life and I was part of his.

'But I'm not the same, now, Juan. My animal side, the spirit that I can't put to sleep, if you want to call it that, still gets excited at the sight of a lovely woman, at the smell of a woman and I still desire her. A nice arse full of mysteries to be unravelled and sweet skin, a deep neck line and I still want to be with the beauty for ever, but my body no longer responds. Sometimes I can't... I don't want to get old, Juan, I don't want to be a Fede [Bahamontes], jealous and selfish, who never wanted to acknowledge that I was a champion. It really pissed him off that I also won the Tour, Juan. He never has managed to get over it, and now, every time you see him, that much older, that much more of a twerp, however much he struts about, and people laugh at him behind his back, like my team mates laughed at me when they saw me drunk and making silly comments. I don't want to be old, and I'm not going to be old. Can you imagine me getting old, Juan? Would you have imagined Anquetil getting old, telling his grandchildren all about his old times, and only his old times? When I die, after I've killed myself, I want to be cremated and then one day I want you, Juan, to bring my ashes, or a part of them, a tiny handful, here, to the Pigmalion. Then I want you to sleep with the most beautiful whore you can see – that blonde over there, for example – invite her to have a whisky and CocaCola and when she's distracted for a moment slip the ashes into her drink. And make sure she drinks it, Juan. There'll be no better place for me than running for ever more in the blood of one of the voluptuous chicks from the Pigmalion, Juan.'

12

The following morning Juan was woken up by Luis's shouts and chants and the splashing of water. He leaned over the balcony and saw him in the middle of the street washing the van, the Espace.

'Luis seems strange to me,' his mother said to him as she warmed a saucepan of milk which he was waiting for, sitting at the kitchen table. 'He seems bad, son, not at all well. He seems subdued as if, bit by bit the life is draining out of him, as if he doesn't have any desire to live any more. He's the same as ever on the face of it: he devours the tripe, he makes flirtatious remarks towards me, he sings while he washes the car, but he's not the same. He has a different look, a sad look.'

'Don't worry, Mum,' Juan tried to reassure her. 'He's only going through a bad patch. He's low on money because he spends a lot and he's earning little, and on top of that he's been left owing a fortune and he's too proud ever to ask for any help. He'll come out alright, he's still a popular public celebrity and he'll be able to continue working on the radio and, if he wants, on television and in the newspapers. He'll be alright, Mum. He's a bit pessimistic right now, because things with Josiane are not going too well. When he got back to the house she gave him a hard time. "Who have you been with? How much money have you brought in?" But it's just a bad phase he's going through. He'll get through it. You know he can't live without Josiane. She's everything to him. He's got too much on and he's tired, Mum. He was telling me he's feeling really bad because he's getting more and more pains because of the problem with his liver, and he's worried because he's got to go for a check up at the hospital in Toulouse… but everything will work out, Mum, it'll be alright. You know his strength of character. Wasn't he the only one to put Merckx on the floor? The new cycling season will begin in a month's time and he'll be fine then; he'll go to the Vuelta with Butano, and that always bucks him up, and there will be money coming in. You'll see. And he has us. He'll never be on his own. He can cope with anything, Mum.'

'I'm pessimistic, Juan,' said Milagros, finally. She would not let herself be convinced. 'Nobody can control him. That's his strength. And his misfortune.'

13

Despite what he had promised Julio that night in Benidorm, when he confessed he was finished, and despite what he had assured him, Luis didn't get to go to the Giro. He died three days before the start of the Italian race. Thursday, 19 May 1994 at 1.45 in the afternoon, instead of getting in the car and driving off to Bologna, where he should have met his broadcasting companions from COPE, Luis Ocaña fired a bullet into his temple. Josiane found him dead in the small office he had on the upper floor of the cottage at the entrance to the estate. The telephone was unhooked on top of the table.

The day before, Luis had called his mother, Julia. He was her favourite of all the children; she worshipped the ground he walked on. 'Do you know what I dreamed about, mother?' he said to her. 'I dreamed you made me doughnuts in the frying pan, the ones that only you know how to make, the ones that taste of you and the family, those that you learned to make in Spain when you got married and which smell of oil and of the earth. You made me lots and I ate them all, Mother. And I was happy. Mother? Tomorrow I am going to Italy. I am going to be away a long time. I want to see you before I go. Will you make me some doughnuts that I can take to Italy with me? I'll eat them on the way and my hands will be greasy and I'll spread that over the steering wheel and the crumbs will fall on the seat. I will clean it all up, but to me they will taste better than ever, mother.'

He also called Milagros in San Fernando de Henares. 'It's been a long time since I saw you, Luis. During the Vuelta I heard you on the radio every day, but you forgot to pay us a visit, Luis. How are you? Is everything alright?'

'Milagros, how is your brother's vegetable garden?' he asked her. 'Has he got some good tomatoes? And onions? I really would love to eat one of those tomatoes, Milagros, just bite it and taste the full flavour of it. I could eat one right now; in fact I could eat a dozen. Have they come out well this year? If I could, I'd get in the car straight away and be over there, Milagros.'

He called Juan that very Thursday, minutes before blowing out his brains. 'I'm going to commit suicide, Juan. I'm going to kill myself right now. I'm going to shoot myself. I've had a terrible row with Josiane, Juan.'

'Yes, alright, Luis, you shoot yourself. No, better still, shoot yourself twice, just in case the first one fails and instead of killing yourself you just remain paralysed... Come on now, Luis, don't be like that... Listen, Luis, we have to get together; I've got an idea which could interest you... when you get back from Italy call me... We have to meet up, Luis. Luis!'

Luis's body was taken to the mortuary in Mont-de-Marsan where it stayed the night, alone. During the afternoon the only ones to go and see him were some neighbours, a married couple. At the entrance to the estate Josiane nailed up a notice. 'The family is not receiving anybody.' On the following day, by order of the judge in Auch, his body was taken to Bordeaux where the autopsy was performed. The investigation carried out by the *gendarmes* in Nogaro, supported by the public prosecutor and the judge, concluded that Luis Ocaña had committed suicide. Despite this, his mother, Julia, and his five siblings, and Jean-Louis as well, appealed against the verdict and brought an action because they believed Luis had not taken his own life. Without naming her, they insinuated that Josiane, who had been the only person in the house with him that day, had killed him, but the judge closed the case; it was suicide.

14

It was not the state funeral of Agostinho. It was not even the burial of Anquetil.

The wonderful, sad, tired gaze of Pierre Cescutti ran over the walls of the chapel and allowed himself to be dazzled by the brilliant colours of the hundreds of jerseys which covered the simple Romanesque walls of the interior of the chapel of Labastide. Weighed down by memories and scarcely taking in the words of Father Massié, who, together with the parish priest Father Lestage, was directing the funeral, Cescutti wanted to recall that same place on that cold day almost 30 years earlier when Luis and Josiane had been married, with the same Father Massié conducting the wedding ceremony. At that time there were hardly any champion's *maillots* on the walls, only Darrigade's rainbow jersey and a green jersey of his. The 'Greyhound of Les Landes' was the most devout of cyclists, devoted to the virgin of cyclists, and to her image, carved in dark stone on the capital directly behind the altar.

One journalist wrote that at the very moment when Darrigade handed over his fine, silk rainbow jersey to Father Massié a real rainbow appeared in the sky and its light shone through the small open windows in the stone. The legend, or rather the miracle which it became as soon as it was written, couldn't be confirmed, but it inspired another cyclist, Henri Anglade, to design a stained glass to embellish the window. And there, that sad afternoon in May, when the grass surrounding the chapel was greener than ever, Cescutti stopped looking at how the stained glass coloured the light, and made out the picture of Coppi and Bartali exchanging the bidon of water. Who is giving it to whom? Cescutti, who was a *Coppiano*, just as he was an *Anquetilista*, just as he was an *Ocañista*, had always maintained that it was Coppi, but it wouldn't have mattered to him if it had been the reverse, since Bartali was also a great and generous champion. And so too was Luis, and some of his jerseys are there – that of 1972 Spanish champion, his yellow from the 1970 Vuelta and from the '73

Tour, and also is his stained glass window, his trademark arched back, like a dome that gives meaning to a cathedral. Cescutti himself had also made his contribution to Massié's chapel. One day he had taken there the bike on which his wife, Rolande Danné, had beaten the world hour record, and her jersey. Cescutti had never seen the chapel so full, not even during the Feast of Penticost, when hundreds attend to eat chicken casserole à la Henri IV. There were at least 500 people. They were there, some inside and the majority in the field, waiting, because they thought about Luis, like Cescutti thought about him. About his life, about a life which brought him to death at the age of 48, the same age at which his father died. Cescutti, when he received the news, was not surprised. It was like a gunshot which brought him down, but one he was expecting.

'Luis could never have put up with the mediocrity of a restricted, penned in life,' his friend thought, as ideas for his epitaph went round and round in his head. 'He went to the edge, as usual. And I understand him,' he thought, also remembering how Luis had told him a few weeks earlier how bad he was and that in the hospital in Toulouse they had given him no hope. There they both were, like on their wedding day, Josiane, now a widow, dressed in black, Luis in a coffin. Eddy Merckx was also there, brought by the fatalism from which no cyclist is far removed. Eddy – and also Thévenet and also Fuente, the two who accompanied him on to the podium in '73 – was one of those who carried the coffin from the chapel to the hearse, which drove it to the cemetery in Tarbes where he was cremated. Afterwards on the lawn, separated from hundreds of fans by barriers which everyone respected, he spoke in a circle with old team mates, all of them more portly, more tired and sad.

'We didn't get on at all well. We very often annoyed each other. We had great battles,' said the Cannibal, 'but Luis was my most stalwart opponent. And in the end we became friends. We used to speak often on the telephone. The last time was just a few weeks ago. He said to me, "Eddy, I am very unwell".'

'He said the same to me, as well, a couple of weeks ago,' said Thévenet, 'But he did not sound to me as if he had given up hope, quite the opposite. He talked to me about plans he had, about whether I could help him to sell armagnac in my area, in Burgundy and around Grenoble. He was a wonderful person, over the top in all sorts of ways, but an adorable person because he was very principled. He always gave it everything, without worrying about the consequences; he'd throw caution to the wind. When I heard that he'd shot himself I didn't want to believe it; I didn't understand it. But then I learned he had a lot of problems and Luis was not the type of person who'd let problems overwhelm him. He always wanted to be master of his own destiny, and he would rather do away with himself before the problems did it for him. He would have wanted to take his own life, rather than let destiny take it. That was the real Luis; that was Luis.'

'Yes, that's right, but in the end Luis couldn't outwit destiny, Bernard.' It was Guimard speaking, his big glasses giving his blue eyes a look of intense bewilderment. Luis, before he died, faced up to enemies he couldn't dominate mentally, like the debts and the illness. I believe that one day he thought about it and came to understand that he was no longer in charge of his life. He'd always wanted to shape his own destiny and then the day came when he couldn't do so any longer. It was his destiny defeated him finally.'

At the funeral the Spanish Consul in Bordeaux was present; he was the only official Spanish representative. They didn't play either Ravel's *Bolero*, nor the *Concierto de Aranjuez* because there was no organ in the little chapel. Nor did they play the music that Ocaña had dreamed about in the service that took place a week later, the last Monday of May, in the church of Priego. There was an organ but Juan couldn't find an organist able to play them. The ashes were divided in three. One part was interred in the grave of his father; another was kept by Josiane in an urn; the third, apart from a tiny handful, was interred in Priego, at the foot of the monument of metal and stone which the town council had raised to its cyclist in 1990.

Epilogue
February 2012

Priego

In Priego, between the line of mountains and that part of the Meseta known as the Alcarria, there are evergreen oaks, and on the patios, fig trees and on the dry, steep ochre-coloured hillsides, the vineyards and dusty olive trees grow. And lower down, next to the river, is the willow. In Priego in the province of Cuenca, from which Luis Ocaña and his family had to flee, persecuted by hunger and by the memory of the war whose wounds had never healed, there are some from his family who still remain. Both old and young they continue to pass in front of the church, where the cross of the fallen, with its Franquista eagle, recalling the number of Nationalists who died, stands as a permanent insult to those who lost. In Priego, Ocaña is a black metal plate, silhouetted in the shape of his time trial profile with his arched back emphasised, which the kids use for target practice with their air rifles. Above the stone pedestal on which Jean-Louis placed a rose on the day when a third of his father's ashes were interred, there are some bunches of dried flowers. And behind him the fortified tower. Juan Hortelano knocks at the door and speaks with the occupants. 'No,' they tell him. 'No, no , we don't want to let you come in and see the house. How much will you pay us?'

Juan had come back to the places associated with Luis Ocaña, to his memory, and to the remnants of what he wanted to build. He wanted to remember his friend through the recollections of his family, of those who were still there. And even so many years later, he immediately realised one thing. No matter who he talks to, they start talking about Luis when he was alive, but in no time at all they are talking about his death. It is clear to Juan that the death of Luis, his friend, is as misunderstood as his life was, and that it caused wounds that would never be healed.

Not far from the monument, Luis's blood cousins have a small fruit shop, Frutería Ocaña. They are the children of Teodora, his father's young sister, and of his cousin. There is little they can tell Juan about the Ocaña who won the Tour, since they had hardly any contact with him. 'We were very little when we knew him, Juan. We do certainly remember the ceremony when they brought the ashes. There was a real row and a lot of noise and Jean-Louis began to have a row with his mother and his sister, right there, in front of everybody. It was very sad, Juan.'

Virginia Pernía – they call her Virgen – has a bar rented to some young Bulgarian women and a large house. She is a cousin of Luis on his mother's side, the daughter of a brother of his mother, Julia. Virgen talks about Luis's life and his visits; he went to the Los Claveles guesthouse when he was a cyclist and drank herbal tea. Then he used to go out alone on his bicycle and come back alone. 'Luis didn't commit suicide, Juan.' Virgen wanted to talk about how the death of her cousin had hurt her, even though it was 20 years ago. 'My aunt, Julia, never believed that her son committed suicide, and I think the same way as her. It couldn't have entered his head. She said to me, "Virgen, my dear, do you believe that Luis, with all the love he had for me, could have done that to me? He had just told me to make him fried doughnuts! They were his favourites, he liked them as much as taking a lovely bite out of a raw onion just dug up out of the earth, and zarajos, callos, mantecadas[1] which Marie-France used to make for him. He didn't get to stop at my house, Virgen, and he had promised me." That's what Julia told me one day when she came to Priego. She told me when we were both in bed, because when she came to Priego to see the family she always like to sleep with me. Julia was like a mother to me and I was like a daughter to her and she confided everything in me, and Amparo is like my sister and I go lots of times to Bordeaux to see her. And we talk about Luis.'

In Priego Matías Soria, who is known as Caquilla, is still alive, a tiny, little old man, and tireless. He's fibrous like you'd think he'd been plaited out of straw. He's alive and now he can go into the bars they used to throw him out of for being a red, for having lost the war.

---

1. Basic Spanish dishes, zarajos being associated with Cuenca.

Bordeaux

In Bordeaux, Juan visited Amparo, who lived a pleasant life there in retirement. Every morning, for an hour and a half, she and her husband and a group of friends practised Nordic walking, going with ski poles at 10 kph through the city's parks, Afterwards in her house, she enjoyed her own private jungle – a house surrounded by planted terraces with orange and lemon trees, and orchids and tropical plants in the lounge.

'I've got green fingers, Juan,' said Amparo and gave him a glass of her brother's armagnac, from one of the last bottles left. She took it out of a small glass cabinet in which two of his racing trophies shone and a small portrait of Luis sat above it. 'Jesús had them, too. I am like Jesús, Juan, except that I am alive. I have his rage, my brother's rage, and the rage has made me be born again. I was no intellectual, I did hardly any studying, but I knew how to set up and run my business. The same pride that my brother had nurtured in me, and with no schooling and without a diploma I got to be head of the kitchen in a hotel. I feel his absence, Juan. I say, "Jesús" and I'm not getting it wrong. If the whole world always knew my elder brother as Luis Ocaña, for us, at home, he was always Jesús, the first name my parents gave him.'

'Yes, Amparo, I do know that. Luis always told me that his name, in fact, was Jesús Luis, and he asked me to call him that as well, but I was already too accustomed to calling him Luis to be able to change.'

'Josiane and my brother went from love to hate in so short a time, Juan, but I don't believe she killed him, although my brothers insisted on it, and my mother. My brother didn't want to be reliant on anybody. He was like that: it was his pride, and it's mine, too. When I told my mother that he was dead, she shouted, "They have killed my boy, Amparo! They have killed my boy!" She told me that a few days before his death he turned up at her house. "I've come to stay the night here, mother' Jesús said to me, Amparo. 'Yesterday I had a quarrel with Josiane and I went to sleep on the sofa. In the middle of the night a noise woke me up and I saw Josiane creeping towards me with a knife.' That's what Jesús told me, Amparo." The day I told her that her eldest son, the pride of her life, had died, that's what she said to me.

'And my mother was hard, Juan, and we took after her. And she never wanted to depend on anybody. She died two years ago. She broke her hip one day and in six months she faded away. She was 89 and carried on living alone in her house. That was her; she never wanted to go and live with anyone else. She did everything herself, washing, scrubbing…the house was always spotless. The day she died I called in at 8 o'clock in the morning and the nurse who was there at night told me she hadn't got up yet, that she was still sleeping. Half an hour later I peeped into her room and she was dead. And then, much later, Josiane also said to me (Juan noticed that she had her brother's habit of jumping from one theme to another without warning and with hardly a change in tone) "I saw him on the sofa, Amparo, and I wanted to kill him, but it was the lounge curtain I cut with the knife."

'The night before he died he got himself drunk with whisky and armagnac, in spite of the bad state his liver was in, as if he were trying to poison himself, and Josiane tried to restrain him, to keep him alive, to stop him dying. "We made love that night, Amparo," Josiane told me. "And I asked him not to use a contraceptive. I loved your brother so much, Amparo." The following morning, however, she thought that he was going to take Marie-Jo with him to the Giro, and she put sugar in the car's petrol tank, and the car wouldn't start. He went up to the office and shot himself. That's how it was, Juan'

Nogaro

In Jean-Louis's farmhouse a framed photo of his father on his bike, riding flat out, dominates the lounge. In the bottom left corner, between the glass and the frame, Jean-Louis has added a small picture, that of the first Luis Ocaña, his grandfather, who died when he was six months old. It is the same picture of a hard, skinny man, looking straight out at the camera, that Luis wanted to turn into an oil portrait. Framed a little further away is the Spanish Champion's jersey that Luis won a few weeks before his father died and which he brought to him on his deathbed. Jean-Louis drinks whisky and CocaCola, like his father did – a swig from the whisky bottle and a swallow from the CocaCola tin, one after the other – and, like his father, he didn't seem to care much for memories. That's all there is. Those are the only visible pieces of cycling memorabilia which Jean-Louis retains. He doesn't even have a bicycle.

'I've never liked cycling, Juan. My father took that pleasure away from me. The first time I went out with him he started to attack me, to insult me and make me suffer. I was 16 years old and he was 40. For me, it's the motorbike, the Ducati.'

Jean-Louis breeds ducks: he receives a batch of ducklings every month, fattens them up in cages by stuffing a mush of maize down their necks until their liver weighs 600 grams. His farm is just a few kilometres from Nogaro, next to where his father had the armagnac estate, not very far from where his grandparents had lived and from Mont-de-Marsan.

'I've lead a nomadic life; I've worked in the Caribbean; I've done all sorts of things, but in the end I've come back, Juan.'

'We all do come back, Jean-Louis. We always do. The land calls us all, as if the roots that we think we don't have grip us tightly and draw us like magnets.'

'No, I didn't come back to Nogaro for that reason. It's not the roots that tie me here, it's the circuit.'

Jean-Louis is a motorcyclist who competes in the French Cup on a Ducati 848 and spends the winter putting together and taking apart engines. It takes him two hours to build an engine, and Juan watched him working in his little workshop. To get there, to that freezing cold room, so low that your head rubbed against the ceiling, you had to pass through a warehouse in which the cages holding the ducks were empty that day, waiting for a new consignment to be fattened up. Jean-Louis also builds up and paints motorbikes, and sells them to pay for the race entry fees. He lives with his girl friend, who comes from Toulouse; her name is Josiane, like his mother, and she's been with him 13 years living in Nogaro, together with a little dog called 'Chien'. From Monday to Friday he lives the life of a farmer, and at the weekends that of a motorcyclist, travelling to races in a camper van, from which hangs his own large banner placard – 'The Ducks Racing Team'. Or, if he's not racing he is practising, lapping the Paul

Armagnac circuit, a stone's throw from his house, and the magnet that keeps him in Nogaro.

'He knows the Nogaro circuit so well that once he went and even won a race,' said Josiane, his Josiane, who sat on the sofa, watching, almost enjoying the scene of her boyfriend drinking and relating his life story in Spanish to a stranger. It was a story of which she had only heard odd bits and pieces. 'I never met Luis, his father, but everybody tells me that as time goes by Jean-Louis gets more and more like him, and that it was more and more inevitable that two such similar personalities, and with such strong personalities, would clash. And I've noticed that even Jean-Louis's back outlines the same arc when he's on the motorbike as his father's did when he was on the bike.'

'The break-up was inevitable, Josiane, and also the reconciliation. Six months before he died I spoke to him, and we each talked about our lives, and finally we gave each other a hug. He told me that he had a lover, and that he was soon going to die. Those two things, just like that! He also told me he was seeing a lawyer in Auch to get a divorce. I went to visit him in the Toulouse hospital where they were doing a liver biopsy and analysis. I rang for the lift and he appeared, pushing his own cot and all the equipment for the intravenous fluids and the catheter. "They've told me I've got a few weeks left," he said. We knew that he would never get to be old; we would never see him old. He also told me that he hadn't had any more children with Marie-Jo, his lover, although he'd been with her for a good many years, and that Josiane, my mother, knew all about it. It was a story that went back 20 years. In fact he told me that once, when I was three, he packed his suitcase and went round to Marie-Jo's house and told her he was going to live with her. But she said, no, he was married and he had to live with his family. So my father returned home and said to Josiane, "I have a lover." I saw his death coming. I saw it coming day by day. It was no surprise to me.'

The day his father died, Jean-Louis had a phone call from his uncle Marino.

'I went as fast as I could. I was out of breath. I climbed the stairs to his office two at a time and I saw my father's brains splattered over the door. Two months before I had taken the revolver, a 9mm, away from him, but he came to my house and asked me for it. I gave it back to him, without the bullets. He must have bought some more. I got out of the little house where he died and went into the wood and lit a cigarette, and while I was smoking and walking about and trying to take in what I'd just seen, I listened to some policemen who were out there getting some fresh air. It didn't seem like suicide to them, I heard them say. And also that they were going to open a murder investigation and that the whole family would be under suspicion. Some days later I saw the photographs of the autopsy, my father with his chest sewn up, and I was surprised that he was cremated so quickly. Normally in a case of murder the body isn't allowed to be cremated, I thought. So, for that reason, it did not seem strange that three days later they told us that the case had been closed.'

Jean-Louis, who was squatting in front of a low table, got up for a moment, went to the back of the house and returned immediately with a large trunk – 'the trunk which my grandfather brought with him from Priego, the trunk my father restored and always took great care of.' Out of it he took a substantial file full of papers.

'All of this is what I sent to the judge. These are all my petitions to a judge who was deaf to everything. He refused me everything and didn't respond to any of my doubts or questions. How can a person commit suicide when he's got 1.9 grams of alcohol in his blood and a destroyed liver? How could he even be conscious? How could he fire a bullet into his left temple when the pistol fell on his right side and he was right-handed? Was it a perfect crime? That day my father told his mother, my grandmother, that he was going to Toulouse with Marie-Jo, but the cases were not in the car and all the tyres were punctured. And I also knew that he had an appointment at three o'clock that day with the lawyer in Auch, about the divorce. But when I saw my mother I said to her, "Now you've won". And that was it. My father was very peculiar. I've never met anybody even remotely like him, but he was not somebody you wanted to be with every day. He didn't feel he was either Spanish or French. That was my father, Juan, nothing more, and after his death I began to understand him.'

Juan looked at Jean-Louis, whose gaze was fixed on the picture of his father arched over the bike, and understood in his look that Jean-Louis saw the same in himself, the young man who had unknowingly inherited from his father those values bound up with work, effort, and above all, pride.

'Everything I have I have built it myself, I have won it. Watching him work I learned to work like he did. I build everything; I am everything: mechanic, farmer, bricklayer, carpenter. I am like my father. I've lived an unusual life, and I, too, like the countryside, the solitude, the vineyards, like he did, but he couldn't live in this world nowadays. He wouldn't understand anything, like nobody understood him in his world. Nor did he ever want to admit to me that deep down, he, who admired rock and the rebellion of Johnny Hallyday, wanted to be like me. The two of us, we both suffer from the same need to be loved.'

Jean-Louis was born on 23rd of February and he always races with the number 23 on the motorbike, and he carries his father with him; etched on his chest above his heart is a tattoo which reproduces one of his father's paintings – a passionate, Goyaesque nightmare. And on his arm is tattooed 'Spain' – the terrible black vision of Spain's nightmare, skulls, a smoking pistol, barbed wire, the mysticism of death and war.

Almost 20 years after that 19th May, 1994 Jean-Louis, accompanied by Juan, went back to his father's estate in Caupenne d'Armagnac. His look, which seemed oblivious, distant, silently ran across the fields, the office in which Luis died, the little house which the new owners had converted into the boutique-showroom of a winery, which no longer made armagnac. They produced white and rosé wines called Domaine de Miselle, denomination Côtes de Gascogne, which sell very well. On the threshold of what was his house, Jean-Louis stopped. He did not dare to enter. He missed the 50 banana trees. He recognised nothing.

'It's all changed, Juan. I don't recognise a thing. A hundred trees have disappeared from the garden, and the swimming pool, and some vineyards.'

'But the fig tree is still there.'

His look now sharper and sadder, he recalled the work his father had put in on the wooden beams of the wine store, the paving of the patio, and he suffered at the unforgivable sight of the paint peeling off, and the dirt.

'That carelessness would have infuriated him, Juan, you knew him.' I don't mind that my mother sold it to pay the debts, to have lost it. What I see now, most especially, are the problems, the complications of maintaining something so big. I prefer a small place. This is a 17th century mansion and all I remember is the work that was necessary and there was no end to it; you were never finished. And I like it when it's finished. Everything had to be recently whitewashed with my father, but now it's lost its personality: he didn't like the wood painted. Everything was ordered; in his mind everything was ordered; the vines had to be straight, all the same.

Artiguelouve (suburbs of Pau)

Before going into the house she had built on the outskirts of Pau and divided into two symmetrical parts, the right for herself, and the left for her daughter, Sylvie and her grandchildren, Bianca and Matteo, the children of the Italian, Josiane made Juan take off his boots, which were covered in mud. Once inside, Juan understood why. He had entered a place so clean, so hygienic as to be almost sterile, ruled over by a 16-year-old chihuahua called Chipi. A carpet shaped like a bull's skin. A number of bookends in the shape of Luis's arched back, and of Luis himself, there were his ashes in an urn and his memory in photos, in the albums presented by his followers and stored in the attic, and a terracotta bust showing his mole and with the winter hat which he liked so much and in which he worked in the fields on cold mornings. It is the only piece of clothing that Josiane has retained.

'I haven't kept anything of Luis's cycling career, Juan. Nor have I kept the furniture from the farm; it was so big, so dark, so rural. When I sold the farm I said to the buyers that they should have the furniture. I didn't want the old stuff. Luis loved that furniture, so Spanish in style. I wanted to be French, but Luis was very Spanish and very jealous.

He always wanted me to be alone; he didn't want me to go out and he made me drive thousands of kilometres in the car to go and collect him from races. He told me everything, Juan, everything, and I told him everything. And wherever he was, he called me everyday on the phone. I never thought that his life could end like that.'

'Luis loved you very much, Josiane. He always told me that. What he said was: "Juan, whatever you might hear, believe me, my only love in life is Josiane. She is everything." He also told me he was going to take his own life, Josiane. I've felt very sorry for you, because of that. You were very much on your own when he died, and you found yourself facing all Luis's family accusing you of having killed him.'

'Things were not good between us ever since the November, Juan. He was so strange when he came back from Paraguay. I told him not to go, and we argued a lot. He cleared off and left me with an insane amount of work in the house, and he'd done some crazy things. You know that well enough because you were with him during some of them. And we had many debts, and there was the illness. The doctors told me he would only live till October. I asked them not to tell Luis that, because I was afraid of his black thoughts, but they told him. His life was destroyed, Juan. He was lost, completely lost.'

'At first I didn't believe you, Josiane, but then I understood. I believed that Luis didn't get to suffer while he was alive and that he wouldn't have died of hepatitis. He got ride of himself because of the economic problems which he didn't know how to deal with. I don't know if he killed himself through cowardice or bravery. You don't know everything about Luis, Josiane. There are things he told me which he never said to you, but of course you knew him better than anybody. Only you knew what went on in his head.'

'For several days he was saying I am going to shoot myself, I'm going to shoot myself, and two days before he went back to broadcasting on the Vuelta for COPE, on the Tuesday, he attempted it for the first time with a pistol, Juan. I had hidden the pistols from him in the wine store, and I hid the key. But he found it, went into the wine store, and got them. At eight o'clock I called his doctor and the police. The doctor spoke with him for two hours and told me he was calm. I told them that if anything happened it would be on their conscience. That was on the Tuesday. That night he wasn't at all calm. He was tossing and turning in bed; he got up very early. But on the Wednesday it was as if nothing had happened; he was happy with the workmen, he planted vines, he worked just as normal. He went to a neighbour's house to ask if he could borrow a machine…and I breathed a sigh of relief.

But on Thursday it all began again, only this time worse. He only wanted to eat bread and milk, although I encouraged him to eat more than that. Then, instead of that he got hold of a bottle of wine and started drinking. I shouted at him that he was destroying his liver, that he had already destroyed it and I threw the bottle in the rubbish bin. He went into a real fit, but he wouldn't let me call the doctor. He snatched the telephone out of my hands and threw it on the floor; he wouldn't let me go to the toilet by myself for fear that I would call on the cordless phone. It was terrible. Then he surprised me because it seemed that he'd calmed down. "Can I go to the office?" he said to me in the kitchen, "to the office in the little house on the other side of the patio?" And I thought it best he should go; that way I could call the doctor in peace, using the cordless phone in the house. But immediately I realised. This is not normal, I said to myself. I ran out to the patio and through the window of the office I saw him sitting in the armchair. He has calmed down, I thought. The crisis is over and he's sleeping. When I went into the office to see him, my first thought was that he had changed his shirt, because before he had on a white one, not a red one… It was the blood. I didn't see the pistol. My eyes were fixed on the telephone that was hanging off the cradle.'

'He had called me, Josiane. He told me that he was going to shoot himself, but I didn't take him seriously. He had said it so many times…'

'He was saying that for some time: "I'm going to shoot myself, I'm going to shoot myself." But Luis was so strong, Juan, that to me it seemed inconceivable. He always said that he didn't think he would get to be old, that his father had died young, that he would not suffer like his father had in dying, nor like Anquetil had. He was in a lot of pain and he didn't want to go to the doctor like his father, and the injections of interferon depressed him; their secondary effects included a tendency towards suicide. "If I'm going to have to suffer the pain my father had, I will kill myself," he used to say to me. It was the illness that changed his character. He was tired , ground down. He didn't see himself with any strength left and I was fed up with everything, too, Juan. It was a terrible end, like a damnation.'

Appendix

Teams*

1966	Mercier-BP-Hutchinson, end of season, amateur *hors catégorie*
1967	Mercier-BP-Hutchinson (FR), amateur hors catégorie
1968	Fagor-Fargas (Sp)
1969	Fagor (Sp)
1970	Bic (Fr)
1971	Bic (Fr)
1972	Bic (Fr)
1973	Bic (Fr)
1974	Bic (Fr)
1975	Super Ser (Sp)
1976	Super Ser (Sp)
1977	Frisol-Thirion-Gazelle (Nl)
1984	Teka (Sp), director
1985	Fagor (Fr), director
1987	ADR-Fangio-IOC-MBK (Be), director
1989	Puertas Mavisa-Galli (Sp), director
1990	Puertas Mavisa (Sp), director

Palmarés

1962   First year of competition in the Vélo-Club Aturin.
First victory, 1st of April 1962 in Mimizan (Prix du Printemps)

1963   Vélo-Club Aturin

1st	Bezolles
1st	Bourdalat
1st	Le Houga
1st	Barcelone-du-Gers
1st	Bretagne d'Armagnac
1st	Forces
1st	Prix des Grimpeurs de Lasseube
2nd	Réans
2nd	Circuit des Gaves de Oloron

---

* Source: www.memoire-du-cyclisme.eu

1964   Stade Montois. Independent second category

1st   Prix Martini de Mont-de-Marsan
1st   Saint-Romain-le-Noble
1st   G.P. d'Ouverture, Bagnères-de-Bigorre
        1st Stage 2
1st   Nerac
2nd   Ceré
2nd   Circuit Bazadais

Independent first category

1st   Saint-Pierre du Mont
1st   Hasparren
1st   Langoiran
1st   Critérium des Espoirs de Saint-Aulaye
2nd   Prix Sicaso de Tarbes
2nd   Mauléon d'Armagnac
2nd   Circuit du Réolais
2nd   Capvern les Bains
3rd   Samatan
3rd   G.P. de Périgueux
9th   Critérium International de Beaulac
11th   Critérium International de Labastide d'Armagnac
13th   Critérium International d'Auch

1965   Stade Montois equiped by Mercier. Independent *hors*
**   *categorie***

1st   Houielles
1st   Lagor
1st   Aillas
1st   Artix
1st   Prix de St. Pierre de Mont-de-Marsan
1st   Hasparren
1st   Villandraut
1st   Critérium du Sud-Ouest, Saint-Aulaye
1st   Estang
2nd   G.P. de France de Laval
5th   Mont Faron
7th   Grand Prix des las Nations
9th   Tour de Combraille
        2nd time trial Stage

**1966   Stade Montois equiped by Mercier. Independent *hors*
*categorie***

1st	Tour of Bidasoa
	1st Stage 3
1st	Prix de la Saint-Pierre de Mont-de-Marsan
1st	Prix Lagarasic de Auch
1st	Stage 4, Tour du Bearn
1st	Lembeye
1st	Pontacq
1st	Cambo-les-Bains
1st	Lamonzie
1st	Vieux-Boucau
1st	G.P. de Poitiers time trial
2nd	Tour du Roussillon
	1st on one stage
	1st in Mountain classification
3rd	Mont Faron
4th	Tour du Gard
	1st Bessèges-Nîmes stage
4th	Criterium de Beaulac
5th	Grand Prix des Nations

**1967   Stade Montois equiped by Mercier. Independent *hors*
*categorie***

1st	Sarlat
1st	Pierre Bénite (Lyon)
1st	Sain-Geours de Maremme
1st	Nersac (Angoulême)
1st	G.P. du Kiosque de Tarbes
1st	Figeac
1st	Saint-Julien d'Armagnac
1st	Tour du Roussillon
	1st - Bourg-Madame stage
	1st - Mountain classification
1st	Stage 1- Cuatro días de las Baleares
1st	Tour du Béarn
1st	Tartas
1st	Meyeymac
1st	Massiac
1st	Reignac de Blaye

1st	Azur
1st	Grand Prix des Nations
1st	'American' Palma de Mallorca (with Jacques Anquetil)
2nd	Haut-de-Gan
3rd	Tour du Gard
5th	Mont Faron
Abanded	Tour des Alpes de Provence
	1st Col de Ganagobie stage
6th	G.P. du Midi Libre

1968 Fagor

Champion of Spain

1st	G.P. de Llodio
1st	Koersel-Louvain
2nd	Montjuic hillclimb
2nd	G.P de Navarra
2nd	G.P. de Estella
3rd	Trofeo Baracchi (with Jesús Aranzabal)
3rd	Grand Prix des Nations
3rd	Vuelta a Andalucía
	1st Stage 1
	1st Stage 2
	1st Stage 6
3rd	Barcelona-Andorra
3rd	La Rochelle
3ed	G.P. de Pamplona
4th	Volta a Catalunya
4th	G.P. de Vizcaya
4th	Beaulac-Bernos
5th	À Travers Lausanne
6th	Spanish Mountain Championship
8th	Kalmthout
11th	Trofeo Serdán
11th	G.P. de Primavera de Amorebieta
12th	G.P. de la Bicicleta Eibanesa _
	8th Stage 4
15th	Setmana Catalana
	2nd time trial stage
32nd	Giro d'Italia
	2nd Stage 19

	4th Stage 21
Abandoned	Vuelta a España
	2nd Stage 10

1969 Fagor

1st	Setmana Catalana
	1st Stage 5
1st	G.P. du Midi Libre
	2nd Stage 4
	3rd Stage 2
	5th Stage 3
1st	Castellón de la Plana
1st	Vuelta a Ja Rioja
	1st Stage 3
1st	Trofeo Dicen
1st	Desierto de las Palmas
1st	Caen
2nd	Vuelta a España
	1st Mountain Classification
	1st Stage 1
	1st Stage 16
	1st Stage 18
	2nd Stage 14
2nd	G.P. Onil
3rd	Subida a Arrate
3rd	Quillan
3rd	Escalada de Monjuïc
4th	G.P. Vizcaya
6th	Vuelta al País Vasco
	1st Stage 3
	2nd Stage4
	2nd Stage 5
	7th Stage 4
7th	G.P. de Forli
8th	Villeneuve-sur-Lot
8th	Á Travers Lausanne
9th	Vuelta a Levante
8th	Super Prestige Pernod
Abandoned	Tour de France

1970   Bic

1st	Vuelta a España
	1st Prologue
	1st Stage 19
	4th Stage 9
1st	Critérium Dauphiné Libéré
	1st Stage 5
	2nd Prologue
	2nd Stage 3
1st	Remiremont
1st	Saussignac
1st	Curac
1st	Plancoët
1st	Londinières
1st	La Souterraine
1st	Trofeo Dicen
2nd	Paris-Nice
2nd	Escalada a Montjuïc
2nd	G.P. d'Ussel
2nd	G.P. de Génillé
2nd	Caen
2nd	Critérium de Saint-Cyprien
3rd	Setmana Catalana
	1st Stage 5
3rd	Grand Prix des las Nations
3rd	Roue d'Or
3rd	Saint-Tropez
3rd	Cannes
3rd	Beaulieu-sur-Layon
3rd	Sarlat
4th	Pluméliau
7th	Tour of Lombardy
7th	Subida a Arrate
7th	À Travers Lausanne
7th	G.P. de Lugano
8th	Ronde de Seignelay
8th	Bastia
9th	Bierre-le-Châtel
9th	La Rochelle

10th	Volta a Catalunya
	1st Stage 7
10th	Circuit de l'Aulne
10th	Quillan
12th	Genova–Nice
13th	Château-Chinon
14th	Monbazillac
14th	Saint-Thomas de Conac
31st	Tour de France
	1st Stage 17
	2nd Stage 23
	3rd Stage 20
	4th Stage 7
	6th Prologue
	7th Stage 11
3rd	Super Prestige Pernod

1971   Bic

1st	Grand Prix des Nations
1st	Volta a Catalunya
	1st Stage 5
1st	G.P. de Lugano
1st	Tour of the Basque Country
	1st Stage 4
1st	Trofeo Baracchi (with Leif Mortensen)
1st	G.P. de Europa de montana
1st	Subida a Arrate
1st	À Travers Lausanne
	1st mass start stage
	1st time trial stage
1st	G.P. de Diessenhoffen
1st	G.P. de Guernica
1st	Circuit de l'Aulne
1st	Circuit des Remparts
1st	Cannes
1st	Curac
1st	Quillan
1st	Saint-Cyprien
1st	Beaulac-Bernos
1st	Quintin
1st	Bordeaux

1st	Bilbao
1st	Mont-de-Marsan
2nd	Critérium Dauphiné Libéré
	1st Mountain Classification
	2nd Prologue (ttt)
	2nd Stage 5
2nd	Vuelta a Levante
2nd	Saint-Macaire-en-Mauges
2nd	Brette-les-Pins
3rd	Vuelta a España
	1st Stage 12
	3rd Prologue
	5th Stage 14
3rd	Paris–Nice
3rd	Setmana Catalana
3rd	G.P. Baden-Baden (with Charly Grosskost)
3rd	Escalada a Montjuïc
3rd	Bain-de-Bretagne
3rd	Critérium de Bilbao
4th	Plancoët
4th	Villafranca
4th	Biot
7th	Spanish Championship
7th	Labastide-d'Armagnac
9th	Ploërdut
10th	Ussel
12th	Commentry
13th	Montceau-les-Mines
14th	Château-Chinon
15th	Meymac
Abandoned Tour de France	
	1st Stage 8
	1st Stage 11
	2nd Stage 13
	4th Prologue (ttt)
	4th Stage 10
	10th Stage 2
2nd	Super Prestige Pernod

1972   Bic

Champion of Spain
1st   Criterium Dauphiné Libéré
                    1st Mountain Classification
                    1st Stage 4
                    1st Stage 5
                    1st Stage 5
                    5th Prologue (ttt)
1st   Circuit des Remparts
1st   Mont-de-Marsan
1st   Bayonne
2nd   Four Days of Dunkirk
3rd   Paris-Nice
7th   G.P du Midi Libre
10th   Plélan-le-Petit
19th   Vuelta a Levante
Abandoned Tour de France
                    3rd Stage 3 (ttt)
                    3rd Stage 5
                    3rd Stage 8
                    3rd Stage 11
                    4th Stage 12
                    6th Prologue
                    7th Stage 7
                    9th Stage 13
7th   Super Prestige Pernod

1973   Bic

Champion de Spain by Regions
Winner   Tour de France
                    1st Combativity Prize
                    1st Team classification
                    1st Stage 7
                    1st Stage 8
                    1st Stage 12
                    1st Stage 13
                    1st Stage 18
                    1st Stage 20
                    3rd Mountain Classification
                    3rd Points classification

	3rd Stage 12
	4th Stage 16
	5th Prologue
	5th Stage 2 (ttt)
	5th Stage 7
	8th Stage 3
1st	Criterium Dauphinée Libéré
	1st Prologue (ttt)
	1st Stage 6
	1st Mountain classification
	2nd Stage 3
1st	Setmana Catalana
	1st Stage 5
1st	Tour of Basque Country
	1st Stage 4
1st	Polymultipliée
1st	Labastide-d'Armagnac
1st	Subida a Arrate
1st	Hénon
1st	Martigues
1st	Biot
1st	Pleurtuit
1st	Maurs
1st	Callac
1st	Mende
1st	Saint-Claud
1st	Criterium de Mont-de-Marsan
1st	Colmar
1st	La Clayette
1st	Biarritz
1st	La Rochelle
1st	Tréguier
2nd	Vuelta a España
	2nd Stage 16
	3rd Stage 6(ttt)
	3rd Stage 15
	3rd Stage 17
	4th Prologue
	4th Stage 11
	4th Stage 13
	6th Stage 4

2nd	Grand Prix des Nations
2nd	Vuelta a Cantabria
2nd	Sittard
3rd	World Championship
3rd	Escalada a Montjuïc
3rd	Niza–Seillans
3rd	Circuit de l'Aulne
3rd	Bagneux
3rd	Meymac
3rd	Bain-de-Bretagne
4th	Volta a Catalunya
	1st Mountain classification
	1st Stage 3
4th	À Travers Lausanne
4th	Saint-Quentin
4th	Concarneau
4th	Aulnay
4th	Omnium of Champions
5th	G.P. de Menton
5th	Ferté-Bernard
6th	Paris–Nice
	5th Stage 7
6th	Vailly-sur-Sauldre
7th	Amberes
9th	Plancoët
10th	Saussignac
11th	La Souterraine
13th	Lièga-Bastogne-Lièga
2nd	Super Prestige Pernod

1974 Bic

1st	Honfleur
1st	Quillan
1st	Soissons
1st	Luçon
1st	Cannes
1st	Tarbes
2nd	Plessala

3rd	Vuelta al País Vasco
	3rd Stage 4
	7th Stage 2
	7th Stage 3
3rd	Grigny
4th	Vuelta a España
	2nd Stage 19
	3rd Mountain Classification
	3rd Stage 18
	4th Stage 10
	4th Stage 14
	6th Prologue
	6th Stage 2
	6th Stage 9
4th	Escalada a Montjuïc
5th	Montastruc
5th	Sérénac
5th	Trophée des Cimes
6th	Criterium Dauphinée Libéré
	3rd Prologue (ttt)
	7th Stage 5
	10th Stage 6
6th	Subida a Arrate
6th	Pluméliau
7th	Trophée Méditerranéen
8th	Grand Prix des Nations
8th	Saint-Claud
8th	Genevre
10th	Volta a Catalunya
19th	Setmana Catalana

1975 Super Ser

1st	Carpentras
1st	Miélan (cyclocross)
2nd	Vuelta a Andalucia
	1st Stage 7
2nd	Setmana Catalana
2nd	Subida a Arrate
2nd	Putanges
3rd	Vuelta a Asturias

3rd	Vuelta a los Valles Mineros
3rd	Castres
3rd	Soissons (cyclocross)
4th	Vuelta a España
	2nd Stage 7
	3rd Mountain Classification
	3rd Stage 14
	4th Stage 15
	4th Stage 16
	4th Stage 19
5th	Quillan
5th	Ambarès
5th	Vuelta a la Rioja
	1st Stage 2
6th	Pléaux
7th	Volta a Catalunya
8th	Vuelta a Levante
8th	Escalada a Montjuïc
9th	Paris–Nice
16th	Criterium Dauphiné Libéré
	4th Stage 7
	6th Prologue (ttt)
	17th Stage 6
	27th Stage 5
Aband.	Tour de Ftancia
	5th Stage
	6th Stage 9
	7th Stage 6

1976   Super Ser

1st	Maël-Pestivien
1st	Beaulac-Bernos
1st	Niort
1st	Saussignac
1st	Salamanca
2nd	Vuelta a España
	6th Stage 6
	6th Stage 16
	7th Stage 15
	8th Stage 19
2nd	Genevre

3rd	Paris–Nice
4th	Meaux
4th	Sérénac
4th	Trophée des Grimpeurs
5th	Saussignac
6th	Vuelta a Andalucía
6th	Villeneuve-Ies-Bordes (cyclocross)
9th	Vuelta al País Vasco
10th	Étoile des Espoirs
	1st mountain classification
11th	Criterium Dauphiné Libéré
	6th Stage 6
14th	Tour de France
	4th Stage 14
14th	Limoges
14th	Plessala

1977	**Frisol**
1st	Alkmaar
1st	Quillan
1st	Prologue Tour del Méditerráneo
2nd	Montauban (cyclocross)
2nd	Villeneuve-Ies-Bordes (cyclocross)
3rd	Trophée des Grimpeurs
3rd	Ronde de Seignelay
3rd	Criterium d'Europe
4th	Championship of Spain
5th	Mée-sur-Seine (cyclocross)
7th	Parisot
8th	Ronde des Champions
9th	Beaulac-Bernos
10th	Grand Prix des Nations
12th	Critérium des As
13th	Gesté-la-Chaussaire (cyclocross)
15th	Les Herbiers
15th	Lampaul-Guimiliau

22nd	Vuelta a España
	3rd Stage 12
	5th Stage 4
25th	Tour de France
	4th Stage 7 (ttt)

Monday 12 July 1971
Tragedy in the TOUR de FRANCE

*On this road transformed into
a torrent of mud by an apocalyptic
thunderstorm
Luis OCAÑA, maillot jaune
abandoned all his hopes
against this rock*